D1094417

July 2014
much love,
Judy Brummer.

SPOTS

SPOTS

Book One in Spotty Books Trilogy

JUDY BRUMMER

BB BOOKS

Published 2013
Publisher – BB Books
ISBN: 978-0-9844957-0-2
Spottybooks.com

Cover design and typeset by Shayla Moller

Dedicated to my late brother,
Bruce Bester.

ACKNOWLEDGMENTS

Firstly, I thank God for life and all that He has blessed me with. I thank my parents for giving me a solid foundation, bricks of faith and family that cannot be broken. And to our Xhosa servants—thank you for helping raise me.

Bruce, my beloved big brother, you made me rebel against being a leopard skinned soul with spots. Norman helped me with research and all the man stuff for this book…thanks, my *boet!* To Wendy, my sister, for tolerating all my latest fashions and fads, thank you.

I am truly grateful for all the people who have asked me to tell my story to audiences small and great. I especially thank the gray-haired man who came up to me after I had spoken at a fireside in Utah and said, "Go home and write your story down. It should be shared."

Kerry Patterson, my famous author-neighbor, gave me most useful tips. Dr. Doug Nielson also enlightened me on writing styles. Thank you both very much! To my other neighbor, Stephen Covey, who loved my "authentic" stories, thank you!

Thank you to all inspiring Relief Society teachers who encourage us to write an honest journal. Mine just happened to turn into three books! I smile when I think of Jill Rae, who came to our home and typed the first few chapters out after I had written them by hand. Thanks! Thank you, Leon Brummer, for mailing me a Typequick CD from Australia. It was the only help that could back up far enough to my elementary level.

I could not have done without the trained sharp eye of my friend, Melodie Bestor. She corrected my mistakes and typos pro bono. And thanks to Ann Woolley, my diligent visiting teacher, who corrected a few last typos and gave me much needed encouragement.

To my mission president's wife, Lorna Wood, I love you and your practical advice. Thanks to my dearest friend, Barbara Sutherland, the world's best listener! She gave me a good gauge of what Americans would like to learn about foreign friends.

Our most handsome sons, Jean Paul and Russell, for keeping me humble. When I mentioned that I am booked up for a year to share my story, Russell said, “It is not that you are such a great public speaker, Mom. I think Americans just like your accent.” I wish the readers could hear my accent. We would sell more books! But it made me strive harder to leave my voice and soul on these pages. When I told my sons that the doctor said I would live to be 100, Jean asked, “Has that doctor seen how you drive?”

Thanks to my two perfectly stunning daughters. Tessa, our beloved bookworm, who edited out repetitions and preaching! Shayla, my beloved baby, who became my boss and got the story printed and published. She deleted tons of sermons as well! (You should thank them!) Shayla also used her talents to design the cover.

How could I forget to thank, André, the most patient husband? He bought me two laptops and encouraged me to get to work! He has loved me through a spectrum of moods and maladies. He brought in his heavyweight connections, like Matt Wright, Jennifer Utley and Rob Davis to help. André makes me feel loved daily.

Thanks to all my Facebook buddies for sharing *Spots* with your friends and book clubs! A portion of the profits will go to help Sindie and Tombie's families. Our trio's lives certainly took different paths, but we remain friends for all eternity.

Spotlight and *Spotless* will be published soon to complete the story of our childhood trio.

CONTENTS

1

FROG'S EGGS

We had enjoyed a good season; the rains had been unusually plentiful. All over the Karoo, the dams were full to the brim. It was a most joyful event to see the Eden Dam wall overflowing with brown, dusty water. Our dam spilled into 'Bumpy,' the undammed stream, behind our farmhouse. The steady trickle of rainwater tinted with mud, meandered into the Fish River. The Great Fish River flowed off the bottom tip of South Africa into the Indian Ocean. There it settled its silt and became blue and salty again. Bumpy's riverbed was scoured clean, with only a few sticks of debris clinging to the banks. Deep pools remained in the eroded rocks for us to splash in.

Tombe, my Xhosa chum, was already tugging off her faded dress. I noticed her panties that had once been pink were now a shade of pale brown. They were, no doubt, stained from being washed repeatedly in dam water. Dam water may remove dirt, but it adds fresh brown stains. At least the waist elastic remained a pretty pink.

Tombe noticed me staring at her.

"*Ibhlumasi yam indala, ndinenthloni gqhitha.* (My panties are old, I am very ashamed.)" Tombe clicked in isiXhosa, her mother tongue.

"*Ayina'nto.* (It doesn't matter.)" I tried not to stare so much.

I was fluent in her clicking language. My nanny, Dinah, spoke only Xhosa to me from birth. Besides Dinah, Mom employed three other full-time maids who clicked merrily all day long in our homestead. Maggie was our matronly cook, Jane, our humble housemaid, and Lizzie, the lazy laundry maid.

"Masikhululeni iibhlumasi yethu! (Let's take off our panties!)" Sindie, Lizzie's child, always came up with an enthusiastic solution.

"Hayi, Ungalinge! Kukwamlungu apha! (No, don't you dare! We are here at the white people's house!)" Tombe warned, far too motherly for the ripe old age of eight.

I hastily yanked my green shift dress with large white polka dots over my head. My bright white panties fair glared in the sunlight.

"Azisenthle ibhlumasi yako, Miss Judy! (Your panties are so beautiful, Miss Judy!)" Tombe gushed, drawing unwanted attention to my lacy panties.

"Abalungu banemali, banezinto ezinthle, (White people have cash, they own pretty things,)" Sindie revealed knowingly, as if I were absent. "They are much better off than us."

Shame leaked into my soul. I was ashamed of my spotless underwear, the ones Aunty Ione had given me for Christmas, all wrapped in red paper, just weeks prior. I became acutely conscious that we were not all born equal.

Sindie ripped off her dress defiantly. Her panties looked the worst! I was shocked at the sight of them. The three of us had all grown up together on Schelmdrift, our ancestral family farm. I was not aware that the state of our underwear was so telling, until that very moment.

Sindie's panties were more stained than Tombe's. Her underwear even had holes through which her chocolate brown bum beamed brightly.

"Jonga, Tombe, ezam zirhazukile! (Look, Tombe, mine are torn!)" Sindie knew that broadcasting the truth diminished the discomforts of reality.

"Ndizakukhulula ezam, (I'm taking mine off,)" I declared, removing the garment as if it were diseased.

"Hayi, Miss Judy, *sizakubetwa!* (No, Miss Judy, we will get spanked!)" Tombe scolded. Tombe had the good fortune of inheriting her mother, Jane's sensibility.

"Andikhathali! (I don't care!)" I refused to endure the culpability of inequality that my panties spotlighted.

SPOTS

Besides a few roaming oxen, crested chickens were the only blinking eyes in sight. The windmill wolf-whistled in the breeze approvingly, turning its spinning head. An old pepper tree shivering in the heat wave blocked the view from our farmhouse. Swimming *kaalgat* (naked) in the Bumpy would most probably go unnoticed.

"*Nam!* (Me too!)" Sindie gleefully followed my example, tossing her shabby panties aside.

Tombe was cautiously observing her two rebellious pals in their all too natural state. She digested the fact that her warnings had fallen on deaf ears.

Above Bumpy, the stone kraal's gate was ajar, allowing red, Africander oxen to surround our water hole. Their hardy hooves were muddied brown, their saliva turned frothy lime green from juicy fresh shoots. The shiny beasts were more attentive to the luscious leaves than us nudists. The pedigree oxen bore BB brands on their bulging rumps to show they belonged to the "Bester Brothers Africander Cattle Stud" herd.

My great-great-grandfather had supplied the speedy, strong oxen to the Voortrekkers, mostly Dutchmen, or so we called the Afrikaners, who had initiated fruit farming while settling in the Cape of Good Hope. Indeed, the great British Empire, for some pompous reason, did not seem to notice that the fertile Cape was already colonized, so they promptly recolonized South Africa yet again and the Boers had to flee inland. Our rugged oxen's strength helped the Afrikaaners to *trek voor* or press forward to reach the Highveld. One needs power to press frontward to higher ground.

My great-grandfather, a generation later, sold draft oxen to pull people, plows and produce to 1820 British Settlers near Grahamstown when Mother England ruled. Generations of BB oxen had hauled loads of wagons over the rocky terrain as they civilized the Eastern Cape.

My grandfather improved the breed and got rid of the spotted cattle until they were only pure red and thoroughbred. His sons inherited the spotless herd of robust cattle with contrasting white horns.

Since trucks had taken over the roads, and tractors now turned the turf, my dad, adapted once more, and bred the cattle for juicy beef steaks.

Sindie and I bobbed up and down in the muddy water. Holding our noses, we immersed ourselves. As Sindie came up out of the water, the summer sun lit up the drops of water which lodged on top of her peppercorn hair, sparkling like dewdrops perched on broccoli.

"*Inwele zakho zinde gqhitha,* (Your hair is very long,)" Sindie observed, clicking her tongue. My curly brown "European" hair was weighed down by the water, suddenly straight, making it instantly longer.

"*Ngawume, ndifuna ukuzibamba,* (Stand still, I want to feel it,)" Tombe ordered, curious at the sudden transformation the water rendered to my curls. Sindie and Tombe crept closer and gently felt my foreign hair between their fingertips, fascinated.

"*Ziyanyibilika!* (It feels slimy!)" Sindie remarked cheerfully, "Like seaweed!"

I shook my head and water flew off, blinding Sindie, who blinked rapidly.

Tombe laughed, artfully dodging the drops. "You shake and smell like a wet dog!"

"When I shake my hair, nothing happens," Sindie complained, desperately trying to get water and hair to fly outwards by shaking her head vigorously. It was a fruitless attempt. Somehow, it didn't prevent her from trying again and again.

Tombe was too cautious to even jump into the pool with us.

"And who do you think you are, Sindie? Trying to baptize yourself like that under the water like white ministers do to our tribe?" Tombe asked.

"So what? The whites are far luckier than us…aren't they?" Sindie defiantly went under the water again. Sindie, too, was sharply aware of the disparity of our born statuses. As she popped up, she repeated, "Aren't they?" She dived under again to pop up once more and posed the same question, "Aren't they?"

All that dunking in dirty water did nothing to dislodge one stubborn hair on her head. Each time drops of shiny water wiggled on top of her hair like nervous quicksilver. Perhaps it was the layer of Vaseline she coated on her hair to make it shine, that prevented water from penetrating her immovable hair.

After the third time, I leant over and laid my hand on her head to feel for myself that it was real hair and not a wig of singed broccoli. Thankfully my movement stopped Sindie from bobbing and chanting anymore.

Soon, Tombe too found a reason to be elated, "I have found frog's eggs! Come and look! Plenty of them!" She paused to pull some slimy strings out of Bumpy with her hand.

"I'm going to dry out in the sun," I decided, putting my cotton panties back on, more for warmth than for modesty. "There must be frogs too then. My granny gave me a book for Christmas that says you have to kiss a frog before you can marry a prince."

Sindie picked up her panties and then tossed them aside again with repulsion. "I don't believe those white people's silly superstitions. I am not kissing any frogs. Come and lay here, Miss Jay, the rocks are nice and warm." She patted the rock beside her. "Miss Jay, please will you give me your panties? Mine are so ragged."

"Here! Take them!" I obliged, promptly removing them, irritated by their damp stickiness anyway.

Sindie pulled them up her dripping wet legs with great gusto, not at all deterred by their dampness.

"Enkosi, Miss Jay! (Thank you, Miss Jay!)" She beamed her best smile. "That baptism worked! I am no longer cursed with scruffy, holey underwear."

Tombe was still otherwise occupied with the frog eggs and did not look up.

Sindie snapped off a twig of driftwood and waved it about. "Look, Tombe! I have been given much, given much…" Sindie showed off, wiggling her protruding bottom. A sudden haughtiness was apparent due to her new apparel. Fresh pride oozed from every pore. Sindie would have made a very sufficient snob in the white society.

Tombe ignored Sindie further.

"Hehala! Heke! (Yippee! Yeah!)" Sindie pushed her Bushman buttocks out farther, arching her back. She was clapping and clicking and singing while she danced in her prize panties. I could only gawk at her sudden transformation of disposition.

"You're in trouble," Tombe sulked, still feeling the frogs' eggs with her fingers, not paying enough attention for Sindie's liking.

Sindie sauntered over to Tombe, as if Sindie were now top of the totem pole. Those "undies" represented a new, heightened status—one of privilege perhaps.

"You better give those back!" Tombe's tone was one of soberness. She was trying to make her voice deeper to mask her envy with warnings, "Or you shall be cursed worse…"

"Ooh!" Sindie interrupted loudly. "Guess what? I know a secret," Sindie exclaimed to defer reality. She knew if she couldn't attract much attention with her new attire, she could try the wisdom of witchcraft.

"Our witchdoctor told *my* big sister, Toto, that if you put frogs' eggs all over your nipples and bake in the hot sun, you will grow enormous, bulging breasts," Sindie boasted with confidence equal to one who could recite whole volumes of encyclopedias.

"Here, Miss Jay, here are some frog's eggs for you," Sindie offered, as if the gift of big breasts would provide restitution for the pretty panties.

"Come, Miss Judy, grab some and let's all try it," Tombe urged, coaxing me further. "Our old witchdoctors know about this stuff. Even Sindie understands that!"

"Witchdoctors say things that are not altogether true at times." Sindie was slightly rebellious. "But this magic works. My cousin tried it and she has mammoth-sized boobs now."

"Are all your traditions true? I suppose we have to just try them out and see for ourselves." I was quite content to be a guinea pig.

"No, we must always just do what the older generations tell us to do." Tombe always obeyed meticulously, when it came to Xhosa tribal traditions.

"Ndifuna amabele amakhulu gqhitha nam, (I also want to have very

big breasts,)" I clicked in compliance with my African friends.

Xhosa was not my mother tongue, however. My white mother, who was descended of pure British blood, with a little blue blood mixed in, spoke posh Queen's English. Be assured witchcraft was not her religion either. As a matter of fact, my family was Methodist or Anglican, according to which denomination minister the weather blew in to preach to us monthly at the Carlisle Bridge County Club.

Our threesome baked our bosoms, sprawled out on the rather pokey rocks. I was stripped, having been recently 'robbed' of my Christmas gift from Aunty Ione. *'Never mind,'* I thought to myself, *'I'll get more such gifts. Aunty Ione always gives me panties for Christmas and for birthdays.'* My April birthday was just around the corner; I would soon be turning nine that autumn of 1965.

Tombe and Sindie, on the other hand, never mentioned birthdays, but we were all from the same crop. Xhosas, traditionally, had not kept written records of anything. My two friends never received gifts or cake on their birthdays. It was not part of the black people's culture in those days.

Tombe explained that African ancestors could not write. Consequently, dates of deaths were not recorded and birthdays were not fussed over at all. Historically, the indigenous tribes were not even aware of the Christian calendar. Xhosas watched the moon to know when a month was over. They felt the temperature with their skin to gauge the seasons. They looked at the sun to tell if it was morning or afternoon. Besides, they had no alphabet, watches, thermometers or calendars before the white Settlers showed up on ships. Numerals and letters were unheard of! Traditional tribal folks could not possibly *read* a cake recipe or *count* nine candles or *write* 'Happy Birthday' with icing sugar!

A favorite celebration the Xhosas observed was a *"sikho,"* when they slaughtered sacrificial animals while doing "work for their ancestors." My mother thought it was a horrid excuse to throw drunken parties. The tribe performed these rituals regularly for their grand-ghosts. I reflected as I basked in the sun about how ghosts could not possibly present their offspring with gifts like my grandparents did...

there was some degree of injustice in their peculiar practice. I preferred grandparents to grand-ghosts anyway.

As I lay there, thinking about my friends' lack of birthday parties, I inquired, "Why do your 'old people' kill cows for your already dead relatives? I ask you. The ghosts can't eat the meat when they are dead, I shouldn't think."

Maybe I should not have thought aloud at all.

The teacher in Tombe erupted like a volcano, "We have fabulous feasts to invite the spirits of the dead to come and live with us again in our huts. 'Old people' say that our dead relatives keep a sharp eye on us."

I hoped no ghosts were watching us just then.

"Ancestors can dish out very good luck to their children who are faithful to customs. But they can also cast very scary curses…" Tombe paused to enlarge her focused eyes and zoom in on Sindie, "…for rebellious behavior." Tombe echoed her old folks' words, while nodding her head and raising her eyebrows. Jane's oldest daughter was more buxom than we were; maybe that was why she assumed she could boss Sindie and me around.

Religiously, the three of us simmered in the sun with frogs' eggs glazed across our flat chests. We roasted our ribcages in the 90 degree weather. The eggs looked like rows of little black spots linked in colorless jelly, slightly firmer than chicken egg whites.

"*Yenzani nje!* (You must do it like this!)" Sindie demonstrated, adjusting her lanky legs to balance better.

We lay there for ages, readjusting our slime-packs as they slipped off. Tombe even went and replenished supplies of fresh frogs' eggs when hers slid off into the mud.

"Who says this works? Are you sure it worked for your cousin before?" I demanded, staring at Sindie.

"It works," Tombe assured me.

"What if our boobs grow too big? Perhaps we should stop now." The fear of growing Jersey-cow-sized udders loomed in my fertile imagination.

I wasn't sure if I trusted Xhosa frog egg magic as much as my

African comrades did. After all, I was a European South African. But I had seen the magic Mommy's egg beater performed on chicken egg whites, whipping them into meringue, which sort of resembled pointy breasts.

"*Nyani- nyani* (Truthfully) it works," Sindie reassured me. "My cousin can hardly hold her boobs up with her back."

"Witchdoctors have special powers to do marvelous magical things." Tombe added her testimony in a matter-of-fact fashion. "You will have to wait and see and only then you will believe us."

"Witchdoctors know these truths from a very long time ago," Sindie was our ever convincing instructor. "Whites don't know these secrets, but we share them with you only, Miss Jay, only you! It is magical *muti* (medicine) from wise witchdoctors who know about it from their training in the bush." She paused to replenish her eggs. "White people just never knew about it or how it works; otherwise, they would all do it too." Sindie seemed to be exerting more energy into convincing me than ever before. "White people do not have these very valuable secrets. Your doctors dish out pills and slice you open and sew you up again like a piece of cloth."

"But how do you know that what your old people say is the *dinkum* (absolute) truth?" I was still a slightly suspicious accomplice. "And who is this witchdoctor that knows so much about boobs?"

"He is that old man from the Gradwell's farm. We trust him." Tombe was obviously a believer. "That wrinkled man put a powerful curse on a young woman and she choked to death on her vomit soon after that."

"Your skin is turning pink already," Sindie observed, examining my European skin and prodding her finger into my side, leaving a white spot. "You will have huge boobs, Miss Jay!" Sindie prophesied boldly. She was quite sanctimonious about the results.

"Your skin is getting blacker, Sindie," Tombe remarked, attempting to harness Sindie in. "It looks even darker next to that white garment that does not belong to you."

Ring! Ring, ring! The dinner bell tinkled. Jane shook the silver bell from the kitchen *agterstoep* (back veranda).

"Miss Judy, *uyabizwa!Yidinara!* (You are being called! It is dinner-time!) Miisss-ss-Juuudy!" Jane called out as loudly as was still elegant in her role as a maid. She was clad in a blue uniform with a white apron that tied behind her back. Jane also balanced a white turban on her head along with a long, flowing, blue German-print skirt under her uniform to reveal that she was a married woman.

We lay still, reluctant to terminate our formal procedure. Each of us was hoping for huge breasts and did not want to break the magic spell.

"Miiiis JUUDY!!" Jane called again and rang the silver dinner bell even louder.

"Ndiyeza! (I'm on my way!)" I called back, in case Jane advanced on our little nudist colony. She was a respectful servant who had worked for my mother for the past ten years already. She was originally hired to work as my older brother's nanny, and then she just stayed on the payroll. My mother had approved of Jane's polite manners very much and soon promoted her to housemaid.

After sloshing off the eggs into Bumpy, I snatched my dress and pulled it over my head. Mom had sewed my skimpy, slip dress for me out of the leftover material from her own cotton frock. Her dress had a more generous flared a-lined skirt.

'Perhaps I should put on Sindie's discarded panties, seeing as she is wearing mine,' I thought, but then I thought better of it.

"Give Miss Judy her *broekies* (panties) back!" Tombe demanded.

"Andicingi! (I won't!)" Sindie retorted quietly, still baking to acquire a fuller effect.

"Ndizakunibona ngoku ngoku. (I'll see you *now-now.*)" I said, quite enjoying the breeze up my shift dress as I set off towards the old white house. I knew that our Xhosa maids never wore panties under their modest ankle-length skirts. I had seen them squat behind a bush and urinate often enough to know that secret. Something told me that it would not work as well in my modern, Twiggy-style, mini skirt, so I walked with my thighs very close to each other like a proper English lady should.

Jane had diligently strolled down to escort me home.

Tombe noticed my odd walk. "Mama, Sindie took Miss Judy's *broekies!*" Tombe ratted on her rival to Jane.

"Hayi, hayi, hayi, (No, no, no) Sindie!" Our loyal servant shook her head repeatedly. *"Zikhulule ngoku! Kawuleza gqitha, ngaphamkwe singxhotwe sonke.* (Take those off immediately! Hurry up before we all get fired.)" Jane clicked and clucked like a mother hen, assertive in her own unassuming manner.

Jane hurried towards Lizzie's child, with her arms outstretched to retrieve the stark white underwear. Sindie looked mournful. She reluctantly lifted each foot for Jane to pull them off. Sindie still clung to her frog's eggs as if witchcraft was her only remaining hope. Social stigma could be avoided by practicing this procedure.

"And you two should not be teaching our white madam's child about the covert operation of frog's eggs!" Jane corrected the girls with a smile.

Pulling me firmly by the hand, Jane strutted back to the farmhouse with me in tow, now fully clad. When we got closer to my home, I could smell a leg of lamb roasting, along with caramelized shallots and golden roast potatoes. Hunger pangs quickened my pace and I ran on ahead of Jane.

Maggie, our plump cook, was pouring white sauce over a dish of steaming cauliflower. We exchanged greetings and I went to wash my hands. Washing hands before meals was the habit of the homestead. Rules, habits, customs or rituals…one just did what your particular old people did, it seemed to me.

Daddy was already at the bathroom basin, vigorously washing his sunburned hands. His khaki shirt had the sleeves rolled up to the elbows. My daddy was the younger Bester Brother. He was affectionately known as Boetie Bester. Dad had inherited our ranch at the age of sixteen when his father died from sclerosis of the liver.

Dad was born and raised on Schelmdrift and knew every inch of the 10,000-acre expanse. He had learned how to dose a sick Merino sheep and exactly when to shear the mohair off Angora goats. He managed to get his servants to control wild cattle during their dipping and dosing rituals. Daddy was excellent at hunting vermin and proved lethal at shooting carnivorous predators. No one dared poach anything on Schelmdrift. Dad's extensive knowledge was ever-expanding. He had studied agriculture from various schools and books, and he was a skilled stock specialist.

Bester is a German surname, although Dad's mother was of Swiss stock. Our Bester ancestors had sailed to the Cape of Good Hope from Europe for a better way of life in the 1700's. They had carved that life out for their families here in the Klein Karoo, on the east bank of the Great Fish River.

This outback of Africa was definitely not for sissies. Only the resilient survive the Karoo. Dad's blood was that of a tough Afrikaner *boer*, with a slight touch of the tar brush, evidenced by his unruly, dark curls. Be that as it may, Dad spoke only proper English in our family. Both my father's grammar and manners were immaculate. An auburn-haired English wife will see to that!

"Don't waste precious water, my girl," Dad said out of habit. "The Karoo is a dry place."

"There are deep pools of water in Bumpy!" I reported.

"Clean water is nevertheless very limited! Don't take the treasure of tank water for granted, my girl." Dad admonished as he left. "One little leak and the level can drop drastically. We never know when it will rain again, so we need to conserve water." He knew we were at the mercy of the random rains. More often than not, they were scarce and it could result in deadly droughts.

My mother had taught me all about the science of evaporation of the ocean resulting in unpredictable rain. We studied the cycle during Nature Study class. No one had yet discovered exactly who controlled the clouds, so we called him the 'weather man.' In the arid Karoo, livelihoods depended on that cryptic creature.

But for now, all was wet and well.

"All right," I said, but allowed the tap to run pure rainwater over my fingers a little longer than usual. "This is crystal clear water," I thought aloud. "It really cleans me and keeps my underwear even whiter." I felt a deep gratitude for cleanliness, but angst for my friends, who did not enjoy the same pleasures.

2

GOOD NEWS

Dad sat in his normal place at the head of the yellowwood table, with natural light streaming in behind him. Through the large window, one could admire neat rows of vegetables and the dark green foliage from our loquat tree.

Mom sat on the right hand side of Daddy. She was the most beautiful lady I'd ever seen. Her reddish hair framed her refined features. Gwenna Bester's skin was very fair, spotted with a few charming freckles on her nose and lower eyelids.

The high-backed chairs smelled like furniture oil. Jane had just polished all our antiques which had occupied that dining room long before any of us had. A side table was adorned with a brass tray, on which stood a tall jug of rain water surrounded by sparkling cut glasses. A bottle of *Oros* orange squash reflected its image on the shined tray. The water jug had a white net draped over it to keep thirsty insects out. Real seashells dangled from the crocheted perimeter, weighing the net down.

My mother's turquoise eyes surveyed me, "Caesar's Ghost, my child, have you been out in that hot sun without your hat? Your face is positively pink!" Mom sensed our sins even before we had time to confess them. "You must be very thirsty."

"I drank the water from Bumpy. We were swimming there just now. We found frog's eggs…" I partially revealed.

"You should *not* drink that water! It is *not* in the least hygienic! And you are *not* to go outside again without your hat." Mom's voice was firm as she removed the lids off the vegetable dishes with each, "not."

"Sindie and Tombe drink it all the time. And they are fine. You can drink that water," I insisted.

"The Natives have been drinking that water for centuries. Their stomachs are used to it. But you, my pet, should only drink water out that jug over there." Mom gestured with her upper-crust English nose because her hands were otherwise engaged.

"Fine," I responded. "But I am not thirsty anymore."

"The servants go to the lavvy in the bushes along the top veldt upstream from Bumpy, and then when it rains, the germs wash down into the Eden dam, which then overflows into Bumpy. That is the reason why I don't want you drinking that water." Mommy was a master of debate, so I kept quiet.

Changing the subject to a more appetizing one, Mom said, "Just look at these veggies…they are all homegrown. Taste how tender these green beans are!" Mom beamed with the satisfaction of a true gardener. Her face lit up to ignite her natural beauty.

Dad was sharpening the carving knife, not listening to us. The familiar scraping sound was part of his ritual before carving a roast. Mom was giving the homemade mint sauce an extra stir in order to dissolve the sugar in the vinegar.

"Everything on the table is produced right here on Schelmdrift. Only the salt and pepper are bought from the shops," Dad noted with righteous pride.

"We are quite self-sufficient." Mom agreed. "The vinegar and sugar are bought, of course," Mom corrected, "but we did grow the mint."

I stared at the vegetables that were irrigated with germy water from our Eden Dam, but boiled in clear tank water.

"The house feels so empty," I said when Dad finished his sharpening. I missed my older siblings. "How long is a term of boarding school?"

"This first term is about eight weeks. They will come home for a weekend after about four weeks. I miss them terribly too. There is nothing we can do about it. Did you say there are frogs' eggs in Bumpy? After dinner, we should collect a jar full. I am going to be teaching you how they turn into tadpoles and then become frogs. It is part of the syllabus that the Education Department sent me. We will also look at that water under our microscope. If you see what else crawls in that water, perhaps you won't drink it anymore." My mother homeschooled all her children for four years before they had to attend distinguished boarding schools in the far away city, Port Elizabeth.

"Tombe and Sindie really like their new school at Carlisle Bridge. They also have a new teacher who comes from East London." I was a lonely child when my siblings were away.

Mom was dishing up the pumpkin. "I am delighted the piccanins like that new prefab building. Your father and the other farmers in the district all donated money to help pay for that new school. It has a couple of classrooms. You can probably fit thirty or forty in each classroom. I was afraid it would get very hot and stuffy in summer. I am thrilled to hear they have a decent teacher."

"Sindie said she wears red lipstick," I disclosed.

"Xhosas don't wear lipstick!" Mom was most piqued.

"She does. They said so. Sindie said she will also wear lipstick when she grows up. She said her father, Jack, will get more cows for her *lobola* (bride payment) that way," I reported.

Something instinctively told me not to mention my induction into the ritual that involved frogs' eggs. My mother was perhaps a little too white to understand fully. "Sindie says she will be sold for cows in a few years. She wants to fetch a high price. Tombe says she is going to get as fat and bulgy as she possibly…"

"SHSHSH, now, my girl. It's time for the news." Dad turned on his brand new radio to hear the national news. "Please be quiet now."

"This is Springbok Radio bringing you *The World* at 1 p.m., Neville Dawson reporting…" a man's voice blurted out the black box.

The news was not very interesting to me, so I daydreamed instead.

I thought about Bruce, my biggest brother, who got a new cricket bat for Christmas. He was chosen to play on the Grey High School

First XI team. He got new cricket pads for his 17th birthday right after Christmas, so he was all kitted out for his passion of playing cricket.

Wendy was about to turn fifteen at boarding school. Mom had posted a vanilla Madeira cake in a cake tin to her. It was decorated with hard icing over marzipan. Mom carefully wrote "Happy Birthday Wendy" in pink cursive. Mother tucked in a box of matches and fifteen candles to blow out while the Collegiate Girls sang to my only sister. We, whites, blew out flames and sang the same song every birthday. My two friends had laughed at our custom when I explained it. They had said, "That's silly. Xhosas only light flames under our food, not on top."

As I dreamed, Jane floated in with the gravy boat on a tray. *"Nanku umhluzi*, (Here's the gravy,)" she whispered.

"Enkosi (Thank you) Jane," Mom replied quietly in one of the very few Xhosa words she knew.

As I swallowed the veggies, I remembered Norman. He was just two years older than I was. He would be home for his 11th birthday during the Easter holidays. He boarded at Grey Junior School for Boys. Bruce, Wendy, and Norman all slept at different hostels. I missed Norman the most. When he left, I felt like an only child.

My siblings only saw one another at St. John's Methodist Church every Sunday. They all wore uniforms and hats to school and church. It was awfully formal and staid and loomed in my future like a dark cloud. Education was a compulsory part of our civilized culture—our white old people insisted on it!

My stomach turned at the scary thought that I, too, would be shipped off to an all-white boarding school exclusively for girls the following year. It made my tummy collywobbles worse than eating veggies grown in germs.

Suddenly I got a bright idea. "Mommy, why can't I just go to the new school at Carlisle Bridge with Sindie and Tombe?"

"SSSHHH! I want to hear the latest wool prices." Dad shushed me up as he turned up the volume.

I waited for the wool prices to be read. Dad cheered, when he heard the merino wool prices had sky rocked due to increased demand. America was buying wool as the least flammable fiber to line aircrafts and other military combat gear during the Vietnam War.

As soon as the opportunity arose, I revised my suggestion, "I could stay on the farm! I have walked to Carlisle Bridge with my friends before! There are *nqhabaza* (berry) bushes along the way! And flowering Cape aloes to suck! I can speak Xhosa perfectly well! I would understand that 'decent' teacher…the one who wears lipstick and short skirts like Europeans. Why can't I just go to school next door with all the piccanins? Oh please will you let me? Please!"

"What utter rubbish! You will do nothing of the sort! White children are not allowed to attend the Native schools anyway!" Mom said emphatically. "Besides, you have to have a proper education." She clearly had no confidence in the "lady" in lipstick. "It is no use even thinking about it! You come from a different world than your piccanins."

"I thought we were all born on Mother Earth?" I cheeked. "This time next year, it will just be you and Dad at the table," I snarled. Perhaps I could reach her heart with that emotional dagger. Anything to change her mind! I had heard about the awful food at boarding school, not to mention the lack of it. I had to do what I could in my puny power to avoid that dreadful prison.

"I want to go to school with Sindie!" I wailed. "And Tombe!"

"Don't be a silly mutt! You come from vastly different cultures and the standard of education is poles apart." Mom emphasized.

"What is this fuss all about?" Dad inquired as he tuned into yet another radio station to hear the regional news.

"Judy will just have to accept the fact that we cannot change the apartheid situation. She will have to go to Collegiate and make new European friends." Mom answered.

"Tombe and Sindie know about things that you do not even know about. They have plenty of useful informa…." I began to protest.

"Ssshhh now! Please, my girl! I want to hear the cricket scores. We can worry about all this later." Dad had the shiny, new knobs all sorted out on his radio.

He put an extra slice of lamb on my plate, hoping to barricade my tongue from talking. Maggie always roasted it to perfection in the wood stove. It was a delicacy, even in South Africa. Karoo lamb tastes much better than lamb that has grazed on grasslands. Karoo-fed lamb has a distinct delicate flavor, not unlike sage.

I chewed my food in a sulky silence. The thought of being separated from my parents and friends made me awfully distressed. My attempts to rectify the situation having been wholly unsuccessful, I had to think harder. I felt powerless and weak.

The sports commentator gushed over the air: "Graeme Pollock continues to hit sixes with such ease, thrilling the crowds. He has his fans screaming on their feet! I trust you can hear me over the din!" Charles Fortune had a smile in his hoarse voice.

That caused Daddy to applaud again. *"Well, I never!* Another six runs!"

"Why can't black and white children all go to school together?" I questioned in a cheeky tone of voice.

"Quiet now! Please!" Dad said, tuning his silver and black wireless to hear the local news. "I need to listen to the weather forecast."

More rain was predicted to make a "hat trick" of good news. "I think we should open a bottle of champagne!" Dad beamed. Mom frowned upon that idea.

This was a brand new wireless. After a fruitful season, Dad could afford nice things. This modern radio had replaced the old wooden box.

"It is half past one on the 31st of January, 1965. This is Springbok radio…" A posh British accent beamed out better now than before from the old-fashioned brown box.

"This is a remarkable improvement," Dad commented quickly to Mom. "I can hear his voice much clearer."

"I am sure all the clouds and rain made the static worse as well." Mom was always practical. "But I must say, this instrument does sound much better, dear."

Radios improve. This new model made it sound like the man talking was sitting at our table. 'So why can't people adjust their minds?' I thought sullenly.

"I like this new wireless, Daddy, it's…" I started.

"Shhh, I want to hear the latest cricket score," Dad frowned at me.

Jane quietly glided in and removed our gravy-smeared china plates onto a tray. A few moments later, she returned with Mom's home-bottled pink guavas in a dazzling crystal bowl.

Yan Xhashimba had paid *labola* to Jane's father for her. She was his bride, fully paid for with five cows. The *Xhashimba* family had a history with our Bester family, as did all our staff. Tombe's dad, Yan, worked for my father, and her grandfather had worked for my grandfather. Our great-grandfathers had also worked together. For generations, our families were connected. Yan once told me that his family would never leave Schelmdrift to work on the gold mines of Johannesburg or to work for any other farmer. Our faithful servants were practically part of our family.

"Thank you, Jane. Tell Maggie the veggies were cooked just right, not too much salt this time," Mom said, quietly removing a dainty jug of pouring custard from the tray. The porcelain glittered with droplets from the fridge.

"Ewe. Enkosi, Mlungkasi, (Yes. Thank you, White Lady,)" Jane almost curtsied.

Both mothers spoke their own languages and only partially understood each other. The nods and smiles conveyed approval. Jane carried her light frame back to the kitchen like a ballerina.

"Maggie tends to be heavy-handed with the salt." Mom really spoke to the walls. She never made too much noise while Dad leaned to his left, aiming his good ear toward the black box.

Maybe *my* grand-ghosts are all sitting in these nine empty oak chairs, I imagined to myself, bringing all the glorious good luck. What else would all those ghosts do all day? Tombe did insist our forefathers live in the home with us. If she was right, our poor ghosts would be doomed to listen to all those news bulletins.

I did not say it out loud, because Mom did not believe in Xhosa superstitions at all. She most certainly did not approve of their ancestor worship. Mom remarked that Natives believed a lot of 'hogwash.'

Dad's right ear was quite deaf, mostly from hunting but also from the World War II. South African soldiers, being subjects of a British Colony, battled alongside the British warriors. Dad fought for four years against the Germans, even though he was of German descent. A framed 'family tree' hung on the dining room wall, with all the names of our *voorvaders* (forefathers) neatly typed on it.

Our own private family graveyard was neatly fenced on the far side of the stables. Generations of Bester bones were buried under tombstones there. Ghosts and bones of one person can dwell separately, sort of like apartheid, I figured. The *spoek* or *spook* (ghost) half could roam around peering at people, gathering gossip, yet remain invisible; while the latter half lay stiff, cold and white.

Luckily, my daddy had survived WWII. His spirit was still inside his masculine frame. Sadly, his brother-in-law had been killed. Dad had learned survival skills on Schelmdrift. He knew how to aim as a child growing up on our farm. He learned how 'to give a lead' to moving targets while shooting flying birds and leaping Springbuck. The same rule applied to bomb-filled approaching planes. Dad had shot down an enemy German plane. It was all about timing. Daddy had earned a reputation for marksmanship early in life. Unfortunately, his right ear was now partially deaf from all the cannons that he had fired. For good reason, the servants, the surrounding farmers, friends, family, and I, collectively, had a healthy respect for my father, Johan Coenraad Bester, alias 'Boetie.'

Dad had an insatiable hunger for 'knowledge.' Even when his tummy was full, he still craved more information. So after midday dinner, he smoked his bent billiard pipe and read the newspaper in his office while his food settled. Just in case he had not been informed enough, he also subscribed to news magazines, which were left in the lavatory for anyone to read. There was no television in South Africa in 1965, so the radio kept us up to date. My father listened avidly to the 6 a.m., 8 a.m., and 9 a.m. news, as well as the 1 p.m., 1.30 p.m., 2 p.m., 6 p.m., 8 p.m., and 9 p.m. news broadcasts on the radio.

Those unfortunate ghosts! They must be dying of boredom.

Daddy was always trying to improve farm methods. My parents enjoyed valuable tips from the *Farmer's Weekly* magazine on all sorts of agricultural crafts, excluding witch's crafts, of course.

Boetie Bester was well-versed in the current affairs of the world, even though we lived in the middle of nowhere. Dad shared snippets of news. I can remember a few. "Computers are going to be the way of the future," he'd mutter as he'd put down a newspaper.

"Those hippies in America think wilted flowers are beautiful. You have to smoke *dagga* (marijuana) to think that." He also had opinions. "They should give those scruffy hippies all a haircut and send them to the Army. Bunch of long-haired sissies, they are. They need some discipline. It is all very well to sit around spaced-out and yelp 'Peace.' But when lunatics like Hitler decide to take over the world by force, we had to step up and stop him. Deranged maniacs do not respond well to all this gushy-mushy peace talk. The only language tyrants understand are bombs dropping on bridges and buildings blowing up. America should draft the whole bally bunch of those pansies into the Army. That would sort them out in a big hurry, I reckon."

Dad thought it was very important to be aware of what was happening around our world. My father's philosophy was "we are never too old to learn new things." So he searched for nuggets of knowledge like a gold digger, ever hopeful to polish his general knowledge.

Gwenna Bester agreed mostly, echoing her snooty mother's rather portentous views. "Education is the key to civilization. Mummy's maid was burnt alive after being falsely condemned by an angry witch-doctor! Some of these black tribes are simply barbaric. My Aunty Ruby's maid was tortured and poisoned by a jealous lover. Look at the Natives all over Africa; they are morally depraved and treat each other worse than the whites ever treated them. A race without books is a ruined race. The tribes have no literature of their own to help them develop acceptable social skills. One needs reading, writing and arithmetic to enlighten the mind. Studying scriptures helps to develop character and instill moral behavior. Just look what happens to civilizations when they forget to learn from good books!" I think she was having a moment because she needed to let off steam like a pressure cooker. I had opened the lid with the idea of going to school next door at Carlisle Bridge.

"Now, you tell me, Billikins, [that was Dad's pet name for Mom] would you call these white, hooligan hippies civilized?" Dad smiled and held up a newspaper, challenging Mom to a debate.

He showed my Mom a picture of a long-haired girl or boy, I could not tell, holding a sign that read "Make Love, Not War." I wondered what my parents were grinning about.

There was another picture that Mom pointed to. "Those disgraceful Women's Libbers burning their bras are equally appalling." Mom smirked. "They simply have no decorum at all. What makes them so unashamed?"

"I have to admit, America has some things to boast about. Look at their technology, for instance. That certainly helped us win the war. When they finally showed up, they produced some very fine soldiers." Dad was teaching us all. "As far as I could see, those Yankee soldiers are a pretty fearless lot."

America had Hippies; New Zealand had sheep; London had fog. I gleaned little tidbits about the wider world as I eavesdropped. When my head had 'had an elegant sufficiency,' I strolled out of his office, down the front *stoep* (porch) stairs onto the front lawn to air my head.

Our ranch was so isolated that when I stood on our lawn and did a 360-degree twirl, there was no sign of any civilization whatsoever! No other human dwelling was in sight, besides our big white-washed Karoo farmhouse with a wide cement *stoep* on the front and south side. Large cement pillars held up the red roof that had a turret on the corner by the tennis court. Wide pepper trees provided shade year round in the driveway.

Bark peeled off the huge gum trees in the front garden, showing the age of the homestead. You couldn't reach the bottom branches. You had to get a ladder to climb those tall trees. Two palm trees were getting taller each year, making our terraced garden look like an oasis in the semi-arid Karoo. We lived in the *boendoes* (outback), secluded from the wicked outside world.

Grandpa Bester built our homestead in 1900 for Granny Bester, long before my dad was born. It replaced the older house that was built a few generations before that. Schelmdrift had been in our family for over a hundred years. Wide wooden beams creaked when you walked on the floor, scattered with Persian rugs. The walls were as thick as a fort. Yellowwood beams from the original house were used to make built-in cupboards and tables in the pantry.

I had thought my daddy owned the whole world. Well, at least, he owned *my* world. It gave me a sense of safety. I never wanted that to change.

"Stop twirling like that, my pet, you'll make your dinner come up." Mom startled me. "You must go lie on your bed and rest for an hour or so until it cools down a wee bit. Then you may play with the piccanins again after tea."

Maggie and Jane strolled up over the hill to their hut village for the afternoon. They would come back to make a light supper at sunset. They always carried enamel dishes full of food on their heads to take to their children.

My spacious bedroom felt empty without Wendy. I lay there and looked at the pink curtains, which Jane had drawn shut to keep out the heat. I stared at a fly on the high ceiling, until it flew away and there was nothing more for me to watch.

How could I change the schooling rules? I was not at liberty to free big people who are trapped in their traditions.

Just then, I noticed movement on my curtain, and I spotted a chameleon clinging to the lace. I got up to greet my new pet, which resembled a miniature dinosaur from ages past.

My menagerie of pets included a grey Cape Vervet monkey, tortoises, cats galore, and some white mice. Orphaned Angora goat kids or discarded Merino lambs were also annual pets. We fed the lambs bottles of milk until they grew up and joined the flocks in the veldt. Sadly, we were not allowed dogs. Daddy, as a teenager, had to shoot his beloved dog when it developed a taste for killing lambs.

After slowly detaching the cautious chameleon from its firm grip, "Even you, little Lacy," I named her after the curtain, "changed to green when I put you on my dress. You can switch the color of your scaly skin," I said out loud. "So why can't I just change the tradition and go to school at Carlisle Bridge? I ask you. Is changing really that painful?"

I was a little too loud, I presume. Even though I was talking to my new-fangled pet, now clawing my dress, Mom heard me and marched into my room. "You cannot change things! Just accept that. Apartheid means the people must develop separately. The whites and black tribes speak different languages. That is why the Natives need to have their own schools with their own teachers who the students can understand. Anglican and Methodist missionaries have tried to convert the tribes to Christianity and now we are trying our best to help educate them."

Wanting to change the subject, I said, "Look how fast Lacy turns brown when I put her on the wooden dressing table!" I was spellbound with my new color-changing pet, and she did it all magically without one battery! Not even Dad's swanky radio could deliver news without four large batteries.

"Chameleons adapt to disguise themselves from dangerous predators. You will be able to adapt to boarding school. You must not worry so much, my pet." Mom's voice had a hint of controlled glum in it.

Tombe's underpants flashed in front of my eyes. The cotton part had absorbed the color of the dam water. I wondered why the elastic stayed pink. Some things change, I thought, but others don't. It was all rather bamboozling. However grim her underwear was, I found myself to be envying Tombe's school situation.

"I would rather live in a mud hut than be separated from you." I finally blurted out what was smoldering in my soul.

Inspecting the chameleon from my pillow, I was wowed by her instinct to turn yellow as it climbed up my pale bedside lamp. Maybe the ancient, wrinkled chameleon carried a clue to her resilient existence. Chameleons were a tiny version of the dinosaur species, and yet the only surviving one. Lacy's bulging eyes rolled in opposite directions, affording her a 360 degree vision. Out of my blurred peripheral vision, I noticed a buzzing fly land on the white lamp shade.

I detested flies.

Lacy struck out her sticky tongue with lightning speed, all while clinging to the light. She extended and re-coiled her tongue with swift stealth and the black spot vanished instantly. That fly became Lacy's lunch, locked in by dry, prehistoric-looking lips.

"Well done, Lacy!" I admired her spot-removing skills. "That was magical!"

Lacy survived with simultaneous backward and forward vision. Ancient creeping things knew secrets, too, surely. Chameleons must have grasped some nuggets of survival talents that dinosaurs did not care to develop. Perhaps Lacy's superior vision, swift tongue and mutable skin color were reasons she remained un-extinct. Could that be the reason why we place such faith in what our wrinkly old people say, for they too have indeed existed for ages.

"Pure magic!" I praised my well-deserved pet again.

The Karoo was a plateau on the bedrock of a rocky reef riddled with evidence of dinosaur dynasty destruction. The derelict bones of dinosaurs had no surviving progeny to boast of, or peep at, for that matter. Evidently, somehow the weak little chameleon had overcome ominous obstacles and outlived, outsmarted, and outlasted the stronger, more powerful species. And they did it all by eating loathsome flies! Eliminating one spot at a time. That was, indeed, the best news of the day.

3

FRIEDA THE FRIEND

The following morning, Jane woke me up, standing at my bedside with my 'early morning coffee' and a homemade rusk resting on the saucer. Rusks were introduced by the Dutch Colonists. Freshly baked buns were immediately dried on a low heat. The *Voortrekkers* used this nifty way of preventing sweet bread from going moldy, during their journey inland. Rusks are *lekker* (delicious) after having been dunked in coffee. Many a baby has cut its teeth while gnawing on brittle, dried rusks.

On my way to the *loo* (lavatory), I overheard my mom mention my name to Dad. My curiosity forced me to resist my bladder's urges, and to eavesdrop instead. I could smell their percolated coffee which they enjoyed in their bedroom every morning.

"We must get Judy to play with white children," Mom voiced her concern. Mother was a mathematician. If there was a problem, she looked at it from all angles to solve it.

"*Ja*, that might be a good idea," Dad agreed. "She needs a girl to play with. Mary-Rose lives a bit too far away. Can you think of anyone? The Bowkers, Snows, Nortons and Gradwells only have boys her age. There are plenty of farmer's sons."

"You're quite right, dear. She will not have a hard time finding one to marry." But that was not the dilemma. "I have a good mind to invite Leenie van Vuuren over this morning, and ask her to bring her daughter. Frieda is about a year younger than Judy." Mom's mind was rapidly doing sums. "They are new to the district and are a bit shy, being Afrikaans speaking and all. They don't play tennis or cricket at Carlisle Bridge, even though the Country Club is right on their doorstep."

"Mind you, Judy will be off to boarding school soon enough, my dear, so she'll mix more with English girls then," Dad assured her, drawing his comfort from a puff on his pipe.

"Perhaps I'll invite Conny Bowker over as well for tea and tennis this morning." Mom continued. "Leenie needs to mix more."

South Africa boasted two white tribes: *Afrikaners* who spoke Afrikaans (a derivative of Medieval Dutch, mingled with German and French) or the *English*, who spoke English with various degrees of posh-ness.

"Perhaps we can persuade Leenie to join our ladies tennis team at the club. She is nice and tall. She should be able to serve well." Mom discerned.

"She is a bit hefty; she won't be as agile and athletic as you are, sweetheart." Dad glanced at his bride with a twinkle in his eye.

At that point, I entered their bedroom with a request, "Please may we make meringues for tea if we're having visitors?"

"Meringues take too long. I'll bake *scones* (biscuits). We have plenty of fresh cream to whip, and delicious homemade youngberry jam that Granny made," Mom made up her mind while making up her face in the mirror.

Just then our robust cook, Maggie, came down the long passage and stood outside their bedroom door. *"Iswekile iphelile!* (The sugar bowl is empty!)" She bleated loudly, not wanting to intrude.

"Judy, hurry and scoop some sugar out of the bin for Maggie." Mom handed me the keys, so she could carry on her conversation with Daddy.

"Ndiyeza Maggie ngoku ngoku! (I'm coming now-now, Maggie!)" I was stomping down the passage to the *loo,* which was added onto the homestead after flush toilets were invented. One had to go all the way through the Breakfast Room to get there.

Maggie was waiting eagerly for me in the pantry where my mother kept three metal bins filled with flour, sugar, and all of my dad's alcohol under lock and key.

I felt very important having those keys. It meant I was higher than Maggie in the pantry pecking order. Maggie was the unstated boss in the kitchen. I leaned over and scooped up sugar to fill the crystal bowl for tea. In order to reach the sugar, I had to balance my tummy on the sharp edge of the deep metal bin. My legs left the ground as I reached for the sugar at the bottom of the bin. Maggie had to grab onto my twiggy leg so that I did not land headfirst into the sweet granules.

"Kasiphe nathi, (Please give us some too,)" Maggie demanded in an entitled tone. I obeyed and filled the enamel mug she had produced from under her apron until it overflowed.

"Pheza! Enkosi, Nohanki! Ndiyakuthanda gqhitha! (Stop! Thank you! *Nohanki!* I love you lots!)" She continued joyfully. Maggie had chosen my very own Xhosa name, *Nomhankazi,* but she shortened it when she was in a hurry.

Before I locked the bins, Maggie grabbed a bottle of *Bols Brandy* and stole a few large swigs then put it back very swiftly. She quickly slipped the sugar mug through the wooden hatch that led into the kitchen. Then slid the little sliding-door shut confidently to conceal the stolen treasure. She walked around to the kitchen to claim it from that side.

I innocently returned the keys to my mom, not mentioning a word about the extra mug for Maggie. I hoped the ever present grand-ghosts were not paying attention.

After a hot breakfast of runny eggs and very crispy bacon, Mom instructed me to start my drawing for Nature Study. I sat at my wooden desk in the Breakfast Room where Mom homeschooled me. I drew a black spot and labeled it 'frog egg.'

Mommy was reminded of her scones when the heavenly aroma wafted across from the kitchen. "I need to go and check on my scones. Maggie seems a little distracted this morning; she burnt the bacon to a crisp."

Maggie was a marvelous cook except when she was marinated in grog.

Presently, I heard a knock on the front door. It was exactly 11 o'clock: time for putting down my pencil and having tea with our new neighbors.

Mom was wearing her turquoise, floral cotton frock. It had a covered belt and buckle to match that I had watched her nimbly create. The belt complimented her slender waist on her tall, elegant frame.

Heading to the door, Mom called out, "Judy, you may have a break now. It must be Leenie. I'll have to change into my tennis dress later. Maggie-please put the kettle on."

I hurried after Mom, curious to see this white, Afrikaans girl. They lived in the flatter farmhouse right beside the Bridge. Carlisle Bridge was the name of the single lane cement bridge that crosses the Great Fish River.

"Hello, Leenie, *hoe gaan dit?* (How are you?)" I heard Mom attempt to speak Afrikaans with an English accent.

"Goed, dankie, (Well, thank you,)" Aunty Leenie replied humbly.

The Afrikaners were called nicknames by the English, who looked down their snobby noses at them. Bruce and his friends called the Afrikaners "Rock Spiders," "Dutchman," or "*Vaalies*" from the Transvaal. *Vaalies* were people who came from far inland and did not know how to conduct themselves properly at the seaside. They wore trousers on the beach, for instance! Some scandalously wore *veldskoens* (suede shoes) on the sand.

In Afrikaans class, Mom had taught me that the "G" in *"Goed"* is a raspy sound that you make when you have a tickle in your throat. Aunty Leenie was very grand at making a raspy G-sound.

"Goeiemore. Goed, dankie, (Good Morning. Well, thank you,)" Frieda rasped.

I was intrigued by Frieda when she started making the same cat-growl sounds.

She was a chubby girl, with dark, straight hair. She had brought a doll, which was neatly tucked under her arm.

"Judy, this is Frieda. They are new in these parts," my mom introduced us.

"How do you do, Frieda," I said politely.

The Afrikaners had trekked up northwards to get away from the British long ago. Since the Anglo-Boer war was distant history, now they were moving back to live next to us. Clearly, I was neither purebred *Boer* or pure British. I was a mixed mutt of a Karoo country bumpkin. One would brand my bottom BB for Bester *Brak* (mongrel). However, my mother was determined to make "lady" my label. Manners were what *breeding* was all about, Mother always taught.

"You two may go and play outside on the lawn. There is a lovely shady spot under the Jacaranda tree. I asked Jane to spread an old rug there for you. She'll bring you your tea just now," Mom continued in her genteel manner.

"Come along, Frieda!" I said enthusiastically, still a little apprehensive about my new friend. The chunky child followed me mutely. We saw Aunty Conny's car stop under the pepper tree. Mom and Aunty Leenie waltzed out to meet Aunty Conny Bowker. She was not related to us, but I was expected to call her "Aunty," just as we called adult males "Uncle."

Mother introduced the adults and after all the "how do you do" formalities, Aunty Conny remarked, "Look how lovely your garden is, Gwenna!" She smiled and breathed in the fragrance. "I love your terraced lawns, and the rockery resembles a rainbow of colors!"

"God gave us a beautiful earth to live on," Aunty Leenie said bravely in English, but with a very Afrikaans accent. She was a stout woman with a neat brown bun on the top of her head. I admired her pluck.

"And He gave us Gwenna to put us all to shame with her gay garden. This garden is like the Garden of Eden," added Aunty Conny, stretching her shoulders after her journey. She was shorter than the other two ladies. One would label her as pear-shaped. "Your daisies are always splendid."

"Thank you very much. It must be the water from our dam. I think that water has propitious fertilizer in it." Mom smiled knowingly. She knew where all that splendor originated.

Uncle Hubert Bowker farmed across the river, but Aunty Conny had to drive all the way around over Carlisle Bridge on the tarred road to get over the muddy Fish River. The river was the boundary dividing their farm and ours. She had to drive miles and miles to have tea with my mother.

We felt fortunate that the government had built a very big H.F.Verwoerd Dam inland with sluice gates that sloshed out permanent water into the Fish River. It made our riverside property much more valuable overnight, Dad had explained. So they all began to plough and put in pumps along the river. The plough blades turned up many bones from the Frontier wars fought along the Fish River. Those anonymous bones were respectfully reburied next to the ploughed fields. They were all buried together as they were all white bones, and no flesh could tell if they were Xhosa warriors or British Red coats.

One school holiday, Dad drove all six of us to pay homage to the Verwoerd Dam. It took all day and Norman was so bored in the car that he stuck his chewing gum in my hair to cause a commotion. Mom had to shave a patch on my head to get rid of the goop.

The dam was named after our current president who constructed grand apartheid. His name was H.F. Verwoerd and he was born in Holland, so he was a true Dutchman. The V sounded like an F and the W sounded like a V. Mom had taught me all of that in my Afrikaans lessons. But she was English and was not at all good at Afrikaans. Mom dearly hoped that friendship kindled with Frieda would help me learn to speak Afrikaans a bit better.

"The soaking rains have helped an awful lot," Mom said modestly, ushering both her guests halfway into the lounge, "along with good composted soil. The servants mix in wheelbarrow loads of manure from the stables. It all helps, Boetie measured another inch of rain last week."

"Gwenna, please may we sit outside on the veranda, so we can enjoy your garden," Aunty Conny insisted. "We only have Colored workers in our yard, and those *gammats* (hooligans) of ours do not know how to prune a rose bush. Perhaps I should switch to Xhosa servants. Only, I can communicate with the Cape Coloreds as they speak Afrikaans. I could never understand these clicking Xhosas. Mind you, those colored *klonkies* (Colored children) swear so much, that my children have picked up some foul words. Steven started talking like a *Kuipie* (Cape Colored) with ghastly adjectives."

"The weather is perfect," Aunty Leenie was brave enough to talk again, "We *is* very lucky with the rain."

Adults always talk about the weather, so Frieda and I left.

"Do you want to play dolls?" I asked Frieda, my newfound friend.

Frieda just stared at me blankly.

"I'll go and fetch mine," I said, pointing towards the farmhouse. "You may stay here or come with me." I gestured toward the checked *rug* (blanket with tassels) and then at me, starting to suspect that she didn't understand anything I was saying.

Sometimes people can understand a language, but not speak it. The lambs on the farm understand when you call them, "lamby-lamby" and they come running. Horses and bulls also get spoken to all the time. They don't talk back, but beasts obey verbal commands.

Frieda said nothing, but she followed me like a sheep as I went into the house. In the Breakfast Room, I headed for the huge toy cupboard. I retrieved my favorite new doll and a small suitcase of handmade clothes. We returned to the rug.

"What is your doll's name?" I asked, pointing at her doll. "I got this one from Father Christmas. But I really don't believe in him any more. Do you? I smelled her new plastic hidden high up in the linen cupboard before we went to the seaside. Sindie and Tombe say that Father Christmas does not exist. They say that Father Christmas is just a silly thing that we whites made up. But my mom says the Xhosas made up the thing about Thokoloshe too. Which one do you believe in? I think Thokoloshe and Father Christmas are both just made-up rubbish to make us be good. What do you think?"

Silence.

"You forgot to tell me her name. What is your baby's name?" I pointed again at her doll. "Can you think or talk in any language?"

Still no reply was forthcoming from my mute mate.

"Ja? (Yes) *Nee?* (No) " I was getting desperate enough to try a little Afrikaans myself.

"Ek weet nie, (I don't know)" she finally muttered in Afrikaans, proving she had not swallowed her tongue!

"Then let's christen your doll a name," I prompted, understanding those simple words after my Afrikaans lessons. She just glared back at me with big eyes, perplexed.

"You could name her Dawn or Sandra or Mary-Rose. Those are all white people girl names." I started nodding and talking in a squeaky voice, as though I was speaking to a baby, but to no avail. She just seemed rapt in confusion.

"Do you want to switch dolls? My doll's name is Rosemary," I said, trying to trade toys. She pulled hers closer to her chest, frowning like I was a robber. We had a serious language blockade. Signs and nodding didn't help. Even the squeaky voice was useless. It merely bounced off her eardrums. There was no bridge for my words to cross into her head.

I was about to call her a *domkop* (dunce), but the ladies were too near.

The Afrikaners, on the other hand, also had rude labels for the English. They called us *"Rooinekke"* or *"Souties."* Name-calling was rampant among the rainbow of races.

Frieda and I were both baffled by then. There appeared to be no bridge to cover our social divide.

"Xa, utheni lomtana? ({Click of tongue when angry}What's the matter with this child?)" I muttered in isiXhosa to myself, feeling exasperated. I was losing patience with this non-responsive newcomer.

Suddenly, Frieda spoke! *"Andisazi isiNgesi.* (I don't know English.)" She was speaking Xhosa with a thick Afrikaans inflection.

Of all the nine black tribes of South Africa, each one spoke their own language. The Xhosa clicked their tongues very fast when they speak. Implosive clicks, were made while inhaling air, not to mention the tricky explosive clicks. Most white people could not unconsciously exhale and inhale fast enough, because they were used to only exhaling while talking. Whites made fools of themselves; usually saliva exploded instead of sounds.

"Ayinanto, khe masithetheni isiXhosa, (It doesn't matter. Let us speak

in Xhosa then,)" I replied in Xhosa, with the correct Xhosa accent. With all my siblings absent, I talked incessantly to our servants and mastered a very pure form of *isiXhosa.* It was very rare for white people to speak Xhosa properly.

The foreign freeze was thawed when we realized we could communicate by clicking in common Xhosa. Frieda had a real barrier-breaking smile. It was most uncommon for European kids to converse with one another in an indigenous language. We had a whale of a time clicking our tongues in the African dialect. We dressed up pale pink dolls. I was raised speaking English and Frieda was raised speaking Afrikaans, and yet we communicated in Xhosa, clicking crazily!

"Well, I might say the girls are getting along quite well, aren't they just?" my gorgeous mother observed as she glided down the stairs of the cement *stoep*. She had the accent of a D.S.G. private schooled girl.

"Frieda is too shy to speak English," Aunty Leenie disclosed, shaking her head. "I was *really* wanting Judy to help Frieda pronounce a few words in English properly." She rolled her r's perfectly.

"Judy never stops talking, I might add," Aunty Conny interjected. "Frieda will learn to speak English very quickly from Gwenna's little chatterbox." The three ladies took a stroll towards the fragrant orange roses.

"Gwenna grows the best Barberton (Gerber) daisies in the district," Aunty Conny floated around, examining the dazzling yellow petals. "Hubert bought me a bunch once from the *Charrah* who sells them on the corner café in town. They were not as pretty as yours." Indians did not escape being called names either; and they were termed *"Charras"* or *"Curry Munchers."*

Name-calling was just part of the culture in South Africa. No one was politically correct with all those condescending names, so no race was going to *trek* away from being called a name or two. It was par for the course, so everyone grew a thick, tough skin, not matter how much pigment was on your epidermis.

There had been too many wars and bloodshed afflicting the races, tribes and colonizers. Poison arrows, gunfire and spears had been the method of communicating death on the enemy. Swearing and name-calling released some steam, so we were all very guilty of it at some time or another. At least name-calling was a step better than killing each other.

"You must take some daisies home with you." Mom glowed with generosity.

"Your geraniums *is* very pretty," Aunty Leenie complimented, while rolling her *r* in *ge-r-aniums* and *ve-r-y* and *p-r-etty*.

"Geraniums grow by slip. You just break off a piece and stand it in a sunny spot in a glass of water. Little roots will start to appear, and then you can plant them in the ground. You just have to remove the bottom leaves like this. Here, do try this one to start." Mom gave *Tannie* (Aunty) Leenie a slip. "Geraniums *are* very rewarding, and *are* perennial in this climate," my mother was instructing the plural verb, always the teacher. She was not rolling her *r*'s, hinting kindly how to articulate English in the proper manner. Mom sounded like she had a hot potato in her mouth.

"*Baie dankie*. (Thank you.)" Aunty Leenie gracefully accepted the peachy pink flower on a stripped stalk.

Correcting others in a nice way is very helpful, not cruel; Mom always said when she taught me. She had made me walk up and down our long passage with a heavy, hard Bible on my head, repeating the words, "how-now-brown-cow."

As the ladies came closer, they remarked on how nicely we were playing. It delighted my mother that I was having fun with a white girl. They strolled within earshot to see if I was nattering in my broken version of Afrikaans, or if Frieda was attempting her sparse English.

Holding up my favorite doll's dress, the one Mom had sown from scraps of material, I said clicking, "*Ndithanda le lokwe gqhitha!* (I like this dress the most!)"

"*Intle gqitha*, (It is very pretty,)" Frieda clicked back. "*Inamaqhosho,* (It has buttons,)" Frieda continued.

"*Nomgqibelo, sizakulqabela ngakuni nathi. Zuze nawe, uzokujongela abazali bam xa bedhala ibholo,* (On Saturday, we are coming over your way. You should come too, and watch my parents play tennis or cricket,)" I babbled on.

My mom stopped and stared in horror, not wanting to believe her ears, when she heard us clicking our tongues. She attempted to distract her guests by steering them to a more glorious show of blue delphiniums. At the same time, she was straining to listen to Frieda and me.

"Ooooh! My goodness gracious me!" Aunty Conny exclaimed loudly. "These little white girls are speaking the most strange black language on earth!" she broadcasted rather dramatically, "How funny!" She roared. "This is too uncanny for words!!" She shrieked, throwing her head back in guffaws of laughter. "Your girls talk like pucker piccanins!"

Aunty Leenie and Mom peered at each other, shrugging their shoulders with discomfiture, relaxing as laughter melted the tense moment. The three moms giggled and giggled as if they were young girls again.

Aunty Leenie put her hand up to cover her face. *"O Here, dankie vir kinders!* (Oh Lord, thank you for children!)" She prayed aloud, not so concerned about being proper anymore.

"How jolly odd!" Mom was still ladylike at least.

"Liewe wêreld!! Wit kaffertjies! (Dear world!! White little kaffirs!)" Aunty Leenie van Vuuren cackled and crowed and screeched. *"Ons kinders is wit pikaninne!* (Our children are white piccanins!)" Both the Afrikaners and English had nicknames for the blacks. Some were nicer than others, but *"Wog," "Houtkoppe,"* and *"Kaffir"* were the controversial ones.

Jane arrived bearing fresh scones and tea on a large tray, looking mystified at the three ladies laughing so raucously. The rules of civility seemed forgotten.

"Molweni, Missis. (Good morning, Madams.)" Jane smiled politely as she set down the tea tray in a most graceful manner.

Aunt Conny was laughing like a diesel tractor engine warming up in winter. An engine that does not take the first time, and you have to keep turning the key in the ignition. But then she took off and could not stop grunting and spattering.

"Hayikhona, hintoni na? (No way, what is going on here?)" Jane directed to me.

"Oh Jane, thank you for the tea." Mother attempted to regain her composure.

"Gwenna, something tells me that little girl of yours will not be muzzled," Aunty Conny declared, still highly amused. "She will talk the hind leg off a donkey in any language she chooses."

Lizzie was in the front dairy separating the cream from the milk and heard the shrieks of laughter; even she got off her fat bottom to come around the side of the house to see what was happening.

"Hayikhona, basela ntoni koloti? U Maggie ufake utywala kwiti yabo? (What are they drinking in that tea? Did Maggie put alcohol in their tea?)" Lizzie stood and whined, "I do not trust Maggie…she is a thief. She tries to steal my husband. I could smell booze on her breath this morning. I will curse her."

"Please don't, Lizzie. Her five children would be orphaned." Jane was well aware of Maggie's improprieties, but always stood up for children. "Her oldest son, Tatey, would become a *tsotsi* (thug). Who would raise him?"

Anyone with eyes could tell that Tatey, Maggie's oldest son, was Jack's child, he being the image of Jack. Lizzie labeled Maggie most viciously, but you could expect Jack's "first wife" to be jealous of his so called "other wife."

Aunty Conny retried to be an English lady, now that she had two servants peering at her and took an elegant sip of tea, but started to laugh before she could swallow, so the tea projected out onto the petunias next to the veranda.

"I will never drink any tea that Maggie makes again, never." Lizzie stated soberly shaking her head, while wiping cream off her chin and rubbing it into her cheeks. "Who would trust a cook like her to make tea anyway? She probably added *dagga* (marijuana) leaves."

None of the three white ladies could hear or understood Lizzie's language, but Frieda flicked her tea out on the lawn with a frown.

"Bahleka thina, ndithetha isiXhosa nalomtana weBhulu. Akasiva isiNgesi tu. (They are laughing at us. I am speaking Xhosa to this Afrikaans kid. She did not understand English at all.)" I smiled to Jane, whom I loved dearly.

"Owu mntana wam, ungumXhosa wena ngakade. (Oh, my child, you are a Xhosa no matter what.)" Jane rubbed my back and stood next to me proudly for a moment, as if she had raised me single-handedly. She whispered. "Please do not play with a child who wastes good tea. Tombe will be here straight after school."

4

LESSONS IN LUCK

For weeks, I observed the black frog eggs gradually grow long tails and big eyes. The wriggly tadpoles learned to swim around in the green water, swelling fatter and fatter each day. Oodles of black tadpoles swam around looking like pregnant black sperm. With warmth and light, they soon bulged, burst, and then gave birth to two back legs, one on each side. Even tinier webbed front arms popped out afterwards. Eventually, slimy baby frogs kicked their way around the smarmy water.

I was spellbound, watching the frog feet instinctively kicking as the outmoded tail shrank away. Those hind legs propelled the frog forward. Such superior entertainment had the special effect of teaching me to be in awe of Mother Nature.

After I had learned about metamorphosis, Mom warned we would soon be setting the amphibians free in Bumpy. Not before, I might add, Mom had thoroughly educated me on the unseen microorganisms that multiplied in the stagnant water under our microscope.

"Now perhaps you will refrain from drinking that contaminated water," Mom chastised. "You are very lucky you did not get a runny tummy."

"My friends taught me to only drink the running water not the sitting water." I spoke up.

I often contemplated kissing my pet frogs, hoping to marry a prince. In order to complete the experiment, I scooped a frog out and kissed it secretly one day, being ever so careful not to swallow the water. At least, I hoped to marry a Carlisle Bridge farmer. Our idyllic life was similar to that of royalty already, I thought.

"We simply have to improve your Afrikaans," Mom declared one school day. "We had better concentrate on that today. Frieda wasn't much help, was she?" Mom smiled to herself.

I was perfectly content having my mother as my teacher. Mom was a gifted teacher. She enunciated the Afrikaans words to the best of her ability. However, she often went to lie down after our language sessions, saying I must practice my Afrikaans *taal* (grammar) on my own.

One day, I heard her say on the phone, "I need to make an appointment to see Dr. Vosloo." The *v* sounded like an *f*. He was our doctor who lived in Bedford, thirty miles inland. Mom drove to Bedford and came home as the sun was setting. "Doctor Vosloo said I have an ulcer in my duodenum. He has to operate to remove it," she soberly informed my father.

He looked anxious and lit up his pipe, drawing smoke deep into his lungs. "Well, the sooner he can fix you up, the better, Billikins." But Dad looked shattered.

It scared me how our circumstances could metamorphose from idyllic to frightening in an instant. Situations, not only tadpoles, can also change their form.

And transform they did. My mother's parents, Granny and Grandpa Stocks, who were very Elizabethan in their ways, arrived a few days later to watch over me.

Granny Stocks was militant about manners. Her favorite saying was, "Manners maketh man," and she would repeat it every day, along with the following:

"Ladies don't chew with their mouths open."

"Ladies don't burp."

"Ladies say 'I beg your pardon.' "

"Ladies, who have any class use common courtesy and say 'No, thank you,' or 'Yes, please.' "

I began to envy my siblings at boarding school, for they had escaped her lectures on the correct conduct of a civilized lady. Boarding school seemed like a respite after a week in Granny Stocks' company.

Grandpa Norman Stocks was tall, slender, and handsome, with fine features. He was a polished English gentleman, ranking high in society. He had no option really, being married to the matron of manners herself.

Grandpa Stocks was also a very fine handyman, and he quickly busied himself making us a wooden go-cart out of the planks from a tomato box. He used the wheels off my old pram. He greased the wheels and affixed a steering wheel to the contraption. Unfortunately, he omitted to add any brakes.

One day, I was riding it down a steep hill and I lost control. I remember thinking that I was about to perish. Suddenly, an outsider influencer told me to relax and become wobbly, like a tadpole. I obeyed, which is why my tail was still in one piece when I reached the bottom of the hill. I wondered who that invisible person was who had helped me. I never told anyone about it, expecting they would say it was rubbish. I considered myself jolly lucky to have only scrapes and bruises to show for the ordeal.

Could those grand-ghosts have morphed into guardian angels?

"It will be a relief for Gwenna to be rid of the pain," my dad said over tea to his in-laws. "We have arranged for Hoppy Gradwell, a young lass from next door, to come and tutor Judy while Gwenna is in hospital for a few weeks."

Hoppy was a most conscientious governess, and I liked her very much. I thought of naming my pet *platana* (frog) after her, but Granny Stocks wouldn't hear of it.

I was relieved that Granny was not going to be my teacher. I had visions of her teaching me how to be a lady all day long. She would have me learning how to eat, walk, talk and act.

For good reason, the servants did not like Granny Stocks. She was very stingy with sugar, and she never entrusted anyone with the bin keys. Servants had a disdain for overly prudent people.

The feelings were mutual and Granny accused Maggie of stealing after every meal. "I gave you eight lamb chops to cook and only seven made it to the table."

Maggie had the chops to lie to her face, "I accidently burnt one, *oumiesies.* Miss Judy only eats half a chop. "

Behind her back, Maggie christened Granny, *"Umgovu,"*meaning the government, which in 1965 ruled with an iron rod.

Oh, how quickly life can be so different! What if my mother died? Fear engulfed my helpless soul for the first time.

"I am going to play at the huts," I said, eager to escape the stiff formalities of the big white homestead.

I found Sindie and Toto, her older sister, at their square modern mud hut with a zinc roof. Jack, their father, had built it next to their old round hut as his family grew very large. White pumpkins and rocks weighed the corrugated iron slabs down. Chickens wandered about on the swept dirt. Lizzie, was slowly smearing specific patterns with white clay around their door and peephole windows. Lizzie used her skilled hands to paint the mud walls very carefully. Triangular symbols around the holes of her hut would supposedly serve to hold the bad spirits and bad luck at bay. Lizzie, no doubt, had Bushman blood in her and was much paler than most Xhosas, which her rivals envied.

Toto and Sindie had just walked home from school. After tossing down their black slates, they each took a long swig of sour milk out of their hollow, dried *calabash* (gord).

"Molo, (Hello) Miss Judy," Toto said with a broad, pretty smile like Lizzie.

"Molo," Sindie smiled, sticking the cork back to seal the calabash container.

"Molweni, (Hello,)" I replied, rather relieved to be in their mud hut.

"Masiyokukha umngqabaza! (Let's go and pick wild berries!)" Sindie eagerly suggested. She always had bright ideas, most of them originating in her tummy.

We collected Tombe further up the hill. She was sweeping their round, old-fashioned mud hut. Yan did not approve of zinc roofs; he preferred the old traditional thatch, as it was cooler in summer and warmer in winter.

Tombe bossed her younger siblings out of the way as she swept. *"Sukani!* (Get out the way!)" She swiped them with the grass broom, and they scattered like chickens.

The three of us hiked up the hill into the top veldt, gathering *umnqabaza* (a cream-colored berry) and feasting on wild, oval-shaped, purple berries called *cum cums.* I was happy to be in their company again.

"Look at these red berries! Let's taste them!" I suggested, spotting a new variety of wild berries.

"No, Miss Judy, they are not to be eaten," Tombe cautioned emphatically.

"How do you know, Tombe?" I inquired.

"Don't you know that if you sit by a tree and watch the birds, you'll know? If the *muisvoëls* (speckled mouse bird) come and eat the fruit, so can you. But if you sat by those red berries all day you would see that no birds of the heavens ever eat them. That's how you know," Tombe scolded, as if I was a stupid white kid who only learned from books.

"Maybe the birds aren't hungry enough," I persisted.

"No, Miss Jay. There is enough poison in those berries to kill you. The old people have taught us not to touch those, even if they do look juicy and inviting," Sindie explained, unashamed of the wisdom she had gathered from the witchdoctors. "Witches use those berries to poison people."

Ignoring their warnings, I picked one and squished it in my fingers. "Ag, it smells bad," I remarked, trying to shake it off my fingers. "I would not want to eat one, but they just looked so luscious."

Tombe marched over, grabbed my fingers with hers, and carefully washed them in the dust. She was unrelenting until she got rid of the red residue that looked like blood on my hands.

"Hayi! Ungaphinde! (No! Don't ever do that again!)" Tombe rebuked, satisfied that I was safe. "Now you can wipe the dust off on your clothes." Tombe was most motherly.

"My mother said that Maggie threatened to plant a few of those berries in your Granny's tea." Sindie laughed aloud. "She said I should tell you to inform her."

Sindie spotted a *litye* tree laden with wild plums. "Those berries are ripe," she announced. "The birds will eat them all if we don't hurry up."

Between us and the *litye* tree stood two red Africander cows with long white horns. Both had calves. The calf was sucking so hard on the udder that white milky froth slid off the sides of its pink tongue.

Sindie started with a joyful jaunt of anticipation towards the tree, which was irresistibly dripping with ripe, red fruit.

"What's the matter with you two? Your minds are not holding onto your brains very tightly." Tombe's words followed Sindie, but Tombe's rigid feet stayed put.

"Look out, Sindie; I can see the whites of that cow's eye. She is fierce. That cow is looking at you," I added my warning. "Tombe is right!"

The red heifers stood their stony ground. Cows have pointy horns to protect their progeny.

"Did your father, the stable man, not teach you anything about cattle?" Tombe was now bellowing.

The warnings dissipated into the royal blue sky and never reached Sindie. She was too daring for her own safety.

Tombe was preparing for the skirmish. She picked up a couple of tennis ball-sized rocks, while still keeping her eyes focused on the cows. I followed Tombe's example.

Sindie plucked a *Swazi* (small stick) off a bush and waved it at the cows, *"Hambani! Sukani!* (Depart! Get out the way!)" She commanded with the same authority with which her father spoke to the tame bulls in the stable.

The cows did not understand isiXhosa, but the birds apparently did. *Dikkops* made swift departures. Feathered *finches* flew and fluttered, falling from dizzy heights. *Boubou shrike* took flight and dived for denser brush, while *buntings* took wing, uttering at take-off. *Pintailed whydah* soared and circled the skies, dive-bombing other smaller birds, dominating the food source.

The younger cow with the firstling bellowed back, its moist nostrils flaring. Half-masticated leaves slid off its large, slimy tongue. No one taught cows not to talk with their mouths full. They had no manners at all, those mooing, munching cows.

Sindie raised her scrawny arm, waving the *Swazi* brazenly. It may as well have been a red flag, which had obviously failed to pop up in her hungry head.

There was suddenly a cloud of dust and the cow charged Sindie, roaring like a lion. For a second, I could not see Sindie at all for dust.

When the dust settled, we saw Sindie posted in the wild plum tree, dangling onto the branches with the agility of a monkey. I have never seen anyone get so high so fast. A diverse array of birds took to the air after discovering the runaway in the *litye* tree. Whether she vaulted off the cow's back, or she was catapulted by the white horns, we will never know.

That left Tombe and me on the ground, heaving rocks at the fuming foe. United we stood in battle, while stones rebounded off the irate cows. Amidst the hullabaloo, a disturbed *duiker* (deer) darted for a *doringboom* (thorn tree). Tombe and I held the front lines, flinging boulders with considerable effort, screeching explosive expletives at the beasts.

Meanwhile, Sindie gave her airborne support, heaving branches from an advantaged height. It literally rained fruit as Sindie shook the tree, creating an aerial attack of pelting plums.

Sombre bulbul birds eerily made babbling trill sounds like "Willie! Come out and fight!"

Except for a few stains on our clothes, the plums never really hurt us. The cows swung their tails violently to shake off the overripe, sticky plums. I had only seen them dismiss insects in that manner before. After some loud protesting, the cows bolted for cover into the bushy banks of Bumpy.

The Battle of Bumpy was won by three little girls!

I watched the top banks to be sure more cows were not going to charge. I noticed our servants had their own open graveyard on those banks. Heaps of unmarked river rocks left a light footprint on Mother Earth. Rocks prevented hyenas from digging up rotting corpses.

I never said a word, not wanting to disturb anyone. Two tiny, stony mounds, side by side, indicated babies slept there.

"You two are real cowards," jeered Sindie, suddenly smug from her roost in the *litye* tree. "Why did you not come with me to chase those cows away?"

"At least we are 'alive' cowards. You are a fool. You could be dead now! You, of all people, should know not to tangle with a cow protecting its calf!" Tombe scolded.

Tombe and I climbed the plum tree and enjoyed some sweet fruit. It was bliss to be with those wild friends in that wild plum tree away from those wild cows. I felt safe.

As we strolled down the hill towards the huts again, we laughed at how Sindie was launched by a cow and landed plumb in the middle of the tree she wanted to reach in the first place. All she had to show for her misadventure was a little rip in her dress.

"Miss Jay, will you please give me one of your old dresses, so my mother does not beat me?"

"I will ask my mother when she comes out the hospital."

I, too, had previously been kicked in the mouth by a calf and had even lost a tooth while tangling with a *tollie* (midsized calf). My brother Norman and cousin, Martin, ordered me to hold the leg while they practiced pulling it over. Luckily, it was my milk tooth. Sindie and I had bovine battle scars, while Tombe played life safer.

"Come and look here!" Sindie's spirit was buoyant as ever as she danced a spry little jig. From that day forward, I knew spirited Sindie was not the type of soul that could be held down. She would always bounce back up again.

I was amazed at her skill of finding a tiny, green, curly stalk sticking out of the ground. It looked like a green pig's tail in my nursery rhyme book.

"It's a *bharu*!(edible root!)" Sindie blurted, excited at her recent discovery. She grabbed a stiff stick and started digging around the spring-shaped leaf, carefully excavating the loose ground with her hand.

"We *are* lucky today." Tombe announced.

When the root was fully unearthed, it resembled a swollen sweet potato. Sindie took her prize out of the dirt and waved it in the air. Bony arms and lanky legs were dangling from her skinny frame. Her spirit was like the wind, blowing her limbs like the branches of a tree, constantly twirling around her trunk. Quite honestly, I always marveled that Sindie's limbs remained linked to her trunk.

Sindie bit off the dirty brown skin and spat it aside, not quite like a lady. Inside was a delicious, crispy, white root. Sindie shared the tasty treat. We sat in a victory circle and passed it clockwise. Xhosas have a healthy habit of sharing.

"It is so sweet," Tombe spluttered, with her mouth full and her eyes bright.

Their nomadic Xhosa tribe had been surviving on this indigenous grub, which was foreign to most white folks, for many moons.

"I like it, too. It tastes a little like the earth, but it is very juicy," I remarked after my first bite.

"You can eat the watery leaves of that succulent shrub if you are still hungry," Sindie pointed at the swollen, fat leaves, obviously proud of her heritage, no matter how different it was from mine.

"No, thanks, I have had an elegant sufficiency," I spoke like Granny taught, only clicking in Xhosa.

I was in awe of their survival skills in the bush. They learned from the birds and wise old people. They taught each other and trained one another. Any Xhosa parent could spank any disobedient child. I loved the way they shared their duties. I admired their closely knit culture. It was in a class of its own.

"My dad calls that *'spekboom,'* I know you can eat it. I have tasted it before," I added, hoping not to be outdone by my indigenous friends. I enjoyed playing with them and learning from them. I loved them.

My dad had allocated all of his laborers a plot of ground below the Eden Dam where they could irrigate and grow their own fruits and vegetables. Some had taken advantage of the opportunity, planting pumpkins, calabashes, and Swiss chard. Others could not be bothered, rather enjoying the buffet of wild berries and prickly pears.

With a belly full of *bharu*, I later slouched at the formal table with my grandparents and Dad.

"Sit up straight please, Judy." My dad gave me a warning glance as if to say, "Granny is watching." I was now being gawked at by ghosts and granny. I was not sure which I disliked more. They seemed like crows circling to pounce on their prey.

I fiddled with my food; it just didn't taste right without my mother present. Change choked in my throat. Why could old people not explain the random things that happen? Why was there no warning at all?

"I don't want to eat. I miss my mommy!" I sniffed.

The next day, my dad drove us to Bedford to visit my mother in the hospital. She sat up and greeted us warmly, putting a smile on her pale face. Her starched sheets had navy blue writing on them that read, "Bedford Hospital." The pristine room smelled like Dettol, a pungent disinfectant.

Dad kissed her and gave her some fresh, blue delphiniums, which Granny had picked out our garden.

"I will be home next week," Mommy mustered up some cheerfulness. "Just in time for the Easter holidays. Doctor Vosloo said I am improving every day."

I daydreamed on the long slow drive home, staring out the car window at the black and white cows roaming out in the Cloete's fields. Their cattle looked so blotchy compared to our spotless red heifers. We only farmed brown Jersey cattle for milk for our family and Africander cattle for breeding bulls.

"These Friesland cows give gallons of milk, more than our Jersey dairy herd, but their milk has much less butterfat content or cream." Dad was teaching us as we ambled along. "Gwenna and I prefer Jersey milk in our tea."

Then there was silence for a while.

"It's such a bother, I might add," Granny stated, attempting to break the silence in our blue Lincoln Zephyr. "Getting an ulcer is a spot of bad luck."

'Who rations out luck?' I wondered to myself. *'Exactly who are the*

givers and takers of luck?' If only we knew the answer to that...so much for all their fancy education from books.

Old English nursery rhymes tell of pots of gold at the end of the rainbow. Xhosa sorcerers sell luck in the form of charms. I knew of a certain tree that shed "lucky beans." They were little red and black seeds that witchdoctors sold for a wicked profit. I had no doubt that my life was more charmed than any of their gullible Xhosa customers—until now. Perhaps I should buy some lucky beans. Why couldn't I just pick them from the tree myself? Do the witchdoctors treat the beans to make them lucky? Do they have some authority to cast a spell on the beans?

A few weeks later, life seemed back to normal. Bruce, Wendy, and Norman were home for the Easter ten-day holiday. The excitement of seeing them cheered up my Mom, who had been convalescing slowly with a long, pink scar on her tummy.

Wendy furiously boiled all kinds of sweet things. On the gas stove in the pantry, she stirred up all sorts of confectionaries. She made fudge and toffee and coconut ice with pink and white layers. I watched and licked. Unlike our cook, Maggie, who could not read at all, Wendy could read recipes. There were most definitely perks to getting an education!

"Please may we put a little extra coconut in it? Won't it taste better?" I ventured to ask.

"Don't be dense! Just follow what the recipe says and it all turns out right," Wendy wailed with conviction while waving a wooden spoon in the air, as if she was conducting a choir.

"Can't we add just a spoonful?" I ate the shredded coconut by the handful.

"No. This is Granny Stocks' recipe. You cannot meddle with perfection." Wendy was always very certain. She definitely had some of Granny Stocks in her blood.

I had mostly observed my Maggie cook on the wood stove in the kitchen. I found great comfort sitting on the laps of my three black mothers while my mom was in hospital. Maggie's *modus operandi* was 'lick, taste and add' whatever the dish needed. Habits spread as fast as germs. You also pick them up from the people who you are with all the time. I preferred Maggie's method.

Bruce spent most of his holidays playing cricket on the top lawn. A blazing display of flowers separated the top lawn from the lower lawn. Bruce had invited Cocoa, his childhood friend, and a few other *kwediens* (black teenagers) to play cricket with him. Bruce Bester batted most of the time, even when he was bowled out. Dad joined in that evening, coaching his sons.

"Alright, Norman, you can come and bat now," Bruce relented, holding out the wooden cricket bat which smelled like linseed oil.

Norman picked up the bat and started to bat left-handedly, swiping wildly as Dad made the first delivery. Norman's bat hit nothing but fresh air. The red ball collided with the wooden wickets, which flew out of the grass like tumbling skittles.

"Howzaat!" (Cricketing term shouted when a batsman is out) Bruce bellowed.

"Bad luck," Dad said, embarrassed that he had bowled Norman out on the first ball. "Try again; keep your eye on the ball. You'll have better luck next time."

"Dad, tell Norman to try batting with his right hand. He is right-handed," Bruce pleaded while resurrecting the fallen wickets.

"Graeme Pollock is the best batsman in the world, and he bats left-handed!" Norman jeered loudly.

"Some people never change," Bruce mumbled, hammering the wickets back into the lawn. He was using a rock from Mom's rockery as a hammer.

"Cricket is all about timing. Haven't you seen Graeme Pollock bat? Watch that ball and don't move the bat too late or too soon. If you relax, you seem to do it better," Dad instructed.

Dad bowled again, a little slower this time, and Norman's bat struck the hard, red ball solidly. It flew across the sky, smashing through the lounge window and landing on the green rug instead of the green grass.

"Six runs!" Cocoa crackled, a grin of white teeth gleaming from a brown face.

Norman was triumphant and shocked. When you hit six runs, it is the highest score you can get off one ball. Norman locked his fingers behind his head, realizing his victory was tainted by the mishap.

"Six of the best!" Bruce predicted, all too familiar with six cuts of the cane across the buttocks, which the school masters readily handed out to disobedient boys at boarding school.

"Caesar's Ghost's alive! That was very bad timing. We are expecting visitors soon for the birthday party." Mom stuck her nose out the lounge door, holding her knitting in a middle of a row, careful not to drop a stitch.

Dead or alive, our grand-ghosts could evidently not catch a cricket ball, I thought. Perhaps my parents should employ Lizzie to come and paint protective triangles around our wooden windows!

"Righto, my boys, I think I'm appealing against the light," Dad announced, indicating the game of cricket was over for the evening.

Dad was reluctant to display a full smile in front of Mom, but the corners of his lips showed pleasure at that mighty six-run hit. And he was just as reluctant to punish his child, as Norman had just got home after weeks away. My father clung to clemency. Besides, cricket was the true religion of Eastern Cape Province.

"Luckily, I am going to town tomorrow, so I will buy a new pane of glass." Dad was always looking for the bright side.

Dad peered up hopefully at the clear sky. "I think we will get some rain tomorrow after this strong, southeasterly wind." Our father taught us to expect rain from a cloudless sky.

"You can tell Mom that a gust of wind blew the ball through the glass," Bruce taunted, clobbering his little brother on the shoulder a little too roughly.

The sinking sun called the game to a halt. "You will have better luck tomorrow." Dad always fed us hope with his contagious optimism.

5

THE LAW OF THE LAMB

Tatey and Rama, Maggie's well-built sons, strutted down the hill towards the kitchen door looking for Norman. They knew that our outlandish Easter egg 'hunting' ritual was all done with. Not to mention the whites' odd cake custom with flames on top. Our traditions were bizarre to those Xhosa *kwediens* (lads).

In our race, white kids' birthdays were not something to be ignored. For instance, in 1956, the year I was born, Norman was a blonde, curly-topped toddler, celebrating his second birthday on Schelmdrift. Mom was still in the Grahamstown hospital with her new baby girl, me. Fortunately, Wendy was already aware of the burning necessity of candles for such occasions. Dad said she was genetically programmed to play the role of our missing mother. As a six-year-old big sister, Wendy methodically mixed up blue icing for her little brother. She glued a stack of *Marie Biscuits* (cookies) together making a heap that resembled a small cake. She lit two candles on top. She was an excellent big sister to her blue-eyed brother, and a firm keeper of traditions.

Wendy, still more domesticated in 1965, helped Mother create a mighty Humpty Dumpty from a large Cadbury's Easter egg. They sat him on a rectangle chocolate-cake brick-wall for my 9th birthday. Licorice legs with boots made of marzipan dangled over the side.

Sindie and Tombe were not invited to our parties, but that was normal in the era of apartheid. One did not invite servants *or* their children to European social gatherings. Sindie and Tombe sat politely out of sight on the kitchen *stoep*, and waited for me.

When I sneaked them a slice of cake to share, they peppered me with countless questions. I found explaining white traditions perplexing at times.

Having never heard of nursery rhymes, Tombe demanded, "Why do you have a fat black man sitting on your cake among the flames? My mother said his body was brown with pitch black legs?"

"No, I'll tell you later. I'll show you him in my book." How was I supposed to explain Humpty Dumpty in a hurry? "He is a man who falls down and nothing can be done as he cracks to pieces."

"Was he cursed? Is he made of eggshells? Is that why he turned black? Could your white-coated doctors not sew him back up again?" Sindie delved cheekily.

"No, he is made of chocolate that is why he is brown." I laughed. "You must see my book, he is white. I'll show you just now."

I darted back to the front *stoep* where we entertained our neighbors, Frieda and family.

Tatey and Rama fully understood that they were not invited to the combined birthday party for Norman and me. When a tradition is repeated for many birthdays, it morphs into the norm. Then it just feels normal. Now, a few days after all our festivities were over, they came to stake their claim in their childhood friend, Norman.

Their stomachs were ready for a tasty feast of a more savory nature. Tatey, the stocky older one, was darker-skinned and closely resembled Jack, our "stable boy," who wasn't really a boy at all. Jack was a full-grown, virulent man. Jack had very large, tusk-like teeth, with a few front ones missing due to drunken fights. Tatey and Jack were both the color of dark chocolate.

"Norman will be here soon. Wait here for him." Maggie handed her sons a slice of bread with butter and apricot jam.

Maggie, felt entitled to help herself to food for her children. Mom mostly turned a blind eye to her thievery.

Maggie was also not shy to come to work when she was drunk over the Easter weekend. Her words were always drawn out and her clicks indistinct when she had been drinking; I could tell instantly. I never ever smelled alcohol on Jane or Lizzie.

When Jane brewed strong coffee to sober Maggie up, our cook insisted she was not drunk. Jane would discreetly do most of Maggie's chores for her on those days. Jane loved Maggie as much as we did.

Maggie had other talents besides cooking.

She was the local midwife and delivered all of Jane's dozen babies as well as Lizzie's big brood. Jane had twins who died soon after they were born, fueling the Xhosa superstition that twins bring bad luck. Those were Jane's twin babies buried side by side on the banks of Bumpy.

Lizzie also gave birth to twins, one of which was Sindie. My friend had a twin brother named Bhoyi. They luckily both lived, but the girl twin was supposed to bring bad luck. Xhosas truly believed the myth that any girl twin was a carrier of bad omens. Mom said that she was befuddled by the fallacy surrounding my friend. Mom deemed Sindie to be perfectly normal, bright and safe for me to play with. But Sindie had not come to play that day.

"We want to hunt for real meat," Tatey stated when Norman eventually appeared. "Not stupid bunnies wrapped in silver paper." He mocked.

"Let's go and hunt some birds," Norman suggested to his two childhood pals. Norman spoke Xhosa, but he had not spent as much time as I had in the huts. His Xhosa was a little rusty, as it was not spoken at all in his boarding school.

"Bring some apples for us to munch," Tatey requested, always thinking of his fourteen-year-old stomach. He had rippling muscles and a deep voice like Jack.

"Please may I come, too?" I pleaded. Norman had only been home a few days, and he was still being quite kind to me. Tombe had also not come to play, so I was feeling lonely that day.

"OK, only if you carry the pellets," Norm replied. "And go and fetch some apples."

I obliged hastily, eager to spend time with my big brother and his pals.

"Enkosi (Thank you) Miss Judy," Tatey relieved me of an armful of apples. He stuffed an apple in his large mouth and tossed one to

his half-brother. Tatey engulfed the apple with his big fat lips. Luckily, Granny Stocks had already gone home.

We walked in a line: Norman in front with the pellet gun strapped over his shoulder; then Tatey, the oldest; then Rama; then me. In Africa, the man walks in front on a foot path. Men are considered more important than women in most tribal cultures.

Traditions were only amended on special extenuating circumstances. Dad heard on the national news that in South West Africa (Namibia), the custom had been revised since SWAPO had landmines buried all over. The women were suddenly told to walk ahead in case the mines detonated and blew up the men's feet. And so it was…the daily habits of Africans were adaptable occasionally—usually to suit the male species of Africa.

"*Kunjani esikolweni?* (How is school?)" Rama missed Norman, who had been mostly absent for the last couple of years.

"*Kubi.* (It is horrible.)" Norman flinched. "It feels like we're in jail. The food is mass-produced and tastes awful. No one can cook like your mother." Norman griped, freely airing his grievances.

Norm led us towards the whitewashed stable, where the Africander stud bulls boarded and lodged. I followed my big brother with great anticipation, feeling most honored that he allowed me to go on the hunt.

One winter, I had begged so much that Dad caved in and took me on a kudu hunt. A majestic, platinum kudu bull, with snow-white stripes down either side of its bulging belly, emerged from the thicket and stood still about fifty yards away, a very easy target. Dad was taking his time, aiming carefully for its head that was crowned with twisted horns. Kudu were the king of all bucks that roamed Schelmdrift, and yet were not considered "royal game" and protected by the government.

Father had the bull in his cross hairs when I burst out, "Daddy, don't shoot it! Look at his lovely long horns!" In a flash, the very wild game was out of both our sights. It simply vanished, darting into the cover of the jungle bush, not to be spotted again. My father was furious. Mercifully, he managed to not turn the gun on me.

"Darn it all, my girl!" Dad swore, as he tightened his lips. "I told you not to say a word. Can you not obey? Never again! You are never *bally-well* coming on a kudu hunt again!" He was quite cross. "You were so perfectly quiet and sat still for so long, and then you opened your mouth at the worst possible time! I should have fitted you with a bally silencer."

Needless to say, I had not been invited big game hunting again ever since then. So I felt extra lucky to go with Norm to hunt birds.

"Molweni. Molo baas Norman! (Hello, all. Hello, boss Norman!)" Jack yelled out the wide stable door with a hammer in one hand, a prize red rosette in the other. They had just got home from their annual *trek* (trip) to the Rand Easter Agricultural Show in Johannesburg. He was about to nail up the new ribbon prizes onto the champion bull pens.

Jack wore denim overalls along with leather boots that Dad had given him for Christmas. It was a hot day, so he had removed the top half of his overalls and tied the sleeves around his waist. Jack was built like a boxer.

Jack greeted us with a huge smile, unashamed of his tarnished tusks. If a white person had those teeth, he would never smile at all. I loved that about Jack. He always beamed a confident smile, in spite of his unfortunate teeth.

"Molo, *Tata*, (Hello, Father)" the blacks replied in unison. In the same manner we called all adults "Uncle," it was polite for them to call all adults "Father." Whites made mean jokes about blacks. One asked…What is the definition of confusion? The answer was supposed to be; "Father's Day in Soweto." Soweto was the black township outside Johannesburg, far away in the Transvaal.

"Molo, Jack," we whites responded cheerfully.

"Where is Sindie?" I asked her father.

"Uthunyiwe, (She has been sent on an errand,)" Jack called out .*"Uyokutheza.* (She went to collect wood.)" Lizzie was lazy, so she regularly sent Toto and Sindie to gather firewood for cooking. "She loves the dress you gave her. She wears it every day. Thanks, sweet girl."

Norman led our procession farther down past our family graveyard. A hedge of salt bush ran flush along the inside of the fence, giving the sepulchres some solitude. Generations of Besters slept under blankets of bluish stony slabs, luxuriously laced with silver lichen. Each deceased couple rested under matching cobbled quilts. Engraved marble headstones served as headboards.

A Cape turtledove descended and perched on the gate enclosing our cemetery. It made the familiar "kerr" sound on landing. It was almost camouflaged, cloaked by the gray hedge, but then the dove made a harsh call of "work-harder, work-harder." The grave repetition of its call was a mortal mistake.

"Naantsa intake! (There's a bird!)" Tatey pointed excitedly, still thinking of his tummy. His appetite reminded him that a dove had more meat on its bones than most *mossies* (sparrows).

Norman took aim at the bird. He pulled the trigger and the dove fell dead into the dust.

"Uyichanile! (You hit it!)" Tatey said with a big grin. There was a distinct resemblance to Jack in his smile, except he, by the grace of God, had Maggie's teeth.

Rama ran to retrieve the warm, limp, drooping dove. He immediately started to pluck its sooty-grey feathers, tossing them to the wind.

"Uyadubula, *Baas* Norman! (You can shoot, Boss Norman!)" Rama expressed his admiration. His skin had an unusual yellowish tint, and so Maggie named him after a popular brand of yellow Rama margarine.

Sindie said Lizzie suspected Rama's father was a Cape Colored builder from the Uncle Hubert Bowker's farm, who came to build us a new cement trough for the bulls to drink out of. Maggie could speak a little Afrikaans, after all.

Jack peered out the back door of the stables and hollered a cheering whistle. He waved the grooming brush and danced a little jig, *"Raakskoot!* (Spot-on-the-mark!)" He showed his teeth again, as he showed off his Afrikaans word. Jack had some sort of charming charisma about him.

"Well Done!" Tatey smiled at Norman, who was marinating in fresh praise.

"You shouldn't shoot doves over our ancestors." I cautioned. "And I thought Daddy said we should not shoot doves at all. Aren't they holy or royal game or something? What will the dead people think?"

"Don't be *dof* (stupid). Dead people can't think," Norman spat.

"How do you know?" I asked somberly. "Who told you?"

"Because!"

"Because why?" I challenged.

"Because pigs can't fly in the middle of July! How do *you* think they can possibly think without a brain inside their skulls?" Norman snapped, starting to get irritated.

"Tombe says, 'You have to keep your ancestors happy.' Sindie said that if we make them cross, we'll have bad things happen to us," I lectured in Xhosa so all three boys could hear my speech. So far, no white old people could properly explain the arbitrary events in life. Those haphazard things that happen without any warning whatsoever remained unexplainable.

"Well, they both talk *twak* (nonsense)," Norman snorted in English. "And you, Judy, you just talk much too much." The normal Norman personality was resurrected.

"You already had bad luck," I reminded him in Xhosa. "You smashed a window pane."

"I don't believe that bunk about ancestors. We white people are not supposed to believe that rubbish," Norman snarled back at me in English, but Rama detected the disapproving tone.

"Hayi (no) Boss Norman, Miss Judy is telling you the truth," Rama said in a tired old man's voice, sighing his words out, with not too much oomph behind his clicks. He did not expect to change Norman's mind, but he still wanted his testimony on record. I knew Rama felt sorry for me after my sermon was rejected so rudely.

"Girls talk twaddle, don't they?" Norman said to his friends, ignoring me.

"You think you know everything since you have been to boarding school. How can you be so sure that my piccanins are wrong?" That was something I would never dare say to my parents, but Norman was a sitting duck and fair game. "Perhaps it is possible that we are watched by some of our dead relatives. Who knows? Who do you think you are? Smarty-Pants! I should tell Mom that you smoke, you would get a *klap* (spanking) for sure. Just maybe the Xhosas are right about this ancestor stuff. In case they are, we should all respect the dead more. You are just a big fat fool with soft feet and a hard head!" I spat viciously.

Norman flew back at me. "You are as irritating as a buzzing fly that never goes away. You ask too many questions. You talk too much and think far too much!"

With stables on the farm, flies were a huge nuisance. Dad read in the *Farmer's Weekly Magazine* about pink poison that kills flies. Soon he had "the boys" (African laborers) chopping branches off salt bushes, which got dipped into the poison and hung all around the stable, out of reach of children. It proved to exterminate countless flies and we were all glad.

I refused to back down, buzzing relentlessly around my brother. I had to live up to my bothersome reputation, after all.

"Norm, how do you know what's true and what's not true anyway? How do you tell? Too much education has made you 'soft,' too," I chirped, standing up for myself, fueled by Rama's support. "Just tell me how you can say what dead people do and don't do! Have you ever been dead before?"

"Oh shut up, we shouldn't have brought you. You are a cantankerous child who never grew out of the why?-why?-why?-stage. You'll chase all the birds away with that big mouth of yours," Norman smirked, exasperated. I knew he wasn't really chasing me away because he said he missed me very much when he was at boarding school.

"I bet you can't even spell that word after all your fancy pansy schooling," I scrapped some more before deciding to keep quiet, just in case he did send me home. "And what does *cantanka rice* mean? I love *fantastic Tastic rice!*" I imitated a radio advertisement for the Tastic brand of jasmine rice.

"*Cantankerous* was on our spelling test and I got it right." Norman was a clever kid. "It describes you perfectly; it means you never stop asking annoying questions."

"Stop it now. Leave her alone." Tatey, the oldest, told Norman.

Norman led the parade down to where the bushes grew dense alongside lower Bumpy. We climbed through the thorny thicket, and continued along the riverbed. We spotted a variety of birds, mostly *mossies* (sparrows), yellow Cape weavers, *whitethroated* swallows, and wagtails.

Presently, Rama was holding six pink, plucked birds by their skinny, scaly feet. He washed the blood and guts off in the trickle of Bumpy.

We found a sandy, sunny spot in the middle of the dry riverbed where we could safely make a fire. Rama and I gathered some dry driftwood and sticks.

"Let us cook now," Tatey kindled a fire, "with the flames *under* our food."

Tatey had cut four long shoots off a tree. He sharpened the points with his new knife that Jack bought him at the Rand Show. We sat around the fire, spit roasting our birds on the long sticks over the coals. The aroma of *braaied* (barbequed) chicken made us all hungrier.

"You shoot well, Boss Norman. Right on target, just like your father, *SngXhoshe* (a name the Xhosas had given my father, meaning strict). Just like your father," Rama repeated with a mouth full of braised bird.

I felt a stab of sorrow for Tatey and Rama. They had never had a father in their home. Maggie was our most capable single cook. She had once married and moved to East London. Her husband had worked there as a waiter in a big hotel, but ignored paying *labola* (bride price) for her. Her husband abandoned her there in the city with her two baby girls. Maggie was apparently also apprenticed to become a *sangoma* (witchdoctor) there. She still wore a string of white beads on her ankles for ceremonies. After her husband discarded her, she returned home to our farm, where she had grown up, and where she belonged. Maggie birthed another three big baby boys. Two of whom were sired by Jack.

All the time she kept our tummies satisfied, she was not a fully qualified witchdoctor, nor was she a fully paid bride for Jack. He had never paid any cows for her, although she was sort of his "other wife."

Tatey talked with his mouth full of food, "You spent most of the summer at the seaside, Boss Norman, so we have hardly seen you since the spring. Did you hear what your father did?"

"What did Dad do?" Norman inquired, spitting out fine bones that landed on his *tackies* (tennis shoe). He had to shake his shoe to get rid of the splinters. Boarding school makes your feet soft. The other three of us, who were not city slickers, were all barefooted. The soles of our feet became tougher from never wearing shoes.

Tatey had just finished licking a homemade *zol* (cigarette) shut. He pulled a burning stick from the fire and shook it until there was just a small glowing coal on the end. He pushed the glowing point to his *zol*, sucking in air hard through the ration tobacco wrapped in brown paper. Tatey was soon puffing smoke out of his lungs like a black steam train engine.

Norman then took out a packet of *Lucky Strike Plain* and shook a cigarette out of the packet, putting it between his lips. He had started smoking before he was ten, but never in front of any adults. Bruce smoked too, but not in front of white adults. The black big people did not tell on Bruce. That was just how the pecking order of privacy worked on Schelmdrift.

Tatey handed the burning stick to Norman and relaxed, leaning back. "I'll tell you what your dad did. When the sheep were lambing, *Ootata* (the African dads) kept finding a few dead lambs. The lambs were not killed and eaten in the same way a jackal would take down its prey. Jackals make flank attacks. These lambs were just bitten all over with teeth marks. The havoc was not caused by a *leguwaan* or lynx or leopard either. Nobody knew what was torturing and destroying the lambs like that." Tatey reflected while shaking off the ash.

"*SngXhoshe* sent Yan on horseback at sunrise to sit and keep watch over the flock. Out of the blue, Yan saw Sergeant Lombard's mongrel, you know the policeman that lives at Carlisle Bridge?" He stopped and looked at us through his knitted eyebrows.

Norm nodded, while his tongue was steering meat around his perfect teeth.

"Yes, we know him." I replied eagerly. "Sergeant Lombard shows up at our house just in time for supper quite often. He does not have a wife. He is a greedy-guts and eats a dozen *mielies* (corn on the cob) at once. Poor Jane had to run out and pick more *mielies.* With all the butter he sloshes on, the glutton got really fat. Then once, he locked himself out of his *rondawel,* so he tried to climb through the round window. His fat stomach got stuck, and his servants found him hours later dangling there, desperately kicking. They had to walk all the way here and fetch my dad. They said they did not want to run, so they strolled over the hill to Schelmdrift. They wanted him to feel what it was like to be stuck for a few hours. Dad said he was hanging limp by the time he arrived there in the Land Rover. My dad drove *ootata* (the dads) over there. Our dads had to kick the cop's door down. Daddy commanded some to help push from the inside; while others pulled from outside till they freed the policeman. Maggie said he should not have eaten all those *mielies* at once," I summarized. "He is fatter than Humpty Dumpty! Mom said he was too fat to find his own wife to cook for him."

"Shh, now, Judes, and let Tatey tell his story," Norman nudged me gently.

"Yeah, those servants should have left the obese pig in the window till he grew skinny. It was *that fat* policeman's ugly dog," Tatey continued. "The white one with big black blotches that always barks at us when we walk to school. Yan spotted that dog on our side of the fence. He observed it burrowing a hole under the fence. Yan was on Rex and galloped home and told your dad." Tatey paused to take a draw on his *zol.*

Taking advantage of Tatey's puff pause, Rama jumped in with the details. "Your dad was furious; my mom told us all about *SngXhoshe's* rage. He only drank half his tea that day. He stormed out and got in his Land Rover, putting his old hat on in a huff."

Tatey continued. "Your dad drove to that policeman's *rondawel* (a round house) and spoke in Afrikaans so that the Sergeant understood perfectly. It was a very cross voice, his servants told us, but no one understood what your dad was saying. He was rasping his throat a lot in *isiBulu* (Afrikaans) but they said he was speaking very harshly. The witnesses only identified the word *"gat"* (hole) a few times. That could have meant *holes* in the fence or *holes* in lambs or *holes* in the dog. They were not positive."

"I think our *SngXhoshe* was threatening to make a hole in the demon dog if it killed any more of his lambs, which are our livelihood. Possibly even a hole in Sergeant Lombard? The policeman was warned very well," Rama surmised, while Tatey smiled around another pull.

"He was thoroughly warned alright, but he did nothing," Tatey stated, blowing out smoke, "More poor little lambs were found dead or half dead, bleeding. Just bitten and killed for the sake of it, not even eaten by that dreadful dog. Yan found the dog, with blood dripping from its teeth, in amongst our little lambs again. He tried to catch it, but the mongrel escaped back to the police station at Carlisle Bridge. Once it crept through the hole in the fence. Yan could not follow it onto police property. Yan made Rex gallop all the way home at full speed and informed your father."

Tatey sat forward and became very animated, imitating what my dad would have done with his hands, "This time *SngXhoshe* took his hat *and* a rifle," Tatey said, as he grabbed Norman's pellet gun for demonstration. "Mom said the wheels spat out gravel behind the Land Rover like buckshot out the shotgun barrel. And *Sngxhoshe* raced off in a cloud of dust in the same direction as before. Maggie, my mom, said the people at Carlisle Bridge told her that when *SngXhoshe* arrived there, he didn't ask to see Sergeant Lombard, the government official. He just asked the servants who were loitering around where the devilish dog was."

Tatey stood up now, pretending he was Dad. "One of our school friends pointed to the kitchen *rondawel*, where the mongrel was cowering under the table."

"'Naantsa, mlungu!' (There it is, white man!) Our friend happily showed *SngXhoshe* who was holding his loaded rifle, with his finger on the trigger. We all hated that dog," Tatey testified. "It made children bleed often. *Noyoki* was bitten on his first day of school."

Tatey's little full brother, *Noyoki*, looked exactly like Tatey. They both resembled Jack, the stable man. Dad could never remember *Noyoki*'s name, so he renamed Maggie's youngest child *NewYorki*.

"That dog chased all the children on their way to school. We were scared. We didn't want to go to school because we feared that dog," Rama added hurriedly while Tatey took another deep draw.

"It was a mean dog," Tatey declared. *"Xha,* (Then,)" he clicked his tongue, "your dad stormed into the kitchen *rondawel* where the dog was still hiding. He aimed at it." Tatey put the gun to his shoulder and aimed, mimicking Dad. "There was a big bloody bang. That horrible dog was dead. Just one shot!"

"Your dad is fearless. He's not scared of the S.A.P. (South African Police). He has the courage of a warrior. He shot the bad dog to save his lambs. All the dads were very happy, cheering and laughing when they heard the gossip," Rama recalled with admiration.

"Our dads said that your dad has a very good sense of justice. The school children were also very thankful." Tatey finished the story with a click of his tongue.

"Things are better with that dog dead," Rama concluded with an air of finality.

There was a glow on the half brothers' faces whenever they spoke of my father. I wanted to share my daddy with Maggie's sons as they boasted of his glory. *SngXhoshe* stood on a pedestal in their male, adolescent minds.

My father, at any length, looked after his lambs, and protected them from harm, even if it meant standing up to evil and pushing Humpty Dumpty over the wall. My daddy was a strict, respected shepherd who cared for his hirelings as well as his sheep, black or white.

6

TRANSISTOR RADIO

"This is Eric Cordell with your 7:30 a.m. edition of World News..." Springbok Radio Station broadcasted so clearly that we could hear the crisp words from our bedroom. "Mr. F. J. Harris, responsible for planting a bomb in Johannesburg railway station last year, killing an innocent Mrs. Ethel Rhys, was hung to death in the Pretoria prison. Twenty three other innocent commuters were hurt by broken glass and shrapnel during the explosion, including children and a pregnant mother, Mrs. Koekemoer."

Wendy wandered over the passage to our parents' bedroom. The Easter holidays were drawing to a close and were not to be wasted by sleeping the precious minutes away.

"Bloody cowards, these terrorists, they are too scared to fight like real men..." Dad lit up his pipe. "Killing a woman waiting to catch a train is the most cowardly act a man can do."

"Daddy, please may I listen to your radio today?" Wendy pleaded politely. "You are going into Grahamstown for stockfair, so you won't need it, will you?" Teenagers felt shut-in and claustrophobic, despite the spacious terrain of the Karoo. That was to be expected from any fifteen-year-old living in an isolated farmhouse.

"Yes, you may, but please be very careful, it cost a lot of money," Daddy conceded reluctantly, not really wanting to lend it but still making an effort to be compromising.

As soon as dust disappeared over the hill, Wendy went straight to Dad's office. She showed me how to turn the three silver knobs and tune into LM radio on the shortwave station. We lay side by side on the front lawn, tapping our feet in time to the lively music.

"Wends, what does LM mean?" I asked enjoying my time with my teen sister.

"It stands for Lorenzo Marques, which is the capital of Mozambique, where they play the best songs, mostly by the Beatles," Wendy explained.

I took the liberty of turning up the volume knob some more.

"Don't put it too loud, Judes. Mom might take it away," Wendy warned.

Just then, Mom made an appearance at the front door. "Caesar's Ghost! Wendy, please stop listening to that awful racket. How can *anyone* possibly consider that caterwauling to be music?" She scoured her forehead. "I am ready to bake *crunchies* for you to take in your tuck boxes. The hens have finally laid enough eggs now. Please lend me a hand, Uncle Sonny loves those oatmeal bars too, and he will be here for tea this morning." Mom motioned with her hand and head, disappearing back into the house as promptly as she had appeared.

Wendy picked up the radio to return it to Dad's office.

I pleaded, *"Ag,* please, may I borrow it?" I tried to stop her by holding it down.

"No, you are too young!" Wendy protested.

"I am almost ten." I had learned to exaggerate with confidence from Maggie. "Please! Daddy is not here, he won't mind."

"Don't be daft. You just turned nine. Dad will notice when he tries to listen to the news tonight and the batteries are flat," Wendy whined, not wanting to take any blame unjustly. She nippily picked it up and placed it back on Dad's desk.

Wendy went to find Mom in the pantry.

I just sat on the front steps in the warm sun, thinking. On the farm, there was always plenty of time to think.

Soon Mom hurried out again, looking very pretty. She had lipstick and mascara on and her eyebrows were browner. "It is Wednesday today, the bus should be arriving presently," she announced.

"You look lovely." I was always aware of her beauty and amazed at how a little lipstick enhanced her natural good looks. She had perfectly straight white teeth and a dashing smile.

"Thank you, my pet. I have just 'put on my face' because Uncle Sep Gradwell and Uncle Sonny will be here any time now, and Dad is not here to entertain them," Mom replied, retreating back to her baking. She popped her face out again. "Let me know when you hear them arriving so I can come out to greet them, please. That eggbeater makes an awful racket. We can't hear from the pantry."

Uncle Sep Gradwell lived on the farm to the northeast of Schelmdrift. Hoppy's father was a very tall, bony gentleman. The Xhosas gave him the name *NoMalambhile*. I thought it was a clever name because it meant "hungry man."

Uncle Sonny's Xhosa name was *NoDyasana*. It meant "one who wears a jacket." Dad's older brother always wore a tweed jacket or navy sports blazer. Sonny Bester had excelled at rugby. He was chosen to play for Eastern Province in his heyday, so he had a variety of golden badges on his navy blazers.

Dad was the youngest in his family of five. The Xhosa descriptive name for my mother was *NoLasti*, because she was the "last" spouse to marry into the Bester clan. Dad's three older sisters had previously married and moved away.

Tragically, Uncle Sonny's first wife, Aunty Daphne, had died along with her fourth baby during birthing complications. Uncle Sonny's second wife, Aunty Yvonne, married into the Bester family *after* my mother, who was already named *NoLasti* (The Last).

Maggie came up with a very creative new name for Aunty Yvonne: *NoAmeni*. 'Amen' is what you say at the very end of a prayer. Only people who have a lot of time to think can think of such suitable names.

Both Uncle Sonny and Uncle Sep had morning tea with us every Wednesday to pick up their post. They lived too far from the tarred national road to have the bus deliver their post to their doorsteps, so they had to come to our bus stop.

The big bus had rows of wheels to churn up the dust; some wheels even had twins. The clanking metal truck delivered the leather 'private bags' full of the week's letters, accounts and of course, the fresh *Farmer's Weekly Magazine*, along with international news magazines. Occasionally, the rugged, dusty lorry transported African passengers, along with sacks of *mieliemeal* (cornmeal) for the servants' food rations and other farm equipment. Sometimes we could even hear goats bleating the blues in an encaged back trailer.

There was not much traffic in the Karoo, so when we heard the sound of a car or truck engine, we all rushed out to see who it was. It was quite an occasion to receive guests, and we always welcomed them with tea and treats.

Dad was always pleased to see Uncle Sonny and Uncle Sep. They exchanged secondhand newspapers, while they all puffed on their crooked pipes. They enjoyed a chat about cricket, rugby, and cattle. Mother was quite capable of holding her own in all three of those topics of conversation.

Dad and Uncle Sonny farmed the Africander cattle together as "Bester Brothers." The red herd grazed on the top camps of their adjacent farms, alongside the kudu in the thick bush. The small stock was farmed independently by each brother. The Merino sheep and Angora goats grazed in flatter pastures nearer the house and Fish River. The brothers always shared advice and new methods of farming, lending a hand to each other if needed.

My thoughts drifted to Grandpa, who I did miss. Grandpa Stocks grew pineapples, chicory and other vegetables near Southwell. He had a few Jersey cows for creamy milk, butter and cheese. Grandpa made his own cheddar cheese. Mom grew up on Glenfillan Park, about thirty miles south of Grahamstown. Granny raised Mom and her two sisters to be ladies with perfect poise.

Mom shared Dad's passion for sports being very athletic herself. She was a leggy girl who beat all her peers in races at her private Anglican school. Mom excelled at Rhodes University where she was the athletics champion.

In my thoughts I visited Granny Stocks, who was not that bad, when she was far away. She grew a more tropical garden that was overgrown with ferns and fairy goblin statues. She had a stone waterfall and wooden bridges in her luscious green garden, where she loved to recline in a hammock and read romantic classics. I think that is where Granny found all her etiquette from reading out of books as well as from her blue-blooded breeding.

Mom rudely interrupted my thoughts when I heard her firm voice behind me. "Judy, run quickly and call Maggie. She went to the stable to get milk; she has been gone far too long. Hurry up, please." Her voice got firmer. "We need the milk right now for tea." English people drink tea prescriptively twice a day, at 11 a.m. and 4 p.m. Come hell or high water.

"Can't Lizzie go?" I snorted, lazy from sitting in the soothing sun and enjoying my wandering thoughts.

"No. You must go at this instant. At once, please!" She urged me along in her firmest voice, giving me a nudge with her toe in my ribs.

I dragged myself up and dawdled along the path leading to the stable, passing through Mom's flowering shrub garden, past the tennis court. I slowly opened the little gate leading to the stables. Our stables were divided into two sections. One half was where *Fikile,* our dairy boy, milked about five Jersey cows into a bucket while he sat on a stool. There was a gallon tin with pure lanolin, which Fickile used to lubricate the udders. The servants "borrowed" lanolin to shine their faces, arms, legs and hair when Dad was not looking. Lanolin is the grease that comes off merino sheep's wool. That section of the stables had a *kraal* (pen) with a *sneezewood* (type of wood) pole fence adjoining.

The main building was where Jack was in charge of the show bulls. There were about eight stalls on each side with a cement manger. There was a little passage for Jack to walk along and fill the manger with fodder in order to fatten the bulls. It was a special mixture of mainly *lucerne* (alfalfa) and yellow *mealiemeal* (cornmeal) with an occasional dollop of black strap molasses. The piccanins loved to dip a stick in the molasses drum and lick it.

There was a huge stack of golden hay next to the lucerne bales, right in the far back. That straw was not for fodder, but bedding. Every day Jack padded the cold hard cement floor with fresh hay for the bulls to sleep comfortably. He scooped up the manure behind each bull with a spade and wheel-barrowed it outside to the compost heap. His stud stable was kept spotless. It hardly smelled like manure at all.

I stopped to lean on the cement reservoir that was fed by the creaking windmill. The windmill was burping up *brack* water from the underground borehole, spurting out a pipe and splashing into the greenish, frog-infested reservoir water. It did not matter what micro-organisms bred in that water, as only the cattle drank it.

"Maa-gie! Maaa-gie!" I called loudly; too weary to walk any further, after noticing the bulls had been let loose to drink at the trough.

New, wilder Afrikaner bulls, recently recruited from the veldt, were sporting new shiny brass nose rings with which they would be led around show arenas, after much needed taming. The drinking trough was filled by a spitting pipe connected to the huge reservoir. The trough was positioned between me and the stables. I had a farm fresh recollection of Sindie's flight into a plum tree launched by cow-power.

There were only very thorny acacia trees close by, so I chose to stay close to the reservoir which I could dive into if needs be. The hard water came from deep under the ground, sucked up by the rotating windmill. I gazed at the long overhanging pipe, noticing the water squirt hypnotically out with intervals in tune with the rhythm of the spiraling windmill. The clear water tasted *brack* and was rich in minerals, a normal feature of underground water.

Something told me not to go any farther. I was wary of those undomesticated bulls, whose coats glinted red in the sun.

Uncle Sonny, too, had recently returned from the *Rand Show*, where he sold most of the older, tamer bulls to other breeders. Jack took pride in how well our prized bulls looked. He spent hours brushing them down from head to hoof. To Jack, the recognition and applause as he walked the champion bulls around the arenas was worth the sacrifice of separation from his wives for a couple of weeks.

Jack didn't always look quite so groomed himself. All the sparse tusks still remaining in his mouth were stained from tobacco and coffee consumption.

"He must have something," Mom always told Dad, "because the Native women all adore Jack." I remembered Mom's comment as I hunted for missing Maggie.

I knew Jack was back. I had seen him on the bird hunt. I leaned against the reservoir wall. "Maaa-gie! Maaa-gie!" I shouted more vigorously this time, becoming more and more suspicious.

"Jack didn't have enough cows after paying ten cows for light-skinned Lizzie," Mom had once told me. This explanation came after I had asked the awkward question, "How can Maggie have babies without a daddy in her hut?" Mom was eager to change the subject. So I never quite understood how Maggie was related to Jack…until just then, when the penny dropped.

I recalled how Granny Stocks had grumbled, "Xhosa men think they can have more than one wife. And we end up feeding all the little mouths." Granny was most incensed at the amount of food that went missing daily. She noticed acute shrinkage while Mom was in the Bedford Hospital.

Eventually, Maggie materialized at the stable door, looking rather disheveled. She seemed a bit flustered, hastily buttoning up her uniform. It was her best new blue uniform that Mom had given her for Christmas, with a white apron and *doek* (headscarf) to match.

It is custom in the Xhosa tribe for married women to keep their heads covered, wrapped in a *doek*. Maggie was re-arranging her *doek*. A piece of straw stuck straight up out the back of her *doek*. It rather resembled the antenna on Dad's new radio. The straw would have looked grander if it were an ostrich feather, like my late Granny Bester wore. Nevertheless, I loved Maggie, straw and all.

"Iza,Maggie. Umama uyakufuna! (Come with me, Maggie. Mom is looking for you!)" I called out to my Maggie.

"Ndiyeza (I am on my way) *Nomhankazi,"* she grinned from under her hefty headdress.

"Mom needs the milk *at once."* I remembered.

"Oops! I left the milk behind," she gasped, swinging back around.

Just then Jack appeared with a yellow jug and a harmless grin. He was shirtless, wearing only his new khaki pants that Dad had given him to wear at the showgrounds.

"Ask Sindie to come and play later," I called to Jack. He had plenty of visitors during the day who would relay messages; it was called the "bush telegraph."

"Sindie loves you, Miss Judy. She is very thankful for the panties you gave her. She said that you got them from your Aunt for your birthday, and you gave them straight to Sindie, brand new." Jack knew how to charm me, too. "We will not tell your parents!"

After midday dinner, when the house was all quiet, I crept into Dad's office. Mom and Wendy were reading books on their beds. Dad and my brothers were still in Grahamstown. The maids had the afternoon off. I stared at Dad's radio. It was just sitting on his desk shamefully quiet.

I looked out the office window, which faced the hill that hid the huts from our view. I spotted Tombe and Sindie skipping down the hill towards our home; I could not resist the temptation of showing off the new radio to them. I grabbed the transistor radio and hurried to meet my friends.

We hid in the maid's room. It was a private room in one of the outbuildings, behind the oily, stinky engine room. That big generator roared at night to give us electricity. The ration storeroom and tool workshop would create a perfect sound barrier between us and the main farmhouse.

The maid's room was used to breastfeed their babies. Maggie, Jane, and Lizzie also used it to change into and out of their uniforms, and to store their personal belongings. Maggie, incidentally, also stored some of Mom's personal belongings there, I noticed from time to time. But for now it was empty, and the smooth cement floor would become our dance floor. Our maids' uniforms hung on hooks like the teal curtains of an ostentatious stage.

I sat the wireless on the cement floor, eagerly demonstrating how to turn the shiny, silver knobs. Suddenly The Beatles blared out, *"She was just seventeen, if you know what I mean….and I saw her standing there."*

"This radio sings very well!" Sindie squealed with delight.

The three of us danced a jig around the instrument.

"You have to stamp your feet like this. Toto showed me," Sindie instructed, with her arms flapping like ostrich wings. Her shoulders seemed as light as feathers, swaying to the beat.

"Who is singing in there?" Tombe urgently demanded.

"*Ama*-Beatles," I answered with a Xhosa prefix meaning "the" and the English name, not knowing how to translate the band's name and not expecting Tombe to care.

Not understanding the English name at all, "*Ama-bani?* (The-who?)" Tombe shouted with a big frown, still bopping and hopping around the new technology.

Xhosa has the most delightful word for insects or beetles: "*rhor-ho.*" The "r" is pronounced like an Afrikaans "g." The sound is made by rasping your epiglottis, as if your throat was itchy. All races in South Africa stole the word because it is very descriptive. In Afrikaans, it is spelled "*gogo,*" but it sounds exactly like the Xhosa word.

"They are called *AMA-RHORHO!*" I translated the Fabulous Four's name literally into isiXhosa.

Tombe didn't say a word, but her eyes travelled from me to the radio and back several times. She was very nonplussed.

"There are insects singing in that box?" Tombe demanded in disbelief.

"No!" I laughed. "That is just the name of the band of boys who are singing."

"There are male insects…in that box…that can sing like peo-ple?" Tombe posed a question while dancing to the drum beat. "Can they crawl out those little holes?" She pointed to the holes in the black leather cover where the sound pounded out.

"No, just dance! I'll explain later!" I yelled, preferring to dance rather than to explain about radio transmissions, because I did not quite know how they worked myself.

In the Xhosa culture, it is very important to have big breasts and buttocks. The fatter a woman was, the more beautiful she was considered to be, and she was the envy of all. That explained why Maggie ate so much lard to make sure she was fatter, if not paler, than Lizzie.

The music was too loud for conversation. I watched Sindie as she tried her very best to make her buttocks protrude. We were all pre-puberty and the frog egg ritual hadn't hatched any visible results yet. But the two of them stuck out their chests with great hope. I imitated them.

When the song came to an end, Sindie had another one of her bright ideas.

"Let's go and show that new visitor from Johannesburg. He arrived on the bus today with a suitcase of city clothes. He is from Fickile's family who live in the big city built over goldmines. That dumb *tsotsi* (thug) will stop saying we are backward farm folks if he sees our radio!" Sindie urged enthusiastically, already claiming part ownership of the silver and black radio.

"I don't think we are allowed to. What will *SngXhoshe* (Mr. Strict) say about his tame insects in the box?" Tombe said soberly. "My mom tells us every day how he loves his new wireless. He will spank us with his sham buck."

"I told you there are not tamed insects in there. And apparently, those Beatles are very wild, Miss Wendy said." I tried to correct Tombe, but she was not fully convinced.

"SngXhoshe has never ever spanked us with his sham buck before," Sindie protested suddenly braver and bolder. "We have to show that stupid city *tsotsi* (thug)." Sindie opened and closed the maids' blue uniforms about her face, "Show the city *tsotsi!"* She made two or three encores between the pretend curtains, chanting over and over the same words; "Show him!"

Tombe's mind was still slightly wary of the mythical insects that might be lurking in the black box.

Elvis started to sing about "Fever" with his smooth-as-chocolate velvet voice. I loved Elvis Presley the most and got lost in the beat.

There was a pause, while the radio talked and told us to try some cigarettes. Sindie did a jazzy step out the room, picked a few leaves off the "salt bush" hedge, and chewed them with zest.

I could tell Tombe was still staring at the radio in awe and surprisingly speechless. Xhosas implicitly believe the praying mantis, for example, is supposed to have enormous powers from the gods. I knew Tombe was mulling over the beetle matter.

The radio announcer promised more rock and roll. I made no further attempt to translate "rock and roll."

So we all just sat and listened for a little bit.

"Those *gogos* can talk a lot, too," Tombe declared, still flummoxed.

"They are people not insects." I repeated.

"People cannot fit in that small box. They must be dung beetles." Tombe avowed.

Dung beetles had provided many hours of entertainment for us as we had watched them fight over balls of dung near the stables. "Robbers" try to steal some other beetle's hard "rolling up" work. We had observed them roll balls of dung bigger than they were themselves. They used their hind legs to make perfect spherical balls. Those beetles are known as "rollers." Then they roll the ball along in straight lines, but cannot see where they are going, as the ball blocks their view.

The beetles also lay their eggs in balls of dung so that the white larvae can feed off dung after the eggs hatch. The larvae undergo metamorphosis; Mom had taught me that big word when we watched tadpoles become frogs. Here wiggly white worms pupate to cocoon themselves and eventually hatch out as black beetles all over again.

When you have observed such mystical transformations of nature with your own two eyes, as well as believe in all the mythical creatures that the Xhosas aspire to know about, one should pardon Tombe's wild imagination. Her mind could be justified in conceiving shrunken ghosts hatching into singing beetles.

Dad had said dung beetles were very valuable to the environment and soil structure. "They are estimated to save the cattle farmers in America $380 million a year in fecal removal." Dad read this from a news magazine, emphasizing how we must not underestimate the usefulness of the black dung beetles and how we must never squash the black crawly creatures. They were considered sacred on our cattle ranch, too, in a sense.

Dad had taught us that the ancient Egyptians incorrectly thought that the dung beetles were only male and that they could reproduce without a female! They deemed dung beetles sacred as it could renew life without a mate, almost like immaculate conception.

If you grew up on a farm, you knew that there had to be a bull and a cow, a cockerel and a hen, a ram and a ewe in order to produce offspring in the spring. Farm folks are not really as backward as those ancient Egyptians or city slickers may think.

Dad had served in Egypt during WWII. There was a photo hanging in his office of Daddy in uniform sitting on a camel with the ancient sphinx in the background.

My conscience pricked me when I recalled Dad's office and knew that that was where the radio should be resting. But the excitement of having my own little birthday party with my playmates, coupled with the intoxicating music, successfully stifled those pesky prods.

Dad had shown us a picture of the Luxor Temple and its massive ancient dung beetle statue. He recalled that people rub the base of the statue, hoping for *good luck* from the sacred scarab. Nowadays they string a rope around the statue to stop the silly superstitious travelers from rubbing away the stone. My daddy was amused by the gullible tourists who believed the faulty information.

Dad also said that the dung beetle was painted on the walls of the Tomb KV6 in the Valley of the Kings. Dad had explained that in ancient hieroglyphics, the image of the dung beetle also meant "to become" and "to transform." He always read aloud to us when he came across interesting trivia like that!

Recently, Dad had read an article to us: "The behavior of the beetles was much misunderstood by the ancients. Jean Henri Fabre corrected the myth that a dung beetle would seek aid from another when confronted with an obstacle such as a rock. He discovered that the 'helpers' were indeed 'robbers' waiting to steal the worker/roller's treasure of a dung ball."

Dad had continued to read aloud: "I ask myself in vain why Proudhon introduced into Scarabaean morality the daring paradox that 'property means plunder,' or what diplomatist taught the Dung-beetle the savage maxim that 'might is right.' " Dad was amused as he read about the good old dung beetle that lived on Schelmdrift, eating our cow manure, and all the myths and misunderstandings associated with the *gogos.*

Any Xhosa piccanin could have told Fabre that long ago. We had spent hours of endless entertainment watching them fighting and stealing each other's dung ball. We could tell that when the beetles' view was blocked, they inevitably ran into rocks in the road. It was during those rough times that they often fall prey to robbers of their own kind. It was, indeed, survival of the fittest for the lowly dung beetles. Impish boys, like Tatey, would even purposely place rocks in the rollers path, just to watch the sports.

Remembering how rocks made beetle rollers prey to robbers, I was even more reluctant to try and translate Beatles singing rock and roll. I did not wish to confuse cultures any more.

I had been ignoring Tombe and Sindie while I danced and daydreamed about dung beetles. Sindie came up to me and literally jolted me back to reality by slapping me across the shoulder. "This city fool thinks we are backward, Miss Jay, we must show him our wireless!"

"He will *not* believe that *Sngxhoshe* has such well-trained singing *gogos* on Schelmdrift." Tombe insisted.

7

TATEY VS. TOWNIE

"Phambhile! (Forward march!) Onward then! Off to the huts we go!" I shouted gallantly, drunken with music. "Where's this brat that said we are backward? Show me the scoundrel!"

"He's a very bad boy. That is what the old people say. He's a *tsotsi* (thug) from Johannesburg. My mom said we must stay far away from him. People from the city are wicked, the old people say," Tombe cautioned. She was echoing Jane's wisdom and warning, preferring protection rather than battle.

"We have to show that blinking blighter!" Sindie persisted, stamping her bare brown feet on the dust outside the maid's room. "City people think they are better than we are. His shoes are all shiny in the sun. He can't even walk barefoot. His feet are too soft. We must show him that we fully know how radios function!" Sindie was swinging her arms in time with the music. Her limbs were still attached to her trunk by some fluke, double joints maybe.

Picking up the radio by the handle, I danced out of the maid's room, followed by my two accomplices. We walked up past the dairy outbuilding, where Lizzie separated cream from the milk by turning the handle of the separator slowly every morning. She did her dairy chores while waiting for the irons and water to heat up on our wood stove.

Lizzie's workload also included sitting on the kitchen floor and turning the handle of the yellowwood butter churn filled with cream. When the blobs of butter coagulated away from the buttermilk, she took it out and worked the butter clots with a wooden spatula, squeezing out every last drop of the buttermilk. Luckily, Lizzie happened to be off-duty that afternoon.

We three cadets marched barefoot up the dirt path towards the huts. We all wore cotton dresses Mom had cut from the same pattern, with slight variations. Hence, we did appear like uniformed soldiers of a sort. Dear Mother told me that I could not give Sindie an old dress without parting with one for Tombe as well. So, in order to be fair, Tombe was given one of Wendy's hand-me-downs, which I had not quite grown into yet. Tombe was much fatter than I was. Mom had sewn all our dresses from the same *Butterick* pattern, but with different fabric. Tombe's dress had old-fashioned puff sleeves. I was not too excited about inheriting the wardrobe belonging to Wendy, six years my senior, because those clothes were out of style by the time I inherited them. But Tombe loved the frilly dress because it made her look larger while she held up the rear position. We sneaked past the woodpile in single file, grateful Fikile wasn't there chopping wood for the woodstove. The laborers took a little longer lunch break when Dad was away in Grahamstown at stockfair.

We strode to the beat of the Beatles. We made it safely past the silo and the car garage. It was a whitewashed cement building where our two-toned blue Zephyr Lincoln was stored and protected by a cream sail to keep off the Karoo dust.

Dad was meticulous about looking after his valuables. He guarded his possessions very well, just like his lambs. The saddles and bridles were neatly hanging on the walls of the car garage, all accounted for and well kept.

When we were almost up to the Land Rover garage, Tombe pointed up the hill.

"Look! There are people! Over there, behind those bushes, I saw them! They will tell on us! Make haste and hide in the tractor garage!" Tombe was losing courage, still uncertain of her choice to follow her wayward friends, but now leading the retreat into the garage.

The garage was made of solid brick and mortar. The cement plaster was whitewashed to match all the other outbuildings and the farmhouse. There remained some heavy wooden yolks in the tractor garage from Grandpa Bester's days. Solid wooden parts of the old ox-wagons remained as silent symbols of the Schelmdrift pioneers.

"Let's dance in here! There is plenty of space because the Land Rover is gone," Sindie said chirpily.

"It will be better here." Tombe was favoring safety of a fortress, halfway between the road and the farmhouse.

"Yes! We can play it even louder in here. No one will hear us," I agreed while I rested the radio on the red toolbox.

Soon more music was booming out of the black box. "Twist and Shout," the Beatles were blaring to the beat. We were rocking our bodies. Xhosas have no inhibitions. They have an innate sense of rhythm, unrivaled and envied by all other races.

Sindie arched her back. "Do it like this!" Sindie yelled, demonstrating.

Tombe and I mimicked faithfully, copying her exactly.

We glanced at the door in unison, startled by amused figures and faces suddenly filling the broad double doorway. It took a moment to identify their silhouettes with the afternoon sun shining brightly behind them.

The strangely-dressed teen was obviously the "townie." He had a few female followers already. Toto, Sindie's older sister, was already wiggling, showing off her voluptuous body. Another girl, whom I recognized from Sunnyside, was giggling and moving to the music. About five other curious teenage onlookers appeared.

This new audience spurred us to peak our performance. Our trio was wild and untamed.

"Colgate toothpaste…for a brighter smile," an advertisement rudely interrupted our euphoric mood. The older girls took the opportunity of the break to flirt with the visitor, who knew all the new slick dance moves from Johannesburg.

Tatey and Rama strolled in last, but not least.

The sun was starting to sink, but it was still light. We danced ourselves silly. We were in a state of euphoria, entranced by more pulsating beats from the beetle box.

All of a sudden, the townie was towering over me. The stranger growled "Give me your radio, child of a *Bulu!* (Afrikaner!)"

Everyone ceased smiling and stared, frozen in shock. He was about sixteen and I was barely nine. When I didn't budge, he reached into his pants' pocket and pulled out a knife. The switch blade was long and hungry. It was bigger than Tatey's new pocket knife that was surely already blunt from shaving sticks on Bumpy.

"Hayi! (No!)" Sindie screamed. She stepped backwards and pulled her head back afterwards, then pushed her head forward again. "No! No!"

Rama quietly crept around and stood in front of the wireless, trying to look taller than twelve. He was acting like a cowhide shield, standing up very straight, with his arms flared backwards.

My legs started to feel wobbly, but they were still rooted to the cement floor near the tractor's back tire.

The city kid was clearly surprised when Toto shrieked at him, "You're mad in your head! You are a stupid fool!"

The adolescent with the blazing blade had hoped he was going to impress his female fans. Instead, he invoked accusations of madness.

"Can't buy me looove…" The Beatles blurted.

Rama was attempting to turn off the instrument of contention so that not a word of this fight would be lost in the legend. He knew this tale would circulate throughout the hut village. Because of his limited technological experience, however, he only succeeded in turning it off the station. The instrument crackled continuously in the background.

"Those singing beetles have become a hissing cobra!" Tombe noted.

In a flash, Tatey snatched a heavy metal spanner off the wall and shoved himself in front of me, almost uprooting my legs. He wielded that spanner like it was a new-age *knobkierrie* (traditional fighting stick with a wooden knob on the top end).

Tatey fiercely showed his teeth in a savage grimace. I wished then that he had Jack's terrifying tusks instead of Maggie's normal teeth. Tatey spat a blob of frothy saliva on the floor at the feet of the fool.

The city boy was still weakly waving the shiny blade, but his smirk had slid right off his face.

"I will kill you if you touch *Nohanki,*" Tatey seethed as he spat out the words. His broad shoulders were swaying, his muscles restless and rippling as he swung from side to side in a sort of warlike tribal dance.

"Whites stole our land and you want to *defend* her?" The city boy hissed with hate. His voice went up into a high-pitched, unintentional squeak. Nevertheless, he stepped back slightly from his menacing opponent.

"She's not white—she's a Xhosa. And we stole the wireless first. You cannot steal something that is already stolen from *Sngxhoshe.*" Sindie was perfectly cheeky.

"She's a Xhosa in a white cocoon," Tombe confirmed with chutzpah, nodding her head up and down for emphasis.

Sindie took a fearless step forward. "Miss Jay is one of us. And you have no clue how well *Sngxhoshe* shoots, do you?" Sindie pointed her chin out, daring anyone to challenge her statement.

"Let the snake out the box!" Tombe added, hoping to scare the *tsoti.*

It was now up to me to change the subject. "My dad would blow your brains so high that the fragments would fall like snow in another hemisphere." I was feeling brave, even though my father was thirty miles away.

"I hate all white people; they are scum, like froth on the top of the sea, who blew over from another hemisphere." The city boy spewed, his popularity fading fast.

"Didn't you hear her? This white child speaks Xhosa much better than you do," Toto taunted, almost boasting on my behalf. "You pollute our language with Zulu and Tswana. You can't even speak pure Xhosa like our Miss Judy here can. You are city scum like the dregs at the bottom of a beer barrel. The only reason *Sngxhoshe* has not already blown your brains out is that you do not have any!"

That was the worst blow to the city boy's ego. It undermined his goal, which was to impress Toto in the first place. Now the lovely maiden was mocking him with no mercy at all.

"Nqanda umtana womlungu wethu. (Protect the child of our white man.)" Tombe yelled.

"Sondela! Iza! (Closer! Come!)" Tatey's growling voice was not just threatening. He meant every word. "I feel like smashing your head, just for the sake of posting you back to Johannesburg where you belong, in a wooden box. We will label the casket 'idiot.' " Tatey's deep husky voice was menacing.

No one laughed out loud, but their ebony faces glowed with admiration for Tatey. There was an instant groupie deflection of fickle girls. Fikile's relative was no longer the new attraction.

"Yes, IDIOT, we can borrow *SngXhoshe*'s stencil and paint from the sheep-shearing shed to mark your coffin," Toto jeered with a killer smile, poking the final deflating needle into the stranger's overinflated ego. "Tatey, here, even spelled 'idiot' right on his spelling test!" Toto was proudly defiant and clearly taking sides with her half brother, who looked more like Jack than either Toto or Sindie did. Toto was a light-skinned beauty like Lizzie. Her skin was shiny due to all the cream and butter Lizzie had access to in her dairy duties. Cream was the original cosmetic face cream.

"Unlike our parents, we can all read and write whatever we like, thanks to *Sngxhoshe* who helped build us a new school," Sindie asserted.

"And he shot the policeman's dog that lived between us and the school," Rama added.

Grabbing the city boy by the shoulder, Zandi, Fikile's teenage son, counseled,

"Masihambe! Masihambeni! Masigodukeni! (Let's go! Let's all go! Let us all go home!)" Zandi was anxious to diffuse the fury before the fight. He also knew Tatey's undefeated record of fighting.

"I was just kidding," the city stray sheepishly stuck his knife away, pretending it was all a joke even though everyone knew better.

Tatey was still wielding the spanner, exactly like the dads hold a traditional *knobkierrie,* except this spanner was a new, high-tech version of the ancient wooden weapon. It, too, had a knob on the end—a heavy spinning bolt, which glinted in the sinking sun like a disco ball.

Jack's offspring spat on the floor at the *tsotsi's* feet and swore again. "You are the semen of a city mongrel!" Tatey was tempting trouble.

The *tsotsi* yanked his knife out again and lunged forward. Tatey cracked one big blow to the visitor's face. Instantly, the youth was French kissing cold cement, bleeding from the mouth. One pink tooth lay on the cement, marinating in his blood. Another triangle of tooth was also chipped off another tooth. The white triangular chip lay next to his bleeding gaped mouth. Lizzie could not have painted a more perfect white triangle to keep out the bad spirits.

"Tsho! Tsho! (It serves you right!)" Toto taunted.

"Heke! (Good work!)" Sindie was cheering. "This is what we call 'bush' justice!"

The confused city juvenile delinquent had to be helped to the huts by his cousin.

The second prettiest girl from Sunnyside whispered something in Tatey's ear, which curled a smile right around his head from ear to ear. That smile never quite left his face for the rest of the day.

After Tatey administered that townie a splendid shellacking, the combat was over. The teens dispersed in different directions.

Tatey and Rama herded the three of us younger girls safely back to the farmhouse, like meek little lambs.

Rama was holding the radio tucked under his arm, as proudly as a missionary holds his "good news" Bible. Tatey was still sporting the huge spanner in his right hand and pumping his fist in the air.

"Heke! Heke! (Well Done!)" Sindie praised her big half-brother. Tatey and Rama had been big brothers and lifesavers to me that day. In fact, I spent more time with them than with my own brothers in those days. Just like Maggie was my "other" mom in a Xhosa sharing sense.

"Akuyohiki tu! (You aren't afraid at all!)" Tombe had great admiration for triumphant Tatey. She was relieved to be rid of the rodent from the city.

"Tatey, you overcame him! You are very strong!" I was grateful for his impressive courage. "And that city slicker looked the age of Boss Bruce."

I hastily returned the radio to my father's desk. It looked more at home there in his office. Two office walls were mounted with solid oak wooden gun racks holding horizontal, well-oiled rifles. They rested there peacefully.

Many neatly-framed photos adorned the other walls, photos of Dad and his teammates in school uniforms, sitting in neat rows. They were photos of the First Teams of Gill College in rugby, cricket, and tennis. Dad was a stud in his youth, indeed, an all-rounder. There were also framed pictures of champion stud Afrikaner bulls, decorated with prize ribbons.

The half-brothers, Tatey and Rama, hung around us a while longer on the back kitchen *stoep*, guarding us while soaking up the compliments along with the last rays of the setting sun.

"I will go and find you all something to eat," I promised as I swung into the kitchen. I found that my mother and Wendy had baked batches of crunchies with golden syrup, coconut and oatmeal. I helped myself to four of the fattest oatmeal cookies and delivered them to my loyal friends waiting on the kitchen *stoep*.

"You overpowered him," I thankfully repeated to Tatey, handing him the hot cookies. He was grateful for the biscuits, but mostly enjoyed the compliment. I returned to the kitchen table, where an abandoned tea tray stood. I filled a large enamel mug with lukewarm tea, adding milk and five spoonfuls of sugar. I stirred the tepid tea and handed it to Tatey.

"Enkosi, (Thank you) Miss Judy." Tatey politely put his hands together, making a cupping shape like a dish to receive the mug. In the Xhosa culture, it is good manners to put out both hands in this fashion when receiving a gift. Tatey took the first gulp, and then Rama, then the girls got a swig out of the communal cup.

"You have great power and strength, Tatey," Tombe concluded, still managing the click of the tongue with a mouth displaying half-chewed crumbs. "City people are soft."

"And quite slow, too!" Sindie added. "Toto will never marry such a dimwit from the city." Sindie smiled contentedly and then swallowed. "And he thought we were thick! Wait till his slummy friends see that his teeth have been knocked out! And they were extracted by a country boy's latest fashion metal *knobkierrie!"*

"We will wait here till we hear the Land Rover's engine." Tatey had decided to stay and protect us.

"That *tsotsi* missed out on tea and crunchies." Tombe stated. "My parents say that when people move to the city, they forget to keep our ancestor's customs and they fall into evil ways."

"Nomhankazi, you had better fetch more food, I need more stamina to welcome our unwanted visitors." Tatey smiled, looking up at me.

That night, Dad, having missed the lunch time news, was extra eager to catch up on the bulletins of the day. He carefully tuned his radio at the supper table.

The voice sort of groaned and grunted, "Thiiis is Springbooook radioooo…"

"What's the matter with the reporter? Is he drunk?" I asked.

"The Woooorld at 7 peee.m., Huuu-gh Rouse repoooort-ii-ing"...and the battery died.

Dad glanced at Wendy for a split second, and quickly quieted his temper. He bridled his tongue with a firm bite on his pipe.

Wendy scowled at me most suspiciously.

8

KEEPING TRACK OF TRAINS

When June rolled around, winter coldly crept into the Southern Hemisphere. Schelmdrift was seventy miles inland from the southern tip of Africa. We endured chilly nights, with the comfort of hot water bottles and Angora mohair blankets. We never saw snow—nevertheless, we often woke up to a white frost crisping the lawns. Soft green grass became bristly brown like prickly front door mats.

At this time of year, our family gathered around log fires in the lounge every evening. Mom knitted Merino woolen *jerseys* (sweaters), socks and booties by the dozen. Dad read copious amounts of newspapers. My brothers had a fireplace in their bedroom as well, but it was hardly ever lit, as they were away most of the time.

I spent most of my time in our servants' toasty huts, enjoying their food, their company, and the warmth of their hearts. Their hearths burned all day long to keep them snug and to cook their food on three-legged pots. In the winter, they enjoyed plenty of venison from Dad's kudu hunting expeditions, on which I was no longer invited.

The Africans who migrated to work in the gold mines in the Highveld usually borrowed words from the eleven official languages of South Africa. They would come back to their tribe with extra words that didn't belong, like the toothless *tsosti* who was promptly posted back to the city. Our well-kept staff never left to work in the gold, platinum, copper and diamond mines of the Highveld reef.

Some had heard the horror stories drifting down the 'bush telegraph' about how over 400 black men were trapped and entombed in the Coalbrook mine in 1960. Despite Iscor drilling through dolerite rock to try and rescue them, they all perished in the hellhole 600 feet below ground. One young Native fellow just made it out alive, but watched for agonizing weeks, as all six of his brothers were all trapped to death. The frantic rescue failed. He was the lucky one. In this tragedy, the government officials had inspected the mines seven weeks before the collapse, deeming it safe. They carried canaries in cages to test for lethal carbon monoxide and methane gasses. If the canary died, the miners left. I had learned from Tombe that we should watch the birds of heaven for examples.

Only six whites were underground on that fateful day, two of them were named Boet. One unlucky Boet was *not* supposed to work that tragic day, but was substituting for another very lucky fellow miner. No educated scientist or prolific research or government investigation could say why some are lucky and others doomed.

Consequently, our loyal laborers, being deterred from the mines—where Fanagolo, a mixed, Zulu-based pidgin language was spoken—still spoke a very pure form of isiXhosa.

Interestingly enough, Dad, Boet Bester, still talked about what he read in the, Rand Daily Mail of 23rd January 1960, that a bull buyer brought him. This is what Dad read:

"Mine officials are finding it difficult to control the hundreds of African workers. The workers believe that mine 'ghosts' caused the hundreds of tons of rock to fall.

They say that the 'ghost' has not been 'paid off' by the mine owners. These raw tribal men believe that the white 'bosses' have to take gold down to the mine 'ghost' every few months.

It is reported that many Africans tried to flee from the mine compound when they heard of the disaster. Officials will neither confirm or deny this."

Boetie Bester always reckoned that the mines were not safe after that, regardless of misconceptions about ghosts.

The isolation of Schelmdrift ensured that the Xhosa language, as well as our air, remained unpolluted. Speaking English to whites, I employed about 44 different sounds. In *IsiXhosa*, I expressed myself in 126 various reverberations and clicks. Xhosa is the most difficult language to learn on the whole earth, unless you learn it as a baby, as I did. I had no recollection of learning to speak Xhosa. I spoke *isiXhosa* as fluently as I spoke English. I naturally switched languages according to the skin color of the person I was talking to. Frieda van Vuuren was the exception to the rule, of course, but I hardly saw her.

Whenever my mother had a baby, Sister Underwood, a white trained nurse came and lived on Schelmdrift with us. She was a fat spinster who wore a nurse's uniform with maroon lapels. She slept in our spare bedroom for six weeks, and the chubby nurse was in our baby photos forever. Dad reckoned she gobbled more food than all four maids put together.

Dinah, my young Xhosa nanny, who had been my nanny since infancy, was with me almost every day for the first five years of my life. She watched me while Mom sewed, gardened, and played tennis. However, carefree Dinah was now no longer my protective nanny, guiding me away from dangerous dipping tanks. We had a small dipping tank for sheep and goats, and a bigger one for cattle. The insecticide killed parasites, and prevented tick fever.

Dad warned all the servants when he read about some other farm *piccanins* who thought they could follow the example of sheep. The kids got themselves immersed in that farmer's dipping tank water. After drinking the dirty water laced with insecticide, they got very sick and almost died.

Dinah always did visit me whenever she walked over to Schelmdrift. She lived with her family at Goodwood, our adjoining farm. She told all the servants that I was "her child." She was the most happy and cheerful person and I loved her.

I loved the peaceful farm. I loved my family. I loved the Karoo. The servants were my "other" family. We loved each other, so the thought of going to Collegiate with a lot of city girls filled my soul with dread. My previous encounter with a city slicker had not been agreeable at all.

I announced to my parents at the supper table, "I wish I was black and didn't have to go away to boarding school." My parents glanced at each other, visibly concerned about my identity crisis. Somehow, I assumed in my innocent mind that if I were black, the dread of relocating would disappear entirely.

"You can't change reality or the apartheid rules," Mom clarified. "We just have to obey the laws." She let out a long sigh as she silently served up the hearty, kudu-bone soup that Maggie prepared during hunting season. The wild soup smelled like home.

Dad turned on the news. South Africa had riots in the cities and bombs that blew up law-abiding people. People were protesting apartheid. Police dealt with rioters with an iron fist. In 1960, police mowed down mobs in Sharpeville like tractors mowed lucerne with a sharp new blade. Times of turmoil lay ahead.

While I sipped the savory kudu soup thickened with barley, beans, lentils, and split peas, I relived the vision of the steam train leaving the Grahamstown railway station. I could picture it over and over again. This scene chooka-chooed around my head as relentlessly as my cousin's electric train…Martin had received an electric train for his birthday. Only the batteries in my brain never went flat!

The following scene replayed vividly in my mind:

The uniformed conductor's pink cheeks ballooned under his captain's hat as he blew the shrill whistle. Then he double-checked the coach doors to see if they were locked shut before signaling to the train driver that all was cleared for departure.

Dad, Mom and I stood on the platform and waved to my siblings, who were leaving for another term of school after the holidays. The steam engine slowly moved to our left as it headed toward Port Elizabeth. Steam billowed out of the smokestack as the engine chugged and chugged, slowly churning the wheels along the steel tracks.

It was our custom, and Mom always saw to it, that we stand there and wave until the snakelike train slid my siblings out of sight. I recollected those squeaking metal on metal sounds and sooty smells as I sipped my Maggie's soup.

That train whistled much louder than the conductor as it departed, picking up speed with every puff.

White arms waved out the pristine first class coach. Bruce, Wendy, and Norman, all neatly dressed in their navy Collegiate or Grey school uniforms, waved from those windows. The Bradfields, Whites, Longs and other British Settler offspring also leaned out that class of the chook-a-puffer. They were off to receive the best public education South Africa had to offer. Starched white sheets and blue blankets awaited them on the bunk beds of their luxurious compartments. Varnished wood and leather seats were oiled to a perfect sheen. Hot water gushed from their bathroom stainless steel taps. The crisp, clean linen all had the S.A.R. logo woven into it, for South African Railways. My siblings would enjoy a comfortable sleep during their overnight trip.

The slightly tarnished second class coach latched onto the first car with steel girders. It was carrying a few poorer white folks, stretching out and waving hands. I heard one girl in red shout, *"Totsiens Tannie!* (Goodbye, Aunty!)" in Afrikaans. I saw another passenger with a big smile. He had a tooth missing on the side of his smile; he waved with his cigarette in his hand. *"VRYSTAAT!* (FREE STATE!)" He yelled in support of his favorite provincial rugby team. Another *Ouma* (grandmother) waved a hanky furiously, almost splitting the sides of her pink *crimpelene* (polyester) dress. She had curlers in her hair, with a white hair net over to hold the rollers in place. *"Ek sal julle mos weer volgende vakansie sien!* (I will see you again surely next holiday!)" Their tickets were slightly cheaper, but they were all Europeans like the first class coach. English or Afrikaans whites could choose first or second class, according to their fee preference.

Next, from the grungy third class coach, I could recall seeing caramel colored arms and limbs of the *kleurlinge* hanging out. Those classified coloreds were a motley breed of Dutchmen, Malay slaves, Bushmen and what not! They waved wildly as they bid farewell in Afrikaans laced with argot, *"Hey my bra, Ek sal hom weer #*$&^ donner volgende keer.* (Hey my brother, I will #*$&^ beat him up again next time.)" I heard a vagabond brag, and then he changed his tune, turning to his girlfriend, *"Ek smaak jou lekka, my cherrie.* (I fancy you much, my cherry.)" A scruffy, toothless male in a bright mustard-colored jacket was waving with a green bottle of *ParaPara* (cheap Paarl Perle wine). He cheered and lisped, *"Ge-th-ondheid! Dankie vir die dop. Dus a Boeing sonder vlerke, hierdie ding, die vlerke het netnou @)&^$&* afgeval. Ons is in die Baai in vyf minute.* (To health! Thanks for the booze. It's a Boeing without wings, this thing, the wings just @&^$* fell off. We will be in the Bay in five minutes.)" He had his hair slicked back like Elvis Presley. A middle-aged woman with too much pink rouge had to grab her wig as it almost blew off her head. *"Soentjies vir almal!* (Kisses for everyone!)" She blew a kiss with one hand. Her other hand secured her straight black wig. Their cheaper tickets only afforded cold water out a communal tap to these lovable folks who had a sense of humor of a premier class. Asians and Indians were also allowed to travel in third class as their skins were also dark tan, but I did not see any that day.

In stark contrast, black bodies made parting gestures of claps and fists out the shabbiest fourth class coach. *"Hlalani* kakuhle*!* (Stay well!)" The most common parting wish was yelled from that overcrowded section. Large women with even larger headdresses waved fat sweaty arms. One Xhosa man noisily waved a beaded assegai, *"UmKhontho we Sizwe!* (Spear of our Nation!)" That was the war cry of the MK, the militant arm of the ANC that had gone underground after they were banned along with the Communist Party. An *igqirha* (witchdoctor) dressed in white-beaded traditional Xhosa garb waved a tuft of horsetail hairs, which rather resembled a fancy feather duster. She hollered, *"Ndizakumnyanga afe!....*(I will give him a death curse!)" With only sitting space, the blacks had to sleep upright. The travelers were provided with only toilets, no bathrooms, which explained the putrid stench. From their platform, their loved ones shrieked, *"Hambani kakuhle!* (Go well!)" loudly, while *toyi-toying* (dancing) farthest from us to our right. *"Usiphathele imphahla entlhe!* (Bring us pretty clothes!)" A group of girls cackled in chorus from the platform to their grandmother.

As the train chugged out the Grahamstown station, peeping cattle pooped out the fifth coach cracks, and mooed to nobody in particular. It reeked of manure, not that I minded the smell too much. Their hooves rattled against the metal as the train truck shook the shuffling animals, destined for the abattoir. The train whistled loudly once more and departed.

That colorful class coach portrait was etched in my mind forever. It was a microcosm of apartheid. Classes were classified by color and that was the law. Whites were not allowed to buy a ticket on the fourth coach. Blacks were forbidden to travel first class, even if they could afford it.

Once Mahatma Ghandi had boarded a train in Durban headed for Pretoria, clutching a first class ticket. When the stocky white conductor came around to punch the tickets, he told Ghandi to shift to third class coach with other Indians. Ghandi who was a lawyer trained in Great Britain, refused. When the train stopped at Pietermarizburg, not far outside Durban, they tossed the slightly built vegetarian, Ghandi, off the train. So no one tried his tactics too often. Ghandi then birthed a non-violent resistant movement.

Ironically enough, all the lower classes looked distinctly more cheerful than those European kids flocking to boarding school in first class. That was the most disturbing part of the scene for me.

"What's the matter, my pet? You look like you have seen a ghost?" Mom asked.

"I am fine thanks." I replied, enjoying my train of thought at the dinner table.

The news blared, "It has been one year since the infamous Rivonia trial ended for eight men, including Mandela. They were found guilty of high treason..." Nelson Mandela, a Xhosa man, and his Communist cronies were sentenced to life in prison in 1964 for trying to sabotage the regime. Mandela was a tall man, born to a chief of the Tembu Xhosas, but the rebellious terrorist was safely locked up. So for now, in 1965, white supremacy was the rigid rule.

Ghandi tried passive resistance and that never worked, so after 21 years he went back to India, only to be assassinated there. Later, Mandela plotted violent bombings to take down the regime by force. After that attempt, he was plunked on Robben Island behind bars.

My mind darted desperately from one idea to the next. I had to do something, but I had no power. At that age, I was most concerned with saving my own hide. I had previously considered that maybe changing the color of my skin might suffice. Brown boot polish would do it, although the smell was too strong. My hair and green eyes would pose a problem. I supposed I could shave all my hair off and pretend I had had a lice attack.

Lizzie had recently shaved off Sindie's hair as well as all her siblings' peppercorns and burned it when they got lice in their hair. Jane did the same for Tombe. The hair was always burned, even if it did not have lice. The Xhosa superstition was that if birds used your hair to make nests, you would go insane.

When Mom noticed me scratching my head, she had rushed me to Carlisle Bridge Cash Store, where she bought Blue Butter. She smeared it in my hair to get rid of the lice. I was the only one of our threesome with any hair left to keep my head warm that winter.

The shop at Carlisle Bridge was about the size of my bedroom, and Aunty Leenie kept a few groceries behind the counter, with bicycle parts, enamel mugs and three legged pots. She had some rolls of blue or brown German print fabric and an old fashioned *till* (register) that she cranked for each sale. She also stocked beads and trinkets that the Xhosas bought. Mom only shopped there for occasional emergencies.

"Judy got lice in her hair from playing with the piccanins," Mom confessed to Aunty Leenie.

"Hee-rrr-lik-heid! (Heavens!) I am selling a stack of Blue Butter lately! You are ve-rrr-y lucky; this is my last jar left! *Jislaaik!* (Geez!) I cannot stock it fast enough. Herrrs is rrr-eally not the only *kop* (head) a-rrr-ound here with lice," Aunty Leenie smiled, without confessing Frieda's faults, or divulging neighbor's names.

Mom bought me a buttermilk sucker and round apricot candy balls. She bought the same for my bald friends. We waved to coy Frieda who appeared briefly behind the counter.

"I am so lucky to have you for a friend, Miss Jay. I am not as cursed as they tell me I am." Sindie smiled. "Bhoyi, my twin brother does not have my luck today!" She stuffed a whole apricot candy in her mouth. It filled her whole mouth and she could not smile anymore, but her eyes popped with pleasure.

"Please tell Nolasti that we are very thankful for the sweets!" Tombe beamed. "Tell her now-now in your tongue so she knows how our hearts feel." Tombe ordered.

Luckily for us, Grandpa Stocks had become well-established in the pineapple boom of the 1930's. My privileged mother with her two sisters had attended DSG, which was the sister school of St. Andrews College. These schools were the most expensive private schools on the African continent. The 1820 British Settlers established those upper crust posh schools.

All three genteel Stocks sisters went on to graduate from Rhodes University in Grahamstown. During WWII years, it was an admirable feat for their gender. Not even all whites could afford such an education during the Depression era.

Twelve years of schooling, meant I faced eight long years of boarding school. Luckily for me and my siblings, my mother was qualified to homeschool us for the first 4 years. Education was the key to success, but random luck remained locked in mystery.

Our family was not to attend those most prestigious Anglican schools in Grahamstown, however, as they did not boast of a first class cricket coach. My sporty father wanted my brothers to be taught by Mr. James Dean, who groomed the famous Pollock brothers. And so it was that my siblings rode in that first class coach in hot pursuit of the finest cricket mentor. In the Eastern Cape, after all, cricket was our creed.

As I scraped up the last lick of kudu soup with my stainless steel spoon on porcelain plates, I could hear the sound of those steel train wheels, screeching, "Insist on school…insist on school…insist on school..."

9

MUD HUT

After a restless sleep filled with nightmares about evil city slickers I sat up straight at the breakfast table and defiantly announced, "I want to live in a mud hut!"

Dad turned down the volume. "Gwenna, what is the matter with this child? Can you please invite Frieda over to play again?" Dad spoke over my head.

"She is just lonely and wants to avoid boarding school. Personally, I think a mud hut is not too harmful." Mom seemed happy to allow a *Wendy-house* (playhouse) to be built.

"We have a few extra staff since I hired Flinder. I can spare you a few servants if that will help," Dad offered. He was crinkling the corners of his mouth into a puckish smile and shaking his head at the same time.

"Incorrigible child, she is!" I heard him whisper to Mom as he turned up the volume again.

But that lenient smile made me smell success.

"Please, please can they build just a little hut for us to play in?" I begged.

My parents agreed to the hut as a better alternative since it did not require major skin graphs, cosmetic surgery, or hair transplants. Dad deduced that a hut could not do any harm.

"If one is having an identity crisis, a new shade of lipstick is better than a tattoo," Mom figured. I jumped out my oak chair and gave them each a big hug and kiss. And so it was that I came to have my very own mud hut.

Two of Dad's laborers, Fikile and Cocoa, who were famous for their woodwork, were soon summoned to build me a miniature hut in our front garden. Our garden consisted of a few acres that were fenced in from the rest of the ranch. Mom allocated a spot that was less conspicuous from the driveway behind the hibiscus shrubs. It was on the way to the stable, but heartily concealed from the tennis court by a healthy hedge. But this was going to be my very unique *Nohan-ki-hut*.

Cocoa followed Dad's instructions, driving the tractor and trailer to the Fish River and returning at sunset with some hand-chopped poles. Cocoa dug deep holes to plant the poles in a perfect circle. He and Fikile tied them together with strips of pliable bark. Fikile then carefully joined additional poles for the roof, all pointing to the sky in the center and overlapping slightly over the circular wall.

Dad even came once to be the building inspector.

"Hold the pole straight!" Fikile would shout at all the willing indigenous local lads who had come to watch and help, hoping for an orange or a biscuit.

The sheer entertainment level was a major draw. No one had seen such a perfect miniature hut before. There was a great chattering and clicking of tongues as we all watched the walls take shape. The women mixed clay mud to meticulously fill the spaces between the upright poles. Cheers of approval from our trio urged all their valiant efforts.

My hut had two round windows, holes the size of dinner plates, with no glass. They were just big enough for our faces to peep out. We could stuff them shut with old clothes if we so desired. Both windows flanked the front door. One looked towards the stable. The other faced our farmhouse.

My Dad paid a few unemployed maids to plaster and smooth the walls by smearing runny mud over the dry clay. Lastly, the Xhosa women, who were most keen to come and help, thatched the roof with their skilled hands.

"Cocoa, will you stop flirting with the thatching maidens and concentrate on holding this plank in position?" Fikile micromanaged Cocoa continuously.

Cocoa had more fans than most young men, due to his effervescent charm.

Fikile, who was the handyman of the farm, nailed together a mini wooden door out of homemade planks and affixed a hinge he cut out of thick cowhide.

Tombe stood nearby and passed Fikile the nails. He carved a little lock as well. It was just a rectangle of wood with a nail in the middle. We could turn the piece of wood to lock the neat door, so we could lock it from the inside.

"When I am a man and find a wife, will you make me a door that locks like this?" Cocoa beamed.

Fikile's heart was swollen with pride at his unrivaled achievement.

"Helala, awusemhle umnyango! (Wow, what a lovely entrance!)" Toto wrung the praises.

An eager audience applauded when they saw the rough door become attached. The door was a stable door so we could close the bottom half to keep out chickens and leave the top half ajar to let in the light.

"Icango lilingana istoroshe! (The door fits the hut!)" Sindie sang and danced around holding my hand, getting in everyone's way.

Lastly, the maids leveled the floor with clay and raised it slightly with mud, creating a ringed ridge in the center to serve as the hearth or *izikho*. There was no chimney, so we had to learn the art of making a good fire without excessive smoke. The round windows, doubled as peepholes and chimneys. The door multitasked as a window, chimney, and entrance. Soot could also filter up into the thatch.

"You three girls can help finish off the floor!" The maids were growing tired of bending. The tall maids could not stand up anywhere in my mini hut except in the center, where the roof pointed to heaven like an upside down ice-cream cone.

The three of us happily obliged. We found some old enamel

dishes and ambled to the stables, pretending to be grownups by attempting to balance the dishes on our heads. However, we struggled as I did not naturally have springy peppercorn hair and my friends' hair had not grown enough after the lice attack.

Maggie soon found a satisfactory solution. "You take an old towel and twist it to make a long snake. Coil it like this, just like a sleeping snake. Then you put it on your head like this. Now you have a flat part to balance things."

Toto taught us the skill of collecting cow dung. "Here is nice fresh dung," Toto pointed, rubbing her toe into the slushy dung. "It's still warm from being inside the cow's belly."

Jack kindly came out the stable with a spade full of stud bull dung to fill my dish.

We scooped up all the warm runny dung we could find with smaller dishes and put it in the larger dishes until they overflowed. It is easier to balance a heavier full dish on one's head than an empty one. Perhaps, the desire to avoid having runny cow dung spill onto our noses was also an incentive!

Of course, I had previous training balancing a heavy Bible while reciting "how now brown cow." But this was much more fun as I had friends to learn alongside me.

"*Yenzani nje!* (Do it like this!) Toto taught me." Sindie tucked her dress into her new purple panties, the pair Aunt Ione had given me for my birthday. Sindie demonstrated how to kneel on all fours and use her right hand to spread the cow dung around. She made an ornate pattern, pushing the dung away from her with her palm. Then she scraped it back towards her bare knees, leaving just the right amount on the floor. It made perfect stripes, sliding away from her in a slushy arc, shaped like a seashell. I was fascinated with Sindie's skill, and learned from the professional. I was soon making perfect seashell shapes by smearing fresh green dung. We used our hands to spread the pungent manure evenly to get a matted grassy rug effect. When it dried, we were instructed to make another layer, until the floor was smooth and looked like my mother's green carpet, only ours was fluffed with reprocessed greenery.

Even Lizzie volunteered to paint white triangles around all the openings, and generously shared the whitewash she had stolen out Dad's tool shed.

After the cow dung floor was dried, the recycled grass did not smell bad at all. We swept the excess manure crumbs up with a miniature grass broom. Dinah had kindly tied the broom for me as a housewarming gift. Much to the delight and envy of all the picannins on the farm, I thus became the proud owner of an authentic, Xhosa-style hut. The completed humble hut was a biodegradable, earth-friendly lodge. I felt like a princess with my very own castle.

"Miss Judy, we need *doeks* (head scarves) as well. Our heads are feeling the cold since we got shorn with the sheep shears," Tombe concluded.

"Go and get another towel for me," Sindie pleaded.

Maggie discovered some small tablecloths in the linen cupboard and wrapped all three of our heads with an African headdress so we could make believe that we were already married mothers. The turban felt like a blob on my head, like a ball of soft serve ice-cream, with tickling tassels melting down my neck.

Maggie said, *"Nohanki,* I am giving you the white *doek,* so you can pretend to be a *gqirha* (witchdoctor). You survived convulsions from a high fever five times when you were a baby. People who survive those are called to be witchdoctors. You have a purpose for your life, or the gods would have taken you home."

"Akusemhle, mntana kaSngxhoshe! (You are so beautiful, child of Mr. Strict!)" *"Owu Wethu!* (Oh, my darlings!) *Nibahle nonke!* (You are all beautiful!)" Jane complimented us sincerely.

"I love those blue checks, Tombe. And Sindie, that yellow and orange stripe suits you well." I noted, following Jane's example.

Jane helped me strap my new doll on my back, just the way she carried her own babies. Sindie strapped my old floppy doll on her back. Tombe tied Wendy's old doll on her back with an old towel. Xhosa mothers never used *prams* (strollers). Babies prefer backs, anyways. I had fond memories of being carried on our maid's warm backs.

We gathered wood, tying the sticks in long bundles, balancing them on our heads, and headed back to our mini hut. Then we filled buckets of water from the pipe that spat into the reservoir and balanced those on our heads as we returned to our hut. We spent many happy hours, days and months playing in that hut.

One wintry Saturday morning, Sindie showed up on the back *stoep*…"Let us go and ask *NoLasti* if we can have meat to cook," Sindie begged. "We also want juicy things to eat like you white people eat."

"Yes, let's go and make a fire and cook stew in our hut," said Tombe, arriving shivering and hungry. "It is too cold to play outside."

Sindie and Tombe had to wait in the warm kitchen while I went into the pantry.

Mom generously provided a homegrown onion, an overripe tomato, and a couple of misshapen potatoes. Maggie sliced us a large chunk of lamb shoulder chops. Jane donated a few empty jam tins and a wooden spoon.

Our ancestors, both black and white, had learned survival skills for living in the Karoo. It required a certain amount of tenacity. To live in the isolated homestead was a tribute to their courage in the face of all sorts of odds. Droughts were recurrent, flash floods occurred sporadically. Those hardy homesteaders battled disease and disasters with gritty determination to civilize the Karoo.

When I came out of the pantry with the food for my famished friends, Sindie told me to go back and ask for salt and pepper. She was never too shy to aim high.

"Also cornmeal, please," Tombe solicited more politely. I hurried and got the goods, and we balanced the dishes on our heads. Off we went to our new mini-hut.

We had become proficient at making a tasty lamb stew boiled over a fire. Out of the cornmeal we made *umphokoqo*, a crumbly corn staple dish. We balanced our empty jam tin pots on a three-legged miniature grid, which Fikile had masterfully woven for me out of thick fence wire.

"You can't taste the salt," Tombe complained, adding more.

"Miss Jay, we want to live alongside you forever," Sindie was plaintive, savoring the stew over the bed of crumbly corn.

"Yes, but soon she will abandon us, Sindie. After Christmas, she leaves for the city to go to the white people's school," Tombe mused rather wistfully, munching with her mouth open, visibly mixing the meat and *mieliemeal* (cornmeal crumbs).

Tombe helped herself to another bowlful of the dry porridge. She shook the miniature calabash that *Yan* had presented me from his own garden. Mom found a cork from a wine bottle, but it was too big for the little hole on top of the hollow gourd. Tatey used his pocket-knife to carve the cork until it was a custom fit. We had soured milk in it. Sindie poured the curds and whey over the remaining corn crumbs for dessert. We shared the dish using the same spoon.

"I wish I could stay, but 'those bloody Nats' say I have to go to a white school," I complained bitterly.

"Who are 'those bloody Nuts'?" Tombe asked.

"I don't really know. My dad talks about 'the bloody Nats' all the time. I think they are the people in charge, the government," I lamented. "My parents belong to the United Party."

The Nationalist Party governed South Africa between 1948 and 1994. They were predominantly *Broederbond* Afrikaners who supported the policy of *apartheid*. They were known as "Nats." They locked the people in class cages, and one could not abscond from one government classified coach to another.

"So, when you grow up, Miss Jay, will you marry Christopher Bowker, from the farm on the other side of Sunnyside?" Sindie ragged. "Then I want to be your servant. I *baggies* (call) being your cook!"

"No, I want to be her cook!" Tombe demanded. "You don't put enough salt in the food. My mom says that a cook has to know exactly how much salt to put in the stew. That is why Maggie has to taste their food all the time."

"No, I said first!" Sindie countered.

"I'm going to be fatter like Maggie. Mom says she eats a lot of their food, which is why Maggie is so much fatter than our moms!" Tombe proclaimed.

"I suggested it first! It was my idea!" Sindie was not going to give up.

"Ok, then, I'll be the housemaid like my mother and polish the wood and silver. The Bowker house will be cleaner and shinier than all other houses in the district. And I will shine my skin with that red rose-smelling furniture oil that your mother steals." Tombe boasted boldly. Jane never stole one thing, unlike Jack's wives, Lizzie and Maggie.

Tombe was just like Jane, her mother, a true conformist: if you can't change a situation, you just make the best of it. That was Jane's philosophy.

"I would love that—you can be my maids when I grow up." I eagerly savored the thought and the comforting food.

"Christopher Bowker is about your age. His cousin, Steven Bowker also lives across the river." Tombe was practically arranging the *labola* (bride price) for me. "Their fathers all have herds of cattle. But I think Boss Frances Bowker is richer." Tombe was talking like a true mother.

"Uncle Frances has three sons; Frank, the oldest is my favorite, then Robert and Hillary." I added. "But I would never marry Christopher Bowker, even if he has pretty blue eyes. He is stingy. When he came over here with his fancy bird egg collection in a wooden box with a glass lid, he wouldn't give me a Hadeda egg! And he had two! Chris could have easily given me the spare one. I would rather marry David Blomfield. He plays cricket at the Carlisle Bridge Country Club with Bruce. Have you seen his big blue eyes?" I asked.

I fantasized further. "Boss Bruce says Boss Dave is very generous when he buys everyone drinks. He gets it from his grandfather, who wrote in his will that his hearse had to stop outside the Albany Club in town. And everyone, all the mourners, had to hop out their cars and drink a whiskey courtesy of 'Old Man Blom.' I am positive David inherited that generosity and will pay you bigger salaries, I hope."

"Whoever you marry really matters to us! He must be generous to us, or you can't marry him," Tombe laid down the law.

"And you cannot marry a city slicker; they are really dumb and dangerous." Sindie added emphatically.

"*SngXhoshe* will want at least 100 cows for you. My mother says she thinks you are his favorite. She says he likes to have you sit on his lap on the rocking chair in front of the fire while he smokes his pipe." Tombe suddenly became sullen, "He will miss you after Christmas."

The reality of the threesome splitting was dawning on their minds as well.

"Now we must all pee in a tin can and we must spread the urine around the outside of this hut, so no evil spirits can enter." Sindie was full of rather unusual ideas. "We want to preserve your life until you get married. How else will we find work one day?" She was most earnest.

"Yes, Miss Judy. That is what the old people tell us to do. It works like a lion, the spotless predator. The cat that is the strongest in the jungle is the spotless one. Your urine will keep bad spirits away," Tombe agreed enthusiastically. "Lion's urine smells very strong; it keeps all sorts of creatures away." True to her tribe, Tombe was very territorial and paid attention to the welfare of both the living and dead.

"But Lizzie already painted triangles to guard the holes in the hut, or to chase away evil. Do we really have to do this ritual as well? I just peed in the lavvy in the house. I don't think I can possibly pee again so soon," I complained.

"Well, then we must make more fire and boil some water to make *rooibos* tea for all of us." Tombe was determined to have me guarded from evil or future misfortunes.

"I'll stoke the fire some more," Sindie volunteered, adding more thorn tree logs.

As soon as the tea was made, we sat and drank on the step on either side of the door, which doubled as chairs. Tombe and I shared one step as there were only two.

Sindie, took a plastic plate, and pretended it was a saucer to her make-believe bone china. Her imaginary tea cup was an empty *KOO* melon and ginger jam tin. She sat up with her back straight against the hut and put her nose in the air. She crossed her legs and imitated a white lady drinking tea.

Tombe grabbed the tin out of her hand and then slapped her not too gently.

"Who do you think you are?" Tombe demanded. "Do not imitate a culture that is not yours!"

We duly performed the urine ritual. I complied in case Tombe slapped me too. I peed in an empty jam tin, hidden away from my white family, in our own little private mud hut.

Tombe said it was not enough, and insisted that they both donate their urine. We stirred the three samples together, uniting our yellow urine in an empty paint bucket.

Sindie then ceremoniously sprinkled it around the outside perimeter of the little hut, singing some sort of chant as she did it. She formed a thin circle of wet wee on the dry dirt. There had to be no break in the complete circle.

"Only good ghosts can cross this line. Now you will be safe forever and ever and ever." A smiled scuttled across Sindie's face.

Tombe clapped her hands in rich endorsement.

"Thank you very much." I appreciated their most kind gesture, even though I never slept in our Nohanki-hut.

FLINDER

As soon as the blossoms popped on the apricot tree, it was once again cricket season. The game played a big part of the English culture; which is why all the other British Colonies such as Australia and New Zealand also enjoy the leisurely summer sport. The farmers gathered each season on the grassy field at Carlisle Bridge, their genuine Club in the Country.

On Saturdays, Dad dressed in his off-white linen shirt and trousers to match. He sported a navy blazer. On the pocket was a fancy gold badge with a kudu bull crested in the middle. Embroidered in gold thread, under the kudu head, was "Carlisle C.C." Dad looked very striking with his dark curly hair and teal eyes.

Mom packed a basket full of apricot jam shortbread for morning tea, cold meats and salads for lunch and fresh coffee cake for afternoon tea. Fresh creamy Jersey cow milk was poured into an empty brandy bottle. It had to be the right breed of cow in order to provide the perfectly flavored tea.

Cricket simply can't be played or watched without drinking multiple cups of tea. The game stops twice for tea, at 11 a.m. and 4 p.m. sharp. It is a British habit. It cannot be broken.

The ladies silently competed to see whose plate of biscuits was favored and eaten up the fastest. It was stiff competition! Mom's shortbread biscuits with chewy apricot jam were always top runners. Aunty Dolly Bowker, Uncle Francis' wife, baked moist banana bread, which was also a fast favorite.

SPOTS

Farmers' trucks, consisting of mostly different colored Land Rovers, would all be parked side by side next to the tennis courts in the red dust. Uncle Sonny drove his cherished old green Ford truck. No one parked next to the cricket field just in case someone hit "a six." The hard red ball would go right through a vehicle's *windscreen* (windshield). Dad always parked his precious vehicle as far away from the cricket field as possible.

We'd all jump out as we arrived at the Country Club, excited to mingle with all the other farming families. The Karoo was a quiet place, where even a passing car was a huge event. Jolly greetings would be exchanged at all such social gatherings.

Each team of eleven men would go into the change rooms to lace up their cricket boots with studs on the bottom. When they came out, the two team captains would toss a coin. That was considered a civilized way of choosing who was to bat first.

In South Africa, cattle were used as the first currency. In 1780, one pound of beads went for one cow. The Xhosas still counted how rich you are by how many cows you owned. But since it was too difficult to toss a cow, now people used coins. Coins also had a head or a tail, just like a cow. If Uncle Sonny, the Carlisle cricket captain, won the toss, he would choose to bowl and field first before the sun got too hot.

Twin, a Xhosa man with a limp, kept the cricket grounds groomed and green. Jennet, his wife, helped in the kitchen. Dad allowed the Xhosa couple to live on Schelmdrift for free. They were zealous Zionist Christians and never caused any trouble. Twin helped the ladies set up their colorful umbrellas, and he was always eager to help unload the trucks. He benefited from generous coin tips for his willing assistance.

Mom was the elected Club Secretary, so she organized all the refreshments. She spent hours on the phone delegating.

Aunt Conny was Mom's assistant, who called me secretly to the kitchen, "Judy, please quickly click and tell this Jennet to hide that goat's milk that the Stephenson's brought. It spoils good tea. She must hide it in her things and take it home." Jennet was too righteous to be part of any theft and sensed something fishy, and her expression was one of suspicion, so Aunt Conny clarified, "Even if she is a Christian, explain to her I am giving it to her to steal."

"Thanks for the superb tea, you lovely ladies," the polite sportsmen lifted up their cricket hats and nodded to my beautiful mother.

"It is our pleasure," my modest mother would reply gracefully. "Please don't mention it."

Mother saw to it that neat and accurate scorebooks were kept for each game. I loved to help her. When I sat on her lap, she taught me how to keep score. Adding up the runs was just another math lesson for her pupil.

"Howazaat!" All the players would appeal when the wickets fell, one by one.

In the evening, the players washed and changed into casual clothes, smelling of soap and Old Spice cologne. Then they'd enjoy cold beers, usually Lion or Castle Lager. The ladies sipped sherry or wine.

Dad always slipped me a mixer like lemonade or ginger ale. "I am sorry that Frieda's family never pitched up." He patted my head.

Soon they would all feel like singing, so Uncle Sonny, with his hair Brylcreamed straight back, would play the piano. People sang old pub tunes. Others played mouth organs, ukuleles and concertinas. My uncle's big brown boot drumming the wood floor kept the beat.

"Waltzing Matilda…I'll go a waltzing Matilda with you!" Happy voices rang out.

There was no generation gap; Carlisle bridged the gap. If you had feet, you stamped them. The older ones waltzed and the younger ones wiggled. That was our entertainment.

"Please, Sonny, will you play, 'From a Jack to a King?' Dad requested his favorite song, spinning Mom around the wooden dance floor. I loved to watch my parents dance. They both knew all sorts of steps.

On the first Sunday of every month, Jennet, the Club maid, quickly swept out the smelly *stompies* (cigarette butts) and empty beer cans from the night before. Wooden benches were neatly placed in rows. A wooden pulpit with a crucifix was respectfully placed in the front by Uncle Francis Bowker. The Country Club was hastily transformed into a church. Farmers with hangovers swallowed Disprin with Guronsan C, using ample amounts of Visine eye drops to get out the redness.

An Anglican minister from Grahamstown arrived in a car to preach to the friendly farmers. The robed minister poured red wine for Communion. The wine was the same color as Jesus' blood, he said. The smell of the wine overpowered the smell of stale smoke and beer. C.C. now temporarily stood for Christian Church instead of Cricket Club. The Reverend preached that Jesus' blood blotted out sins, too.

Mom sang so loudly that I was sure she hurt the headaches on purpose. Dad always put paper money in the collection plate, which was actually a purple velvet bag with gold tassels rather than a plate. Mom stuffed green paper money with an Afrikaner stud bull printed on it for her contribution, and I tossed in coins to make the bag rattle even louder. Then the farmers went home to rest and recover.

One such Sunday afternoon, Mom and Dad were snoozing. I could hear Dad snoring from across the passage. Then I heard louder noises and banging on the kitchen door. Maggie came staggering down the passage.

"BAATH BOET, kom gou! (BOSS BOET, come quickly!)" Maggie spoke in intoxicated Afrikaans.

On seeing me, Maggie hollered, *"BIZA UTATA WAKO!* (CALL YOUR DAD!)" As if I was her maid servant.

Maggie was swaying and holding the wall. She smelled like smoke and a few other smells that she often collected at their African parties. I summoned Dad to the scene. Maggie was speaking in too many tongues, and Dad was not able to understand any of her garbled jargon.

"Judy, what is she saying?" he asked anxiously.

"She said Moses has been stabbed."

"What?" He frowned. Dad sounded shocked and worried and annoyed all at once.

Dad soberly walked out and down the kitchen steps. A crowd of about twenty was gathered. They were all yelping tales of terror in a very excited frenzy.

Mass hysteria was now calling for Flinder to be hunted and shot. Arms and fists were pointing and punching the heavens.

Maggie was waving her arms up and down declaring, *"HY IS □ SKELM! HY IS VOL TWAK! UGHEZA GQHITHA!* (HE IS A HOOLIGAN! HE IS FULL OF RUBBISH! HE BEHAVES VERY BADLY!)" She was telling tales of Flinder's base character.

All the dads were trying to talk at once, each one louder than the one next to him.

Dad intently nudged through the crowd. He kept asking "Judy, what are they all saying?"

Dad was hard of hearing, and with everyone yelling, he was very perplexed. It was one big din. I translated select phrases that made some sense.

The men had carried Moses down the hill from the huts by his wrists and ankles, all staggering along unsteadily.

As we reached Moses, I saw blood blotches on his checked Sunday shirt. His head was dangling like a dead sheep's head. The sticky blood was gluing his yellow shirt to his dark skin. Moses was wobbly and limp. Blood was oozing out of him and clotting like gobs of gummy sap out of a Mimosa thorn tree. It was the same color as the communion wine. I could smell his blood. It smelled salty like fresh meat.

I translated for Dad:

"Flinder stole Moses' beer."

"Moses went to get it back."

"Flinder denied stealing."

"Flinder stabbed Moses."

"The blade was sharp on both sides."

"That *tsotsi* from Jo'burg sold the knife to Flinder."

"The thief tried to finish Moses off, but we brought Moses to you."

"Simthathe sambetha ngegqudu samgqiba wawa phantsi lagheza! (We knocked that lout out with a knobkerrie!)" Yan proudly confessed,

but I didn't translate that part for Dad. I did not want Yan—Tombe's dad—to to go to jail.

Most of the Dads were dithering around in different degrees of drunkenness. Maggie was clearly a trifle inebriated. A few other rustic-looking nymphs of ill repute lingered alongside her. Jane and Lizzie were at home with their children.

Fikile, the only sober one, was now preaching the Gospel to make up for the fact that his rebellious relative had provided the wicked weapon. "This is why we should all be at church on Sundays instead of drinking beer!" He was tall enough to stand out above the crowd; he did not need a soapbox. "Keep the Sabbath day Holy and this would not have come to pass!"

Dad took one quick glance at Moses and ordered, "Judy, run and tell Mom to phone for an ambulance. We'll meet the ambulance halfway." Just then, Mom appeared on the kitchen *stoep*, so he told her himself. She hurried off.

Dad asked, "Is he breathing?"

"No! YES! No!" came the answers.

"They don't know," I translated.

"Well, let's look," Dad said as he quickly bent over the lifeless, dangling Moses. "I can't tell either. If he is breathing, he isn't breathing very well. Let's feel for a pulse."

There was a hush as Dad quickly grasped Moses' wrist. "There is a feeble pulse."

"Judy, tell them to hurry up and carry him around the front of the house to the driveway, under the pepper tree. I'll bring the Land Rover down. Tell them to cover him with blankets to keep him warm."

Fikile was still making amends for his wayward weapon provider: "Thou shalt not steal! Thou shalt not lie! Thou shalt not kill! Those are the commandments of God! Why can we not obey those simple laws?" He used his most virtuous voice, elongating the vowel sounds. Fikile was indeed a ferocious vicar preaching to the least sober congregation I had ever seen. Fikile had the noblest of intentions, but I did not translate his oration for Dad as Dad had already been to church. Fikile was truly converted to Christianity and was quite adamant in letting everyone know, "If only we all obeyed all the Ten Commandments…there would be peace…no fighting…on earth."

Maggie ran to grab the old blue checked rug that we used for picnics. Dad collected his keys, pipe and wallet from Mom who had thoughtfully brought them out to him.

"Thanks, Billikins. He'll be dead by the time the ambulance gets here. We are thirty miles away," I heard Dad mumble to Mom before he jogged up to the garage.

The dads managed to heave Moses into the back of the Land Rover *bakkie* (open back truck); I had seen them hurl a dead kudu carcass in the back of the *bakkie* in the exact same manner. Moses' wife was given a hand up as well. Yan also rode with the unconscious man in the back. Dad drove off very fast. Yan grabbed on the side with both hands, when Dad never slowed down for the bumps. Moses almost got sloshed off the back, but Yan managed to grab onto the bleeding man.

"Fancy that! How about that?" Mom said indignantly standing on the front *stoep*, with her hands on her hips, "It is all very well for Dad to go off like that on a charitable mission. Caesar's Ghost! Daddy just left us here with a violent murderer on the loose. It is perfectly obvious it never occurred to your father that we might be in any danger."

"I fear Flinder may also have some injuries. Yan said he knocked him out cold with a *knobkerrie,"* I translated hesitantly.

"I shall phone Sgt. Lombard at Carlisle Bridge," Mom said as she walked briskly through the stained glass door onto the tiled hallway, where the phone was attached to the wall. Our house had two front doors. The one on the south was called the "telephone door."

"There is no reply." Mom was livid, plunking down the receiver. "Insufferable man that policeman is anyway!"

"Phone Uncle Sonny then," I suggested.

"Uncle Sonny left this morning to take bulls to the Queenstown Show." Mom stated curtly.

I watched the servants rumble back up the hill, still waving their arms dramatically, broadcasting the details and carrying all the noise and clamor with them.

Mom and I found ourselves alone in that big spooky house. The servants returned to be with their families and retell the news. Besides, it was the Sabbath—their day off. I wanted to go and call Tatey to protect us. But I had never told my parents what a wonderful hero he was. That tale would have to include my confession of stealing the radio.

Mom dialed the police station a few more times, but got no answer.

"He is probably sleeping, the lazy old sod. Or he is out eating another farmer's food. Let's go and put the kettle on." Mom tried to regain her composure, but the words were uncomfortable.

Usually tea calmed most situations. You just talked about it over tea, and all fear vanished. Not that day.

"Let's go and get the shotgun," I said. I presumed it was an opportune time to protect ourselves. "I know how to use it. Bruce taught me how to shoot. He let me pull the trigger a few times last time he was home."

"Don't be a silly mutt! Flinder won't harm us," Mom said with too much confidence. It had to be stupidity or blind faith. Whatever it was, she was not too enchanted with my bright idea.

We drank more tea to calm the nerves, but to no avail. The minutes felt like forever. Mom kept glancing up towards the huts. An ominous gloom settled on Schelmdrift. Such an incident tainted the fresh air with an unpleasant rancor. The happy village of the Xhosas had been flung into disharmony over homebrewed beer and a flick knife.

"Why do people fight over beer? Can't they share?" I asked.

"The Natives have nothing else to do. They don't have books to read, sports to play or cinemas to watch. They sorely lack recreation." Mom was emphatic. "It is in their culture to fight. Maggie admitted they have a sort of lust for the sight of blood. Fighting is their sport. The Zulus Impi's and Xhosas have been slaughtering one another for as long as they have existed. That's just their mentality. That's their way of solving a problem. When our ancestors came to this continent, the Africans were barbaric savages. They clubbed each other then, and nothing has changed. They ran around in loin clothes with spears and shields and knobkerries, killing one another for amusement. Now they have knives. Perhaps their weapons are different, but nothing else is new. That is how savages and uneducated bloodthirsty barbarians behave." Mom was visibly distressed as she vented her feelings.

That was the third sermon I had heard that Sunday.

"Oh," I said. "But Flinder and Moses are brothers-in-law. They are both Xhosas. They are not savages."

"Well, then, I don't know. Flinder behaved like one today. If you behave in a barbaric manner, you are a barbarian. Have I not taught you anything about verbs and nouns? If you tell lies, you are a liar. If you steal, you are a thief. If you behave in a savage manner, you are a savage. It is perfectly simple. People are thus titled after their behavior. That is why Granny says 'Manners maketh man'—the way you behave tells who you truly are and how you are bred and what class you belong to."

"Our servants do not always behave like this. Perhaps someone put too much yeast in their beer." I was more worried about our safety than about sermons.

"The Kaffirs just all had too much *kaffirbeer* to drink." Mom dismissed my suggestion. "Alcohol makes people do ghastly things. Drunkards have no scruples at all, regardless of whether they are black or white; the dimwits resort to the base behavior of a baboon." She paused to sip more tea. "We ration our servants with food because the maids complained that their husbands would waste all their money on alcohol. But then their men simply take the *mielie* (corn) meal and use it to concoct the vilest toxic brew. They make the *food* rations into *foul* fermentations. You just can't win—it's their tradition. What are we supposed to do?"

"Why haven't their old people been to school?" I asked, annoying her further. "Can we not change traditions?"

"A leopard never changes its spots. They just do what they have always done. The Natives had no schools or books or education when the whites landed here, that's why. Schools cost money. And who do you expect to pay for it all?" she barked. "The blacks outnumber the whites forty to one! Who will foot the bill? And who do you propose will train teachers and buy their books? They can't go to the white schools, even if they were allowed to. They speak different languages and have a very different culture. Caesar's Ghost, child, you cannot just quell an ancient culture of quarreling overnight. They live by a different set of morals and have an anomalous belief system. Christianity and witchcraft do not mix. You understand that, don't you?"

"That Anglican minister said today we should love one another. Why can't they come to church with us? Or you and Granny Stocks could start a school to teach manners. Did your ancestors not start a Methodist School? Didn't your Stocks family have something to do with Kingswood College?" I had stretched her frayed nerves to the limit, I sensed it.

"I need to *spend a penny* (use the toilet)," Mom announced after copious cups of tea.

I thought of holding my urine in until I had enough to sprinkle around our farmhouse, but that would surely require gallons. Mom was not in the right race or mood to donate her pee, even if I produced a collection potty. I was not too eager to share witchcraft remedies at that moment either.

I got up to leave as well, but she jerked her head up and said, "Where do you think you're going?"

"To the *stoep!*" I announced.

"Stay inside…just a minute, my girl." Mom hurried up the passage to the lavvy.

Unlike my mother, my mind had been thinking many more thoughts than my mouth had been splurging. My mom was too girly to really know how to shoot. She never had brothers to teach her.

Flinder knew that we were defenseless without Dad. I, too, glanced up towards the huts as I walked out the front door onto the *stoep*, then into Dad's office. It was a little eerie in there that ugly afternoon.

In one of his black and white photographs, Dad was uniformed as a soldier in Egypt. Soldiers had guns to protect their families. I had a right to defend myself and my mother. Mom was clueless with a gun, I knew as much.

I also understood that my worthy dad had fought in World War II, which was not exactly what you call loving one another. Apparently, fighting is okay if you are defending yourself or your family. Africander bulls' eyes stared at me from the photos on the wall. I had the instinct of an Africander cow with a newborn calf. We had been chased by angry cows often enough to know that survival instincts are natural.

The rifles were all resting reverently on their racks. They were keeping the day holy, not blasting holes in anything. Hunting rifles were never used in the cricket season, because you never shot in the spring when the kudu cows have calves. That was too cruel. How would the calves survive if their mothers were shot? Mothers were supposed to protect their young.

I had a mother who could not shoot, so I thought her young should protect her.

Maggie had warned Dad that Flinder was a trouble-causer. She had even advised Dad to fire Flinder. He was not one of the original boys who had grown up on Schelmdrift, whose fathers had faithfully worked for my grandfather. He was an outsider, a newcomer.

Dad had employed Flinder when there was extra sheep-shearing work, and on the recommendation of Moses, who was now hovering near death.

Earlier, I had overheard Maggie tell Jane that Flinder was fired from another farm for fighting. I had not translated or told my parents that part. So now I felt guilty. Maybe I was to blame for not telling Dad about Flinder's firing in the first place. So perhaps it was my duty to now fire at Flinder.

I knew Sindie and Tombe would be hiding, huddled in their huts. Maggie had no man to protect her, but Tatey was tough enough. Sindie would be safe with her full-grown brother, Ping-ping, even if Jack was at the Queenstown Show. Then I thought of Tombe. Their hut was right next door to Flinder's hut. Her dad, Yan, had gone with my dad. I fretted about her safety, and for petite Jane and all her little ones.

My eyes lingered on the shotgun. I gently caressed the cartridges. Suddenly Mom barged in.

"What do you think you are doing?" Mom demanded.

"Just looking."

"Well, get down off that table at once! Don't you dare touch that shotgun!" Her voice was curt and clear. "Come with me. We'll go and try the police station again. Just maybe we'll get a reply this time." She yanked me down very forcefully by my dress. "There are other ways to solve problems! More civilized ways!"

Just then, we saw Dad stop at the turn off, where Yan jumped off the back of the truck.

"Thank God Above," I heard Mom breathe again.

Dad was livid. You could tell by his boots on the *stoep*. His boots would have dented the cement if it had been any softer.

"Please may I have a cup of tea, Bill?" He called Mom that sometimes; it was an affectionate term that they shared.

"And do you suppose you deserve a cup of tea? You abandoned Judy and me here all alone with a malicious maniac on the loose!" Normally, she never scolded Dad in front of me.

"I am sorry, dear. You had gobs of guns. I forgot you don't know how to use them," Dad apologized, his angst dissipating with his confession.

"I know how to use them!" I said quietly raising my hand, but they ignored me.

Mom and Dad were kissing and hugging. I started to feel like a gooseberry (third wheel), so I went inside to put the kettle on the gas stove all by myself.

Later, Dad vented over tea, "The ambulance was so slow. I was through Hell's *Poort* (Pass) before we met the ambulance. I was at Tommy White's farm when they finally came crawling along."

Dad sipped his tea, and continued, "The Natives have different ambulances to the Europeans. Theirs looked quite shabby and dirty. And the medical staff looked very incompetent. They obviously weren't trained very well. They say Moses is still alive. He looked dead to me. They may kill him along the way, that *bally* useless lot."

"And where do you suppose our policeman is?" Mom asked, less frantic now.

"We stopped at the Carlisle Bridge Police Station on our way home. He was snoozing in the sun. He jumped up and promised he would come and take Flinder to jail. Yan said Flinder was 'sleeping' in his hut. Mind you, I strongly suspect our boys may have helped put the blighter to 'sleep.' " Dad lit his pipe.

"It sounds like they gave Flinder a good *klap* (smack) with a *knob-kerrie*," I added.

"If he is beaten up too badly, they will also go to jail. I'll have no labor left." Dad puffed away on his pipe.

An eye for an eye appealed more to me that day. Why should we allow Mercy to stab Justice? I would prefer Justice to hit Mercy over the head. That is how I felt in the outback of the Karoo, where it was simply the survival of the fittest.

"Well, Flinder won't be coming back to Schelmdrift. What about his wife and children? I can't just throw them off the farm. Mind you, she is probably glad to be rid of the dodgy character, too. Yan tells me now today that Flinder beat his wife up regularly. I wish I had known. Maybe I should have listened to Maggie and fired Flinder long ago. I'll talk to Maggie tomorrow and see what they all say. I understand them better when they are calm and sober." At this point Dad was much more unruffled himself. "I would not be at all surprised if Flinder has given up the ghost by now."

It haunted me that the Anglican minister in a white dog collar and long, black robes, with jingling chains, dangling a shiny crucifix, preached, "Love one another." Was that a realistic expectation? Flinder chose to steal, to lie and to kill. It was not easy to love him anymore.

Cricketers get a second chance to bat. No matter if you made a *duck* (no score) the first innings, you got a second chance. Dad granted Flinder a second chance and look what happened! All people, well-read or uneducated, young or old, make big bloody blunders.

11

RAMONA CAFE

I knew deep down that the balance of power was in my favor. I don't know how I knew exactly, but I knew.

Flinder went to jail forever. Moses' organs were damaged and he had to have part of his liver and lung removed. He could never work again. He survived on a permanent disability pension—compliment of the tax payers.

With everything back to normal, Dad planned to go on a fishing trip to Kasouga, where our family holidayed every summer. It wasn't quite summer yet, but the weather was sufficiently sunny.

The radio was blaring: "This is Springbok Radio. It is August the 10th, 1965. This is Eric Cordell with your 7.30 a.m. edition of World News..." The date was a harsh reminder that my carefree days in the country were running out. Boarding school began in January, and that change was looming.

Before we left for town, my family enjoyed our usual hot breakfast, courtesy of Maggie. We sat at our placemats and munched on our poached eggs, sausages, and tomatoes—fried slowly in farm butter until they had caramelized.

The relentless radio reported, "The Springbok cricket team, representing South Africa in Great Britain, triumphed over the English Team by 94 runs at Trent Bridge yesterday."

"I look forward to reading the newspapers when we get to town. Will you please get the servants all loaded up quickly, while I go and tell the staff what to do while we are away?" Dad directed his request towards Mom.

"Yes, Dearest." Mom savored the last mouthful of buttered toast spread with her favorite grapefruit marmalade. During the winter, Mom thinly sliced homegrown citrus and boiled it up with sugary syrup. She preserved it in *Consol* jars, labeling each jar 'orange' 'lime,' or 'grapefruit' accordingly. Marmalade was another English tradition.

I soon found myself nestled between my parents in the front of the cream colored Land Rover. Maggie was seated in the open back, with Sindie and Tombe cuddled on either side. Suitcases held our weekend clothes. A plastic bag held theirs. Our three little hearts beat with excitement. The two girls had never seen the sea and I was excited to show it to them.

With fishing rods securely tied on the back, we set off to the seaside via Grahamstown. A red scarf fluttered from the end of the rods. Dad tied it on so the busy metropolis traffic did not bump into the points of his precious rods that extended out the back.

As we approached town, Dad drove straight to the garage to drop off a piece of farm equipment for repairs. "They say it will take about an hour," Dad reported, climbing back into the Land Rover. "I'm thirsty; I think we should go to the Ramona Café for a cup of tea while we wait."

"Have a heart! You've just had tea," Mom flashed her teasing smile. "Are you possibly craving newspapers?"

Daddy smiled sheepishly. "You may go shopping while I wait there, if you prefer. But why don't you come and join me first for a cup of tea? Aren't you thirsty for the news too?" He smiled invitingly at my mother.

Dad was a ruggedly masculine man. His eyes almost crinkled closed when he smiled.

Dad bought all the newspapers he could lay his hands on. At the front counter of the Ramona Café, sweets were displayed in open containers with their respective names and price tags. Some were wrapped in paper and others were not. They were not protected by a glass counter like the ones at the Carlisle Bridge shop.

"Please may I buy my piccanins some sweets?" I asked as Dad was taking his change in coins. Greek and Portuguese immigrants in South Africa usually owned the corner cafés and fruit shops. They were a mottled breed, and we used to call them the "Greasy Greeks" or "Portu-Goose."

These groups of café owners were not large enough to have a coach of their own on the class trains. If they did, it would be below the Afrikaners and above the Coloreds. The Greeks would have been slightly above the Asians, in the slice of rainbow of races. The races were classified by the 'rock spider' regime. They defined who you were according to a specific skin color code. If there was a discrepancy, the government officials inspected people's gums and bums to see what color they actually were!

Greeks and Portuguese were lighter than Gandhi's Indians, and were barely classified as whites—by the skin of their yellow teeth. Greece and Portugal were part of the European continent, after all.

The posh Englishmen still turned their noses down on that assortment, however. One had to know that within the two white coaches, money separated the spectrum of social classes further. Then within those two coaches, the whites were still split further by a finer prism of lightness. That was the unwritten continuum law of apartheid, or separate development. Apartheid was not as simple as black and white. Manners, indeed, played a distinct role in all the rainbow of races. A colorless glass prism intersected parallel peoples into axes of good or shades of evil. Each coach had an enforced glass ceiling.

"Too late, my girl, we'll buy some sweets on our way out. Let's go back there and sit with Mommy at the table now." Dad replied, pointing towards the rear of the Ramona Café.

"GLORIOUS TEST VICTORY" was the headline of The Johannesburg Rand Daily Mail.

"What is a test?" I asked.

"Can't she go and sit on the back of the Land Rover with Maggie?" Dad groaned, petitioning Mom with narrowing bushy eyebrows.

"No. She is going off to school soon; she needs to learn how to behave properly in public." Mom meant "civilized public," but she didn't say it.

Mother decided to distract me instead. "Look here, my child." She had my attention. "Let's read, and do some comprehension exercises. That's how you learn. You read this article and I will quiz you to see how well you understood it."

Instead, my question only resulted in homework. I should have known better. My mother could not cure herself from automatically switching into teaching mode. Teaching was innate to her personality. She came from a long line of school teachers.

"What is a test match?" I asked, wishing now that I had been banished to the back of the Land Rover.

"You get all kinds of tests. At school when you learn about History or Geography, the teacher asks questions to see if the knowledge sunk in. That is how teachers find out how much information you retained. However, these newspapers are talking about a sports *test match.*"

"A cricket test is when the team of the 11 best players from one country play against the 11 very best selected to represent another country. Whoever gets the most cumulative runs from both innings wins the test match," she patiently explained. "A test match can go on for four or five days."

The English prided themselves in the competitive gentleman's sports. It was part of their culture of recreation and a healthy pastime.

The newspaper article gushed of glory:

"What a finish to a great test, a test that will go down as one of the most thrilling on record. There were thrills galore. There were moments of tenseness as both teams fought to recover from collapses, and there was the glorious last hour when England fought with all her might to save the match, and threatened to do so." I continued reading. "Then came the 'over' from Peter Pollock which lifted the Springbucks back into the seat. Victory came with twenty minutes to play."

I already knew that an "over" is when a bowler completes bowling six balls in a row. Another bowler then commences a new "over" from the opposite end of the long pitch. I had learned a lot about cricket at Carlisle Bridge.

"SOUTH AFRICA WINS WORLD ADMIRATION" reported *The Star*. The cafe was abuzz with Albany District farmers reading the magnificent news. Dad greeted a few with polite nods, still keeping his nose keenly in the freshly-printed press. All papers exulted the youngest Springbuck, Graeme Pollock. His sensational batting talent amazed cricket fans worldwide.

"POLLOCKS' FINEST HOUR," another headline caught my eye. Peter Pollock's bowling stunned the world. Graeme Pollock was the left-handed wonder of the world.

"I detest these thick tea cups," Dad grumbled as he took a sip of steaming tea. "Tea tastes better on Schelmdrift out of proper crockery, don't you think, Bill?"

"Well, Dearest, you can't have bone china in a Café. They'd all get broken," my mom replied, practically. "Personally, I think it is the Friesland cow milk they use. It does not taste as good as our Jersey cow milk."

Mom then tested my knowledge of the cricket match and I passed with flying colors. She was satisfied. I started to get bored and fiddled with my dad's hunter green felt hat, the new one he wore to town, now resting on the fourth chair of our table

"How many more newspapers are you going to read?" I demanded of my dad for the second time, spinning his hat.

"Please leave my hat alone. Would you like to go and sit with Maggie outside," he suggested politely, peering over the crinkly paper.

'Victory is mine!' I thought as I wandered out to the Land Rover parked in the street. I had learned enough about tests for one day.

"My dad is reading newspapers," I explained to my neatly dressed friends, who were patiently waiting in the back of the truck.

Tombe was savoring all the unfamiliar sights of a bustling city street. Her dark eyes were *out on stalks* (wide-eyed), searching for stories to tell to her less-traveled younger siblings.

Maggie was chatting to an acquaintance from another farm. They relaxed in the shade of the Land Rover, sitting on the curb of the street. Gossip has no better means of travel than by an unbridled tongue. The traditionally-turbaned women whispered, snickering together about lovers lost, stolen, and found again.

"Sifuna ilekeze! (We want sweets!)" Sindie announced lustily, her face shining in the sun from an extra layer of Vaseline. Neither girl had ever traveled the thirty miles to Grahamstown before.

Tombe nervously sat very still staring at the traffic, semi-detached shops, and bustling pavement full of people of every shape and shade, absorbing every detail of High Street. She would later entertain her family with the news of this adventure, no doubt. Tombe was skilled at taking detailed mental notes of all the noisy movements, smells, and sights. She would have made an astute journalist.

"Let's go and buy some sweets at the shop then." I wanted them to taste the town treats as well. "I've got cash."

My dad had bribed me with 25 cents so I would be silent for five minutes while he read the news. I had rightfully earned it, 5 cents per minute. It was hard work for my tongue. I held up the silver coin for display.

"Hayi (No) please Miss Judy, we will get lost," Tombe begged not to go. Fear emanated from her glinting, round, chocolate-colored face. She clung tightly to her familiar sack of clothes. No *tsotsi* was going to rob Tombe of her earthly possessions.

"I won't get lost. We'll just go into the Ramona Café. Right there," I told them, pointing towards the door. "They sell sweets. Are you thirsty as well?"

"Hayi (No) Miss Judy," Tombe pleaded, clutching one side of the Land Rover anxiously.

"You come with me then, Sindie," I commanded my less-fearful friend.

"All right," she obliged, jumping over the side with great agility. Her lanky legs flew in a cartwheel style. "I want to see the city."

Maggie noticed the flicker of leaping legs out of the corner of her eye. Our observant cook had the eyes of my chameleon.

I had often examined my pet chameleon's eyes with fascination. Chameleons had goggle-like eyes on either side of their heads. The eyes rolled around independently. They could see where they have been and where they were going at the same time. One eye looked forward while the other eye peered backwards. Maggie's eyes and ears never missed much either.

Lifting her hand in a preventive gesture, Maggie clearly called out, *"Hayi* (No) Sindie, you are not allowed in there. Blacks have to wait here."

"We've waited soooo long!" Sindie protested, stretching her long limbs. Maggie turned her back to us, resuming her conversation, hungry for salacious gossip from clicking tongues, dribbling delicious details.

"Masihambeni! (Let's go!)" I urged, grabbing Sindie's arm and leading her in the direction of the door. We quickly shot into the Ramona Café while Maggie was distracted by juicy gossip.

"Hayini! (No, you two!)" Tombe howled, intentionally attracting Maggie's attention away from the tabloid of tongues. She stood up and was nervously shaking both hands agitatedly at the wrists, obviously in great despair.

"Hayini!! (No, you two!!)" Maggie and Tombe repeated, this time in waning harmony.

"Abeva! (They don't listen!)" I heard Maggie's exasperated voice fading behind us. But I knew she wouldn't dare follow me into the "whites only" domain.

"Khetha apha. (Choose from here.) You can choose apricot balls, Wilson's molasses toffees, or Wick's wintergreen bubblegum." I was giving Sindie a guided tour of all the sights of sweets on both aisles.

Sindie was a grand tourist, touching and smelling all the new flavors with aplomb. She was gliding like a duck on the dam. She ceremoniously dipped her face into the bins, like a duck dips its beak into water. She even licked a *niggerball* (type of hard candy) to test the taste. She placed the black licorice ball back very politely, with the wet side discreetly concealed.

I glanced over at my dad; he was safely tucked behind the stiff newspaper, reading about the Pollock Brothers. My mom had her back to us, sipping her second cup of tea. She was equally absorbed by the news of triumph at Trent Bridge.

"Sorry, you are not allowed to buy here," the man with a thick Greek accent said in a low voice, pointing at my black playmate. He glowered at Sindie as if she had leprosy.

Sindie was most well-dressed that day, the most preened I had ever seen Sindie look. She wore a flared pink skirt with a smashing red *jersey* (sweater). Her borrowed buckle-up school shoes were a size too large.

The Africans wear woolly jerseys even on hot days. It is a way of announcing to the world that you own one, a status symbol of sorts. Not everybody could claim ownership of a chunky, hand-knitted red jersey, even if it had been handed down from Wendy to Toto to Sindie.

The Greek's manners irked me no end. How dare he insult my friend like that! Especially when she was in her Sunday-best attire! I had never seen Sindie look more spick and span.

He was a foreigner from Greece, and actually belonged on the lower crumbs of the upper crust scale of British class system. Sindie was a true-blue Xhosa, belonging on the soil of Africa more than he did. Maggie may have had chameleon magical eyes with all-round vision, but Sindie lacked their splendid camouflaging skill in that scarlet sweater.

"She's not buying! She's choosing!" I mouthed back cheekily. Continuing the tour, I demonstrated, "Look here, Sindie…Here are fruity Sugus and those are sugar coated joob-joobs made with lots of gelatin from cow's hoofs."

"Well, I'm afraid she's not even allowed in here. It is clearly written 'Europeans Only' on a sign above the door. Can't you read?" he said, frowning at me accusingly. His fat cheeks wobbled like jaundiced jellyfish.

He omitted to recall that I was Boetie Bester's daughter, the very good customer who had bought all the various newspapers, boosting his Café's coffer. I remembered how politely he had treated Dad.

"Well, she has white bones, just coated in chocolate skin, like those peanuts," I fought fiercely, pointing at the bin of dipped nuts. Sindie had defended me once against a city *tsotsi.* Now it was my turn to tell off this lowlife townie.

"She has to leave right now," the oleaginous Greek spat, becoming louder and less polite by the minute. "Before I lose my customers and call the police."

"Why? What's the matter with choosing?" I squawked, annoying him further.

"You—*voetsak!*" The unctuous man used a term only used to get rid of dogs, as he shooed my friend away.

"No!" I said stubbornly, stamping my foot and holding onto Sindie's arm. "She is not a dog or chameleon. She cannot change her skin from brown to white, you stupid twat!"

Hearing my floor-stamping tirade, my mom glanced around. She sprinted over to us, clutching her leather handbag furiously, like it was a baton in a relay race. She could do hurdles over chairs and tables if she needed in any cotton frock.

"Didn't I tell you Sindie is not allowed in here?" she scolded.

"Why not?" I fumed indignantly, feeling a temper tantrum rising.

"Dad said that you can buy her sweets, but she has to wait outside," Mom explained in a fake polite voice.

"Why can't she choose for herself?" I stood my ground. "She is allowed in the Carlisle Bridge Cash Store."

Sindie huddled closer to me.

"I'm paying." I boldly held out my money, "Just let her choose!"

"Don't be a silly mutt!" Mom carped, grabbing me by the arm firmly, squeezing tighter than what was publicly proper.

Pointing to the door with her other hand and hissing, "Sindie, *wena hamba* (you go) and get in the Land Rover *ngoku* (immediately) and please stay there." Mom had inserted a few Xhosa words that she knew into her English sentence just to be sure Sindie comprehended the message.

Meanwhile, Dad merely lowered his newspaper, shaking his head slightly. I noticed a half smile on his face, before raising *The E.P. Herald* again.

Degraded, Sindie slowly climbed into the Land Rover, using the tire as a step up. She slunk back down next to Tombe. We were defeated.

Mom marched me back into the Café, with a quick step. I bopped around, helping myself to four of each of the best sweets, adding three 'Fanta orange' for each girl. I grabbed a grape artificial flavor soda for Maggie, protectively cradling the drinks against my chest. I saucily helped myself to five straws as well, taking my time under the glare of the grumpy Greek. I knew Maggie would share her favorite flavor with her friend.

Mom, who was very apologetic and embarrassed, dutifully paid the Greek for all the extras. She was hoping to avoid another commotion and to compensate the man for her noncompliant child.

"You are never bringing your piccanins to town again if this is how you behave," Mother seethed under her breath to me, while she maintained her calm outwardly. She waltzed me out of the Ramona Café.

"That ghastly man is not my cup of tea." I protested to my mother.

"Abeva! (They don't listen!)" Maggie bleated like a lamb having its tail cut off as she tattletaled to her madam. Gratefully she accepted the loaf of white bread and luxuries. *"Enkosi, Mlungkasi wam!* (Thank you, my White Lady!)"

"I'm going to pay the *sangoma* to put a deadly curse on that ugly man," Sindie clicked away in Xhosa under her breath. Fortunately my mother didn't understand isiXhosa well enough to decipher her threat.

I hopped onto the back of the truck. Mom instructed Maggie to watch us more carefully, and then she went back to join Dad.

"May his ancient Greek ghosts hover over the filthy fool." I added to Sindie's insolence. "And haunt him!"

Tombe was visibly relieved to see Sindie and me again. She gloated with the feeling of satisfaction, the kind you only get from having fully obeyed. Her face brightened at the sight of the sweets. Perhaps the road trip was worth the distress after all.

"Tombe, you are tame like a sheep. You will make your mother happy," Maggie muttered as she broke the fresh-smelling bread. Mother Maggie then rewarded Tombe with an extra large chunk of warm bread. Sindie and I got slightly smaller portions.

"You two! You are the feral ones! Creeping away like stalking leopards!" Maggie glanced over her shoulder at Sindie and me. "I don't know what will become of you two! I will whack you both if you climb out of this Land Rover again."

Maggie turned and faced the Ramona, "Don't worry, Sindie, the grisly ghouls will take that uncouth man out!" Maggie spat almost far enough to reach the door of the café. I was highly impressed at how far my Maggie could spit even when she had chew tobacco in her cheek.

Maggie then turned to break the remaining half a loaf with her tittle-tattle companion in peace. She boasted two straws out of one Fanta grape. I was aware that was her favorite flavor. She always instructed me to sneak her one out of the Kasouga drinks cabinet at Christmastime.

I coveted Tombe's compliant spirit and ability to blindly obey old people and traditions. She was more like a dung beetle, moving in a straight traditional line, even if the ball of dung was so big Tombe could not see where she was heading. Lowly dung beetles used the ancient Milky Way as a source of light to guide them straight. They have compound eyes to detect the light galaxy of stars in heaven. Conformity was much more difficult for Sindie and me. We had wiggly spirits, sort of like tadpoles.

12

THE PLACE OF THE LEOPARD

Dad steered the heavy four wheel drive vehicle south, towards the coast as we left Grahamstown. "I see the servants made short work of that loaf of bread. Are you sure we have enough groceries," Dad checked, as he changed gears, "…to feed all these extra little faces?"

"Yes, dear, we won't have to buy much, really," Mom replied. "The only things I needed were a few spices and sunflower oil to fry the big fish you're going to catch for me. Actually, if we stop at the market on our way out of town, I'll buy a few gem squash, if you don't mind. Mine are not quite ready to eat yet. That horrid porcupine eats them before they can ripen."

"Never mind, I'll set a trap for it when we get home," Dad reassured her. "My spring gun will eliminate that pest." Dad had a shorn-off shotgun that went off automatically when the intruders tripped over a wire strung across their forbidden path.

"We'll need to buy more bacon on our way home on Monday," Mom remembered. "But we have plenty for the weekend."

"I plan on catching you a big Jan Bruin. I know that is your favorite fish." Dad glanced at his wife with a twinkle in his eye.

We continued down the curvy, narrow, tarred road. I looked out the window, admiring the grassy hills dotted with white farm houses.

"It is greener here; they must've had good rains," Dad said. "I heard on the news…"

"Why does this place look so different from Schelmdrift?" I interrupted.

"Rain is more plentiful," Mom answered. "Down here they produce mostly vegetables and cash crops. The farmers here can make a living on a smaller piece of land, planting potatoes, pineapples, chicory and the like. That is why we see houses spotted every mile or so. The Karoo is much drier and the farms are larger."

"What is chicory?" I should never have asked…

"Chicory is a root that looks sort of like a brown carrot. They dry it and roast it and grind it up. It has a rather bitter taste, sort of like coffee. It was first planted in 1895 around here. In the olden days, the *Voortrekkers* mixed bran and crushed acorns into their ground coffee to make it last a little longer. Our parents used to drink chicory when coffee was scarce during WWII. Chicory is blended with coffee, to make it go further."

"How much farther do we have to go?" I asked.

"Not too long," Mom patted my knee.

"The Eastern Cape is a picturesque part of the world," Mom remarked. She was elated to be on the greener side of town, where she was raised.

"Well, the Eastern Province has certainly produced two of the best cricketers ever." Dad recalled proudly, still savoring the good news.

Picking up *The Cape Times* newspaper, Mom summarized, "The newspaper described the match as 'The Pollock's Test. Any controversy will be largely limited to whether the thundering batting of Graeme, or the demon bowling of his brother, Peter, was the biggest contribution to the victory.' "

You could almost lick the sweet taste of victory off the newspapers. The press oozed with pride for the Springbucks in sports-crazed South Africa. One would think South Africa had taken down the entire British Empire.

"I'm certainly delighted Bruce and Norman can have the same coach as the Pollock's had at Grey High School. Mr. Dean is the finest cricket coach around these parts," Dad observed. "Mind you, which was why we chose to educate our sons in P.E. in the first place, isn't it, Billikins?"

"James Dean is a superior coach, indeed, dear. They say here that Graeme Pollock played his first competitive cricket match at the age of eight for the under eleven team at Grey. In that match, he scored 117 runs and took ten wickets for 25 runs. At age sixteen, Graeme Pollock was selected to play for Eastern Province. He was the youngest player in South African cricket to score a *century* in first-class cricket. At 19, he became the youngest hitter of a *double* century in South African history," Mom rambled on, quoting bits and pieces out the paper.

"When are we going to get there?" I interrupted, sick and tired of hearing about cricket heroes.

"In about half an hour," Dad answered. "That van der Merwe has been a brilliant captain for the Springbucks. I reckon his smart decisions also contributed to the Springbucks' success. "

Wild springbuck grazed on the plateau above Bumpy in our sheep camps. Our little threesome had often watched the agile gazelle on "the flats." They could leap up to about eleven feet, higher than our heads. As soon as they landed, they leapt again, simply to show off, just in case you missed the first display. The wild game had sleek white underbellies. They were tan on top, with a dark brown stripe running from the front legs to the back legs.

"The springbuck on the farm jump around on four legs. They can't even play cricket. Why are the cricketers called the Springbucks?" I queried.

"Perhaps it is because they are so quick and athletic. Springbuck can run up to 50 miles an hour, faster than I would take this Land Rover over rough roads," Dad stated.

"Perhaps it is because springbuck are multi-colored, like the people of South Africa," I put forward my tender proposal.

"I am afraid not, my girl. There are no coloreds or blacks on the team. Did you know that when they are '*pronking*' or springing, they excrete a sweet floral odor? They can lift the flap of white pocket-like skin that extends along the middle of their backs onto their tails at the same time. They can multitask effectively and confuse their predators by smelling like vegetation rather than flesh, so perhaps that's the reason," Dad amused himself.

"Let me tell you a little more about the springbuck." Dad looked relaxed, puffing away on his pipe contentedly. "Long ago, millions of migrating springbuck were the largest herds of mammals ever spotted. My grandpa reckoned it would take a herd several days to pass over a settlement. At least, that's what his old chap used to say."

The tutorial from my mom resumed. "The springbuck is just a symbol, my pet."

Presently, we drove into the quaint river town of Port Alfred and turned right to cross the bridge over the Kowie River. I glanced out the back window to see Tombe with her eyes shut and her hands covering her ears.

"Tombe is scared," I reported to my parents.

Mom responded calmly, "She's never seen a two way bridge before. Not everybody is as lucky as you are. Maggie's with her. She will comfort her."

We drove out of Port Alfred, heading west onto the coastal road. A road sign read "Port Elizabeth, 90 miles." That jerked my memory to my encaged siblings. I felt fortunate, but was acutely aware that my luck was to expire shortly.

A herd of lazy, fat brown cattle roamed the green pastures, their buttocks and bellies bulging from the luxury of sweet, waving grass.

"Kasouga means 'The Place of the Leopard' in isiXhosa." I translated the road sign, where Dad made a turn onto a narrow dirt road.

Squished in between Mom and Dad, I could not escape further schooling.

Daddy considered it fitting to then edify my mind about leopards. "Did you know that leopards are called opportunistic hunters? They will eat anything that moves. The spotted predators will munch on something as small and smelly as a dung beetle, but also devour a giant 1,800 pound male eland. My grandpa, who hunted them, said leopards stalked and pounced on monkeys. They will literally eat anything they can catch. He reckoned they also liked the taste of rodents, and even snacked on snakes. If those big spotted cats had half a chance, they ate frogs and fish as well. No living thing escaped the leopard's palate. "

Mom followed Dad's comments, "My grandfather, who was fascinated by leopards, believed their favorite food was slower antelope, such as steenbuck, duikers and bushbuck. Kasouga farm is a sanctuary to loads of little *steenbokkies.* There are some right there, grazing on that luscious-looking grass. Can you see them?" She pointed at a group of little auburn buck. "So I am not at all surprised that the leopards once loved to hide out here at Kasouga, close to their favorite food." She made the most of an opportunity to educate me while I was sitting captive, stuck in the middle seat.

"Will leopards eat people?" I checked, glancing back to see if Tombe and Sindie were still safe.

"Probably not, unless a leopard is injured and can't catch other edible creatures," Mom reassured me. "But I don't think there are any leopards left here nowadays. There used to be when my granny and grandpa first started camping here. Someone's cook apparently went missing, and they found her half-eaten corpse up a tree. It sounds like a bit of a tall story to me."

Dad then chipped in, "Leopards have a selfish, but clever, habit of hauling their prey up a tree so they can hide it from lions, hyenas or jackals. Evidently, they can carry carcasses three times their own weight. Mind you, I have not heard of any leopard attacks on sheep lately, either. I reckon the farmers have shot all the roaming leopards in order to protect their flocks. Do you remember that they once found that very rare species of leopard here in the lower Albany District, Bill?" Dad asked Mom over my head.

"Yes, quite so! Those leopards were so spotty that the spots all joined up to make the leopard appear solid black on top." Mom recalled.

"I thought you said leopards never change their spots?" I asked too quietly for dad to hear, not wanting to have to listen to more leopard lessons. "When Flinder stabbed Moses, you said that!"

"That simply means people never change their old habits. For instance, Flinder was an aggressive bully and thief before he ever came to Schelmdrift. People do not change their ways at all." Mom explained.

The Greek's manner had switched from courteous to loutish. I had seen him go from polite to rude in less than an hour, with my very own eyes.

"You are quite right, Sweetheart. I seem to recall it was between 1885 and 1934 that six pseudo-melanistic leopards were spotted around here. I remember reading a fascinating article about them. Some experts thought it indicated a mutation in the local leopard population." Dad never ceased to amaze me with his broad general knowledge.

Mom was just as informed as Dad, which created stimulating conversation. She went on, "The spots became almost confluent on their backs. That is why it appeared as if there was a broad black stripe running down their backs. I remember they were seen in the hilly land covered with scrub jungle, mostly down over nearer Glenfillan Park. My father's friend, Uncle Neilly McDougall, spotted one when he was younger."

I was only vaguely interested in their chatter.

"But every leopard keeps the exact spot pattern it is born with…" Mom tidied up the loose ends of my thoughts like she would tie up her knitting loose ends.

Eventually, we came over the hill. That is when Dad started his usual ritual chanting: "Who-can-see-the-sea-ea? Who-can-see-the-sea-ea?" Dad sang that every time we drove over Kasouga hill. It was our family tradition.

Standing up to make myself taller, I responded, "I can!" quite relieved to end the leopard lesson. I could see it in the distance, but my friends on the back had their backs to it, so they did not see it then. As we drove downhill we lost sight of the sea again.

Kasouga was South Africa's first holiday resort developed by the 1820 British Settlers. It was also the least developed since then, mainly because it was a privately-owned farm. Back in the olden days, leopards, elephants, and hippos had inhabited the resort, lolling about in the blind Kasouga River.

As we drove onto the peaceful "green," a flat-grassed area alongside the *Kasouga* River, I saw Maggie pointing at our shack. She was identifying our beach cabin at the very end of the neat lineup.

Finally, the laden Land Rover came to a steady halt.

"Naantsi indlu yethu! (Here is our house!) *Siselwandle*! (We are at the sea!)" Maggie announced with the jubilance of an *air hostess* (flight attendant) who had just completed a rather arduous journey.

We had the newest and biggest shack on all of the green, I thought to myself proudly. There were no other people to be seen. All the other asbestos cabins were standing empty, only to be occupied during the Christian holidays, Christmas and Easter. We had the whole "green" all to ourselves, and I would not be lonely.

The purpose of our trip was for Dad to fish leisurely and for Maggie to spring clean vigorously before the upcoming Christmas holiday rush.

"We'll unpack while you girls go stretch your legs and you may show your friends the sea," Mom directed as she lifted out her basket full of heavy library books.

We had been to Kasouga every summer of my life just as my mom had done during her childhood. I explained this Stocks' family tradition to my fellow travelers, Tombe and Sindie, as I introduced them to the empty holiday homes, "Our shack is shack number one, closest to the beach. Granny and Grandpa Stocks' shack is that one next to ours, shack number two. Mom's younger sister's family, the Fischer's, own the house next door to my grandparents' shack number three. Mom's older sister, Aunty Ione, and the Murrays are farther up that way. She is the one who gives me pretty panties all the time, like the ones you are wearing, Sindie." I could not help seeing her panties when she did another cartwheel off the Land Rover.

The three of us scampered around the corner to see the sea. There was a distinct buoyant bounce in their stride, fuelled by great expectation.

"Yoo! Yoo! Yoo! (Wow! Wow! Wow!)" My companions harmonized together, as we suddenly came upon a deserted beach currently being licked by a mass of blue leaping waves.

"Yoo! (Wow!) Miss Judy, aren't you afraid?" Tombe wondered in a state of shock.

Tombe's nerves had been sufficiently strained for one day. After visually absorbing the sheer enormity of the Indian Ocean, Tombe stepped forward with marked hesitation. The shock of seeing the watery world coupled with the sensation of soft sand under her feet was too much for her. She had seen High Street and high tide in one day. Her mouth remained pursed in a whistling tight circle for all her inhaling and exhaling. *"Yoo! Yoo!"*

Her toes grew into roots and sank securely into the deep sand. Tombe suddenly held her breath in awe. She covered her breathing cavities with her hands in case her spirit was to jump out of her body.

Quite to the contrary, Sindie's face reflected excitement as the sea air entered her nostrils for the first time. She breathed in deeply with wonder. Her face crinkled into a coy smile as she bit her lower lip. *"Ilwandle lihle.* (The sea is beautiful.)" She raised both eyebrows, blinking her eyes vigorously to make sure they were telling the truth.

"Let's go closer!" I coaxed. "We can wet our feet! You can taste the salty water if you like!"

Curious Sindie was waving her arms and legs in delight, like a tree in a strong wind, sucking in the wondrous sight, tasting the freshness, the newness, with sweet discovery. "The air smells like salt!" Sindie enthused. "Where does all this water come from, Miss Jay?"

Pondering for a few seconds, I proclaimed out loud, "God put it there when He made Mother Earth."

"How?" Sindie's thirst for answers was unquenchable.

"I think maybe He must have had a very big bore hole and windmill," I concluded.

"I don't want to go any closer," Tombe confirmed her fears. "Miss Judy, won't those lashing tongues lap us up?" Finally Tombe was exhaling again, her lips like the velvet purple purse of the Anglican minister's collection bag—resembling fabric that is too thick to have gathers. *"Yoo! Yoo-oo-yoo!* (Wow! Wow-wee-hee!)" She was fearfully howling aloud, this time with a trembling vibrato in her voice. "It seems to have lots of curling, frothy tongues at its mouth!" Tombe needed reassurance as she cinched both of her hands around my arm.

"Is the water boiling over like your mother's whistling teakettle?" Sindie was trying to make sense of it all.

"No, *mtana wasekhaya* (child of my home)," was my answer, "don't be scared, Tombe. Those are soft waves, made of cool salty water, Sindie."

"I'm not going any closer," Tombe was dogmatic as she firmly buried her brown feet in the golden sand. "Evil spirits live under the water and eat foolish people."

"The sand is so soft!" Sindie rejoiced as she did a little dance and wiggled her feet, exploring the newly-found texture. Fine sand stuck onto the layer of Vaseline, making her feet a lighter brown. Her ankles resembled the exact color and texture of sandpaper. "My skin has changed color!" Sindie laughed, enjoying the strange sensation. "Why is the sand so white?"

"Pity you did not have any sandy arms and legs when you were in town." Tombe sulked.

"Because the sea washed the sand all clean, I suppose," I replied in the reversed role of educator now, although I was just making up answers that sounded sensible. "That amount of water ought to make anything spotless!"

"Can we go and swim?!" Sindie wished aloud, fiddling with her red, hand-knitted sweater, ready to remove it.

"No!" Tombe said with a distinct determination, holding me back with both her hands still sucking onto my arm as tightly as octopus tentacles.

"Sindie-put your jersey back on right now!" Tombe was clicking her tongue in angry Xhosa. This time, Tombe was prepared to use brute force to prevent us from getting into any more deep water.

"Look at the sea," Tombe continued. "It is alive! It's not sleeping still like the dams on the farm. It sucks itself back and then sits up like an angry cobra, and then its head comes forward to strike. Those many hissing tongues then crash into frothy, angry foam. The sea is awake. It will swallow you, Sindie!" Then buxom Tombe made a testy threat: "And if you dare go near it, I'm going to beat you up. And I'll tell your mother of all the wicked things you've ever done. I'll tell her you *think* you are white and you *think* you can go into the Café and drink tea out of cups with *Nolasti!*"

Sensing impending consequences, Sindie cautiously changed the subject. "Is the water really salty?" she quizzed me.

"Yes. You cannot drink it." I was stern in my caveat. "It will make you thirstier."

"But witchdoctors say you can drink it for *muti,"* Tombe corrected. "It helps mend your stomach."

"Why would the gods put water there that you can't drink?" Sindie probed. "And if all the unsalted rivers run into it, why is it still salty?"

Running out of answers, I had to resort to the truth. "I don't know. Perhaps it is just to swim in. An old person has to be watching, though. We are not allowed to swim alone. Every Christmas holiday, I love swimming in the sea. Nothing has eaten me yet. You see, Tombe, don't be so frightened. I always come back home to Schelmdrift alive, don't I?"

Still unconvinced, Tombe alerted, "Hark, you two! Your ears hardly ever work, but pay attention for once. Listen, this sea hisses like an angry snake."

"What are those black things that keep popping out?" Sindie pointed farther along the virgin seashore.

"Those black things are not bobbing up at all. They are solid rocks. They never change. They are just like the rocks at Bumpy. The waves just swell up to cover them and then shrink back to reveal the rocks." I attempted to console Tombe's terror and Sindie's curiosity at once.

"What is on the other side of the water?" Sindie questioned.

"The South Pole," I volunteered.

"Who lives there?" Tombe demanded. "I know about the 'river people.' They are the people who live underwater. The witchdoctors teach about them." Tombe glanced suspiciously at the taciturn green river to our right. "They are the ones who look after the spirits of all the people who drown." She glanced back at the Kasouga River, just then a mullet fish sprung in and out the water, and Tombe jumped a few feet into the air.

"Thiza wam! (My Golly!)" She yelped.

In Africa, many bodies are pulled into rivers and streams, by hippopotami, crocodiles and currents, never to be seen again. So there are many folktales and superstitions surrounding the dangers of water. Wicked spirits were always to blame.

"I don't know who lives at the South Pole," I replied, "Eskimos, perhaps. I think they live in igloos. That is a hut made of ice."

"What is on the other side of that?" Sindie piped in, still prying. The sight of the shore made her imagination stretch further than usual.

"More sea, I suppose. I'll have to ask my mom. There is enough salty water to share with all the continents. It evaporates and forms fluffy clouds. Then they drop raindrops for us in the Karoo."

I was filled with a deep gratitude for a generous Creator. The sight of the desolate, unspoiled, non-commercialized, natural seashore was indeed a wonder to behold.

I gazed far out to sea. "Look!" I alerted. "There's a ship on the horizon. Can you see it?" They stood in unadulterated amazement as they spotted a ship for the first time.

"Won't it sink?" Tombe was alarmed, her anxiety deeply rooted in a lack of education and exposure.

"No," I said hopefully, repressing the image of Gulliver's Travels, my favorite storybook. I wished that Sindie and Tombe could have had a more experienced teacher to educate them—someone more well-read, like my mother.

"Those are the vessels that carried white people across the sea to steal our land. That is what that dumb *tsotsi* (thug) from Jo'burg tried to tell us," Tombe said with great solemnity. "He told so many lies. I did not believe anything he said after a while. Ghosts must live on the other side, in huts made of ice like Miss Judy knows about. Real people could not live in ice. It would be too chilly. And if they made fire in the middle of the hut like we do to keep warm, their homes would melt." She was having a desperate grapple with reality and common sense. "I am glad that you brought us here to see to 'The Place of the Leopard,' Miss Judy. How else would we have had wheels to reach here?"

"And who else would have bought us sweets?" Sindie was eager to agree.

"As a matter of fact, we never stole anyone's land. And my ancestors bought Schelmdrift many moons ago from the Peterson family," I related the truth.

That night I went to bed on my wooden bunk. There were three beds in the girls' room. I had the bottom bunk, Wendy normally slept on the top bunk, and visitors used the spare bed. Sindie and Tombe, however, slept with Maggie in the servants' quarters, which consisted of two outside bedrooms hidden in the bushes. They all shared Maggie's big feather bed for warmth. Meanwhile, I lay alone in my bedroom with two empty beds. I sort of envied them, cozily huddled together.

When my mom came to tuck me in bed and kiss me goodnight, I shared my impasse, "Sindie wants to know what's on the other side of the South Pole and why God made the sea salty so we can't drink it."

"When we get back to the farm on Monday, you can invite Sindie and Tombe into the Breakfast Room and I will show them our globe. I will teach them about the continents that Almighty God created." She rubbed the blanket over my legs.

"But why is it so..." I yawned, "...salty?" I repeated, exhausted from all the excitement.

"God can do anything He wants to do, my girly. He was very clever to make the sea salty. The reason being, I am convinced, He did it..." she yawned as well, "...is...so the water doesn't become stagnant and smelly. Salt kills the germs in the dirty water, just like salt saves our *biltong* (jerky) from getting putrid and ruined. The old folks say that yawns are only contagious if you like the person who yawns first, so Mommy must love you."

"I caught yours, too." I yawned again.

"Remember, my pet, God is so very, very intelligent. The Bible teaches us that God is omnipotent, which means He is all-powerful."

Mother paused to reflect. "Almighty God can do anything, anywhere, anytime!"

That golden nugget of truth sunk into my heart forever.

13

LABOLA LAWS

The following day, Tombe begged to stay put, so we didn't go to the beach. She wanted to make very sure that her chance of being eaten by a Great White shark or swallowed by the Indian Ocean ghosts was zero. Instead, we safely played around our rustic fisherman's shack.

Mom had allowed me to bring the girls that weekend in order to keep me entertained. It freed her so she could read her stack of books. It freed Dad to go fishing in peace, and it freed Maggie to cook and clean. Maggie dusted all the sand off the wooden furniture in the lounge, and then she swept the wooden floor. Oiling the thirsty oak chairs and shining her legs with red rose-smelling furniture oil was next.

Maggie always volunteered to accompany the family to the seaside for the Christmas holidays. She enjoyed all parties and social life with other servants, being an honorary Kasouga-ite herself, our seasoned cook knew the scene.

"I hope Dad catches a big Jan Bruin for our supper. It is the most scrumptious, flaky fish." Mom squinted up in the sun from under her straw hat. "I brought plenty of potatoes. Maggie can fry *slap* (semi-soggy) chips to go with the fish."

I had not even seen Dad that morning. He and the Land Rover were missing in action by the time I woke up.

"Which way did Dad go?" I inquired.

"He said he was going to Ship Rock. I might take him a flask of tea later. Would you girls like to take a stroll up? It's only about a mile or so; we can hitch a lift back in the Land Rover."

"Do you want to go and watch my dad catch a fish for our supper?" I translated into Xhosa.

"No, I want to stay here." Tombe was adamant. "But if you two do go, please get my mom some bottles of salt water; she uses it for *muti* (medicine)." Tombe remembered one of her missions for coming to the seaside.

"Shall we go and play on the swings then?" I invited, pointing to the swings across the dirt road like a tour guide.

"Are we allowed to?" Tombe inquired with the Ramona Café incident still fresh in her memory.

"No, not really. At Christmastime, when everyone is here, you are not. They won't let you. But no one is here, so I say you can." I tried to sound as if I had authority on the matter. "Mom and Dad won't mind."

The swings hung on a sturdy, stinkwood pole frame. Strong steel chains suspended each smooth hardwood seat. There were only two swings, so we took turns. They both knew how to swing. We had a homemade swing on Schelmdrift, which now seemed so very far away. Fikile had carved it out of an old truck tire, suspended by ropes. The ropes hung from a strong branch of the pepper tree in our driveway.

"The 'Place of a Leopard' is a quiet place," Sindie observed. "Where are all the people?"

"Did the leopards eat some of them?" Tombe was jittery, still not quite sure of her surroundings. The shacks stood empty like ghost houses.

"They all live inland and just come down here to celebrate Christmas when it's too hot on their farms," I explained. "You can see the birds getting ready for summer too."

A pretty pair of yellow Weaver birds, wearing black-feathered hooded cloaks, bustled about. They were plucking grassy reeds to thread through their basket nests. There was a cluster of neatly-woven nests craftily suspended under the tall trees near the Berriman's shack. The Forest Weavers' nests hung with longer entrance halls dangling down lower than those of the ordinary Cape Weavers around Bumpy. Birds were busily preparing and feathering nests for the breeding season.

"Holiday makers only come to stay in these houses in December, so there is no one here now. You are safe to use these public swings in spring." I assured them.

My words weren't even cold, when a blue Land Rover rumbled down the dirt road to prove me wrong.

Tombe leapt off the swing rapidly, squealing, *"Hayi* (No) Miss Judy, you lied! You will get us arrested!"

Sindie simply laughed. She was innocently leaning on the pole chewing a piece of river reed, waiting for her turn. Sindie spat it out smugly. "Yes, Miss Jay, you don't know the laws. You'll put Tombe in jail," she jibed half-accusatory, half-amused.

I could tell the girls were slightly homesick. They hadn't been seventy miles away from their huts ever before. Their dads didn't have cars. They only owned bicycles, goats and a few cows for sacrificing or buying brides.

The gentleman driving the blue Land Rover, with fishing rods sticking out the back, waved politely to Mom and drove towards the beach.

"Dad is not home yet. The fish must be biting!" Mom called out. "That was Uncle Freddy Ford." She settled in her Morris chair that she and Maggie had carried outside, so Maggie could scrub the floors.

My two friends sat inconspicuously on the ground, while I perched on the swing, not really swinging any more, but just dangling my feet. Their brown bodies were perfectly camouflaged on the muddy ground.

We watched the seagulls looking for tidbits to eat along the river. Coots were building their nests on the floating reed debris. A male and female Bou Bou Shrike sang a duet, the call for spring mating. I could hear a colorful Red Fronted Tinker Barbet making the sound of a squeaking bicycle pump.

"That old man lives here all year round. He owns this Kasouga farm. He has never been married." I tried to explain his presence to my peers, as well as subdue Tombe's fears.

Uncle Freddie Ford owned some of the fattest, laziest cattle I had ever seen. Graceful snow-white birds perched on the tame red cows grazing on the green.

Those lovely, large white "tick birds" with filamentous plumes on their backs fluttered around the docile herd. Tiny black ticks are not easily visible on a hairy cow, until they have sucked up adequate blood. The beast's blood swells the parasite's abdomen enough to protrude above the hairs of the cow. The blood suckers then serve as a tasty treat for the Great White Egrets with black "breeding" beaks. Beautiful Great White Egrets oddly change their beaks from yellow to black during the breeding season. Nature is full of magical illusions. Black beaks pecked and picked the blood-sodden ticks off the beasts with regular rhythm.

"Those bulging beasts looked too pregnant to chase anyone." Sindie smiled safely.

Those cows had been inseminated by a BB bull that Uncle Freddie Ford had bought from Bester Brothers to improve his beef herd. Dad always smiled with pride when he recognized the bull that had been bred on Schelmdrift.

"Why would that man not buy himself a wife with all these fat cattle?" Tombe could not fathom anyone not wanting a family. "He must be awfully lonesome. Who looks after him? Who feeds him?"

"White people don't buy wives with cattle like we do," Sindie corrected curtly as she sat back on the swing. "It is a Xhosa thing."

"Our fathers will sell Sindie and me for cows. Then we have to serve that man for the rest of our lives, even if we don't like the person," Tombe dutifully recited the *labola* laws like the Catholics recite the catechism.

"What if he is a mean old man with a fat hairy stomach like Flinder?" I asked.

"Then I will put that red berry *muti* in his beer," Sindie retorted.

"They are allowed to beat us if they bought us." Tombe knew the Xhosa customs all too well.

"Come and swing!" I invited Tombe on again as soon as Uncle Freddy Ford's Land Rover had safely disappeared onto the beach.

"No, Miss Judy, remember what happened with the pomegranates?" Tombe was feeling insecure. She recalled my biggest mistake of the previous year.

"That wasn't entirely her fault." Sindie was trying to be fair.

"Well, you two don't know anything," Tombe said distrustfully. "Between the two of you, I might never see my family again."

Not wanting to recall the awkward pomegranate incident, I suggested, "Shall we go and cook with Maggie?"

Maggie was grateful, and she cheerfully assigned Tombe, Sindie, and me some chores. Mine was to go ask Mom what the menu was for supper.

"We'll wait and see if Dad brings us a fish. Tell her to peel half the sack of potatoes so long," Mom instructed.

Her father, Grandpa Norman Stocks, was a renowned fisherman. He had won many competitions. Grandpa Stocks had taught Dad how to read the sea colors and examine the tides, as well as how to select the best current fishing spots.

Dad arrived home triumphantly with a beaming smile on his face—so big, in fact, that his pipe almost fell out. Using both hands, he held up two stumped nose silver bream fish by the gills. The Jan Bruin suddenly flapped violently.

Tombe leapt away from it, yelping.

"*Yoo, yoo!* (Wow, wow!)" Tombe yelled as she sped towards the bushes with her arms flailing in the air, her hands agitating wildly at her wrists.

We all chuckled at her reaction. Tombe had never seen a live fish before. The muddy dams and river on the farm only bred frogs and water tortoises. Ironically enough, we had never seen a fish caught in the Fish River either.

In desperation, Dad's fish flopped, furiously gasping for saline solution. There was no drip to save it from its fate. The fresh-line fish, which Daddy had so cleverly hooked out of the sea, was our supper. Maggie filleted it outside on the grass with an audience of three.

First Maggie dipped each chunk of boneless fish flesh into beaten eggs, with just the right amount of salt and pepper. Sindie helped sprinkle the salt and pepper on, with Maggie leaning over her to give instructions.

"I have to learn how to do this properly because I am going to be Miss Jay's cook one day," Sindie boasted, wiggling with delight and smacking her lips. "After she marries David Blomfield who has blue eyes."

I had always had a little crush on Bruce's friend.

Then our cook tossed the dripping fillets over and over in a dish of crushed corn flakes. Tombe had helped crush the cereal with a rolling pin.

"Tell Maggie that she and the girls can also have fish and chips. There is plenty," Mom told me to interpret for them. I loved to be the interpreter of such unusual good news. I was not sure what book Mom was reading and how it affected her in such a manner that she felt that my playmates deserved a treat too. The servants usually ate different food from us. So I was most overjoyed to relay the news.

"Fish always tastes extra delicious when you eat it the same day it is caught," Dad said as he sat at the head of the oak dining room table, with Mom and me on either side. He picked up his *serviette* (napkin) to wipe his chin like the well-mannered gentleman he was. My fish tasted even better, because I could see Maggie, Sindie, and Tombe sitting on the kitchen floor, having the feast of their lives.

I heard Sindie's voice boasting from the kitchen, "Wait until Toto hears what we ate! I-Fried Fish!" She tried to speak English with an *i*-prefix, common to isiXhosa.

"Mama, please don't forget my mom's sea water," Tombe was conscientiously thinking of her family but not volunteering to scoop up the salty seawater *muti* herself.

"I'll get up at sunrise on Monday morning and go and fill your mother's bottles before we leave," Maggie promised, sopping up the grease in the plate with a piece of fish. She licked her fatty fingers loudly. They ate off blue enamel plates, sitting in a circle around the food, in their traditional manner.

"*Nohanki* will go with you," Tombe volunteered my services, wiping the grease off her face, using the top of her hand as a *serviette*. "She knows all about the sea." Tombe surmised. "And how to stay alive."

I was startled at her faith in me.

"Are these chips oily enough? I want them to make me fat fast!" Sindie said.

After they washed the dishes, the three of them disappeared to the servants' quarters, which were completely hidden in the shrub jungle. They had no view of the sea or river.

I sat lazily on my dad's lap, waving the smoke from his pipe away from my nose.

"Why didn't you come up to Ship Rock to play in the pools? It was low tide, and there were lots of shells and sea creatures to show the girls," he complained good-naturedly.

"I know. I'll come with Mary-Rose Dell when we come down here again at Christmastime. My piccanins are too scared of the sea," I whined. "They just wanted to stay here and cook with Maggie. It is all about *labola.* They want to get fat so that they fetch a good price." I stared across the Kasouga Green to look at the Dell's shack, with its royal blue door locked down.

Later that night, as I lay on my foam mattress, my thoughts turned to life on the farm…

My dad kept a lot of well-loved fruit trees. It was his favorite hobby.

The flocks of Merino sheep, Angora goats, and herds of Afrikaner stud cattle were his vocation. The animals all had to be individually dipped in insecticides, dosed with medicines, and inoculated against disease.

The sheep had to be shorn by "the boys," and the wool had to be sorted by my dad. Then they squished it into big Hessian bales and bussed the bales to the F.C.U. in P.E., where the prices could rise up or sink down, depending on our lucky stars. It was not as predictable as the tides of the sea that are pulled in and out by the moonbeams.

It was one of those random things that "old people" of all tribes cannot ever explain. On the farm, we witnessed the law of the harvest daily. We saw that honest hard work paid off healthy dividends. But there were always things that went right or wrong at random times for no reason.

There was a factor of mystery that was put down to…"that's life" or "you were just lucky" or "he was in the wrong place at the wrong time." We had to solve the mystery with no clues from any of the adults in the world.

Our income on the farm was not constant; we had good years and bad years. It rained or it did not. We were not involved in the weather man's moods, and he changed his mind often. He made us rich or poor according to his whim and fancy.

I lay on my bunk bed and thought about my hard working Dad. When a fleece was shorn off a Merino sheep, Dad would throw it on a slotted table in a special professional way. It landed in a shape of a sheepskin which had been skinned off a dead sheep. It is also the shape you see on handbags or purses to symbolize that they are made from genuine leather. Dad had a big cement shearing shed down on Goodwood, our other farm that Dad owned. His father always told him to pay premium price for land that adjoins yours, so my father paid a lot of money to buy Goodwood.

That is where Dad judged and separated the good and bad wool. He tossed the long parts of wool that grow on the sheep's back into one bale. Dad then determined where other sections would go, throwing segments of the fleece into specific bales.

Dad's big masculine hands were always smooth when he sorted the wool. Lanolin, a by-product of wool, is an ingredient in hand lotion that makes ladies' hands silky soft. His hands switched from rugged rough to sissy soft during shearing time.

The manure and urine-stained parts, which were shorn off the sheep's rear end, went into a separate bale. Farmers got less money for those parts of the fleece. It was labeled lox. They painted "lox" with a stencil on the bale because it is a bit smelly.

"Factories wash the wool clean, dye it different colors, and spin it into balls of yarn. Then we buy the wool back, at a steeper price, I might add, to knit our jerseys." Mom had once enlightened me while she was knitting me a pink jersey.

"They also weave material for men's suits," Dad had added. "I read in the paper that they are using wool to line the space shuttles because it is less combustible. You just can't beat natural fibers. No synthetic fiber can beat good old Merino wool. Mind you, we have had a decent mohair clip from all the new goats." Mohair prices went sky high once when fashions changed. Fashions and fads and trends of the human race change and affect the demand and price that the farmers fetch for their produce. No one wore ostrich feathers in large hats anymore, so those ostrich farmers all felt the pinch, since my Granny Bester was dead. She loved those hats and kept the consumer confidence alive on her own.

Stock farming was Dad's occupation, but taking care of the fruit trees was his diversion of choice. He would meticulously prune the plum, nectarine, apricot, and peach trees. He'd even cut down the unruly grapevines. The orange, lemon, and grapefruit trees didn't need much attention. *Naartjies* (clementines) were my favorite citrus to pick because they were so easy for me to peel.

I, too, started to long for our family farm from the Kasouga shack when I thought of our huge fig trees. They were most fun to climb. My Bester grandparents planted about ten juicy fig trees. Some yielded small black figs, others a green variety or brown figs. The brown Smyrna figs were the tastiest. The *muisvoëls* (Speckled and Red-faced Mousebirds) and other birdlife agreed and pecked the figs as well. Mom expertly sewed nifty cloth bags with drawstrings to cover the figs. She had figs to spare to make jam. Fig jam was my favorite.

Dad summoned builders to erect a huge chicken netting wire cage over his fruit orchard, but our lofty fig trees didn't fit in and had been left out. The fig trees had grown too tall and proud for protection.

"This fruit *hok* (cage) keeps out all two-legged marauders—piccanins and birds alike," my dad would say as he locked the big brass padlock on the gate of his prized orchard. "The servants cannot complain. I have allocated each of them a spot of fertile land to grow their own fruit trees."

"I planted six pomegranate trees, one for every member of the family," my dad said with satisfaction. Fikile had actually planted the shrubs while Dad gave detailed instructions. Even though I felt like an only child, we had a row of six trees yielding a good crop to remind us we were still a full family of six. These shrubs were not in the caged orchard, under lock and key.

"Don't pick any pomegranates just yet," Dad had said, carefully inspecting the yellowish fruit turning red in the autumn sun of April, 1964.

"They need a little longer to be fully ripe, so you may NOT pick them yet. You see?" He wandered around inspecting his pride and joy, his walking stick in one hand. His other hand was busy alternating between caressing the pomegranates and holding his bent pipe.

Dad always wore a 100% wool felt hat, whether they were in fashion or not. His farm hat was his old town hat, which had become too shabby to wear to town. It was stained with greasy fingerprints where he'd put his finger to lift it. Daddy would not part with his cherished old green hat.

"Yes, Dad," I promised my old man in the fall of 1964, around my 8th birthday.

Old people do have strict structure sometimes. But at least, for now, in 1965, I was confident my dad would never sell me for a cow as that was not our family tradition. I was thankful for that.

I knew Dad had bought some *tollies* (calves) to fatten up and sell and save to pay for Wendy's wedding one day. He would also do the same to pay for mine, I felt sure. Dad, my farmer father, liked to plan ahead, just in case a drought hit us, or a flood, earthquake, plague, disease, fire or locusts to demolish our crops. Those are the haphazard hit or miss events that occur unexpectedly for no rhyme or reason.

As I lay dreaming about my future wedding feast and life on Schelmdrift, from 'The Place of the Leopard,' I thought that my friends are not really leopards. They preferred their mud huts to the seaside. Kasouga reminded me that we are not stuck in one spot. A leopard may never change its spots, but I wished that some things of the Xhosa Culture could be modified. *Labola* seemed like a form of slavery to me. Girls needed to choose. Choosing made one feel free.

I still had not forgiven that horrible Greek for not allowing Sindie to choose her own sweets.

Choices can also land us in a dung heap, though. On the farm, I once made a very bad choice regarding pomegranates…

14

FORBIDDEN FRUIT

Still not sleeping, wondering who was flashing a light outside my window every now and then, I lay on my bunk bed wide-eyed, and recollected my pomegranate lesson:

Late one afternoon, before the pomegranates were quite ripe in 1964, there was great excitement because the Natives had been to a talent show at their new school's grand opening at Carlisle Bridge. It was attended by all the surrounding farms' Xhosa children. The Sunnyside *piccanins* were passing through our backyard to walk home to Uncle Sonny's farm when one of them spotted the six laden pomegranate trees.

I was playing with Tombe and Sindie in the maids' room.

"Hey Miss Judy, won't you give us a pomegranate to eat on our way home? We are very hungry," the Sunnyside boy, Sandile, solicited.

"What's the matter with you?! Have you no shame?" Tombe affronted him.

"Please, I haven't eaten all day," one of the *piccanin*s implored, exercising his dramatic stage talent.

"Miss Judy, just one. Please! No one will notice!" they pleaded.

"Go and eat your own fruit at Sunnyside!" Tombe told the hungry boy off, who was now clearly the object of her contempt.

"It's sooo far away. We'll starve along the way," was one skinny boy's pitiful plea.

"There are no *mnqhabaza, cumcums,* or any other berries for us to eat," another boy piped up. "There aren't even any *tolofia* (cactus fruit or prickly pears) left either."

"We'll perish along the path," one child implored.

"We'll ask Sophie, my mother, to bake you some bread and bring it to you," a hungry Sandile pledged, hitting my weak spot.

Maggie baked the heartiest whole-wheat bread. We always ate healthy brown bread on Schelmdrift. Sophie, the Sunnyside cook, made white crusty bread that was unrivaled, the kind that makes butter melt and apricot jam taste like pudding.

"All right then, I'll pick you only one," I caved in. *"Qha!"* I clicked my tongue again, repeating the word "only."

Brazenly, I went and picked the biggest one, rationalizing to myself, "This is *my* tree. I can do what I like with my own tree."

That pomegranate was demolished and devoured in seconds by the ravenous boys. The red, almost ripe pips disappeared down their throats without much munching.

"Oh, Miss Judy, please get us one. Those greedy boys ate it all. I never got one pip," skinny little seven-year-old Sindie complained.

"She is OUR friend!" Tombe reprimanded, turning to them and trying to shoo them away rather possessively.

I hurried back and picked three more and passed them over the backyard fence, feeling guilty, afraid I might get noticed if I walked all the way to the side gate with the forbidden fruit.

Cheers of applause erupted. Suddenly new faces appeared, begging convincingly. I picked a few more off Norman's tree. He was away at Grey Junior School. You can't put pomegranates in the post, I deduced. So I'll help myself to his, too. Even more persuasive *piccanins* suddenly appeared out of the bushes.

"We never got any!" the forlorn ones cried.

After a few trips, I stripped fruit from Wendy's and Bruce's trees. Then I stole a few more off Mom and Dad's trees—not all, but just a few. I left a couple for my parents to taste, but I almost stripped the other four trees completely clean, filling my skirt with four or five at a time. I handed them to eager faces over the fence.

The Xhosa kids thanked and praised me most profusely:

"Akavimbi tu, loMiss Judy. (She's not stingy at all, Miss Judy isn't.)"

"She gives!"

"She really knows how to give!"

"She shares!"

"When she comes to Sunnyside, we'll ask Sophie to bake her bread."

"And cupcakes."

"She is most generous."

The adoration was perfectly intoxicating. Flattery worked its maleficent magic.

Sindie was indulging with relish, thrilled that sensibility had been defeated, or should I say, knocked unconscious, by impulsive appetite.

"She is generous to a fault," Tombe triumphantly announced, once her belly was bulging. Tombe was also starting to realize what we had done, so her motherly instincts came to the fore, *"Hambani! Godukani! Ninyolokhe gqhitha!* (Leave! Go home! You're very greedy!)"

Tombe was clearly irritated with their gluttony. She was more than willing to confront these farm boys at the age of seven. She clouted a small one across the back of the head vigorously. Pips flew out his mouth, which he quickly caught with his hand.

Of course, we were not professional thieves. We left a trail of pale peels right there at the fence where I had passed them over. More skins were scattered along the path, evidenced along the lane leading up to the huts. The footpath trodden to Sunnyside was also littered with rinds. But at least every brown face was sufficiently satisfied, and a few pockets were stuffed, no doubt.

The ecstasy of forbidden fruit faded fast. I went to bed with a bellyache, not saying a word about my gushing generosity to my parents. When I saw Dad, his words echoed in my ears, *'Don't pick any yet.'* I felt very guilty.

At lunchtime the next day, I was just starting to believe that it was good to rob the rich to feed the hungry. Perhaps more pomegranates would magically grow on the tree to compensate for my extreme charity.

But the imminent moment of accountability arrived.

I heard my dad's big army-type leather boots banging on the wood floor of the lounge. I could not lay the blame at the feet of a robin in a black hood. I was "red-faced" and "speckled" with the spots of sin, as guilty as any *muisvoël* (mousebird). Blaming monkeys, porcupines, leguwaans or any other primate was not going to fly. And my skin was not black enough to blame *Tokoloshe* (Xhosa mythical goblin) either.

"Those bloody diabolical piccanins! The insufferable swines stole our pomegranates!" Father fumed between more frequent, indignant puffs of his pipe. "I'm sick and tired of them stealing our fruit. I should have built a *hok* (cage) over all the fruit trees. I feel like giving them a bally good thrashing!"

He stomped down the passage into the hall where the telephone was attached to the wall. "Dash it all! I give them land to plant their own gardens and the lazy looters *still bloody-well* have to steal mine." He belted out to mom, "Gwenna, where is Sergeant Lombardt's phone number?"

My life had ended. I slinked onto the small bed which my parents had put in their bedroom corner for me because I'd been having horrible nightmares. My stomach ached from collywobbles. I curled up in the fetal position.

"That bally policeman sits there all day with nothing to do. He can come and find out who the thieves are. Then, I'll get their fathers to spank them with my sham buck," He muttered, as mad as a striking snake.

Switching to Afrikaans, I heard Father say, "Hello, Hello, HELLO, *Goeie middag, dit is Boetie Bester. Ek het 'n probleem met die swart kinders. Hulle het al my granaate gesteel. Ek wil hê dat jy asseblief onmiddelik hiernatoe ry om uit te vind wie dit gedoen het.* (Good afternoon. This is Boetie Bester. I have a big problem with the black children. They have stolen all my pomegranates. I want you to please drive over here immediately and find out who did it.)"

"Dankie. Totsiens. (Thank you. Goodbye.)" I heard the phone slam down. I did not understand most of what he said, but my imagination ran wild.

I am going to jail! Jail is dreadful! I want to die! I panicked. *Maybe if I hold my breath, I'll die.* I held my breath. I did not die.

Mom had read enough Enid Blyton *"Noddy"* books to me, so that I knew that Mr. Plod, the policeman, enjoyed putting thieves in jail. I had seen the real jail at Carlisle. It was a round *rondawel* with big iron bars across the high peepholes. There were three round prefab huts: one for a kitchen, one for the policeman's bedroom, and the third for an escape-proof prison.

Dad interrupted my panic attack as he stormed into the bedroom. "Judy, do you know anything about the missing pomegranates?" he checked in a very gruff voice.

"No," I lied in a frail voice.

In a few minutes, that felt more like seconds, Sgt. Lombardt, "Mr. Plod" himself, drove up and parked his grayish blue van, the one with a steel cage on the back for thieves, directly under the pepper tree. I could see it out of my parents' bedroom window. Dad was ready and waiting to greet plump Sergeant Lombardt. His leather belt was straining to synch his bulging belly, a black leather holster housed a loaded pistol.

They spoke Afrikaans, as most of the government officials did, and shook hands.

Mom came into the bedroom hurriedly to "put on her face" as she called it. It meant she quickly painted her lips pearly peach preparing for guests. It was usually a happy occasion to greet visitors in the Karoo. Only on this occasion, the policeman was a most unwelcome visitor.

My little ears heard Xhosa clicking near the *stoep* by Dad's office. It was actually "the boys" or "the dads," depending on what tribe you belonged to. Faithful Fikile was preaching very loudly, "Thou shalt not steal!" Yan, Jack, and all the rest of the dads were present.

They had lined up all the black school children outside my dad's office. They were shooing the ones that got out of line with their sticks, just as they so often herded the sheep. The solemn policeman walked judiciously past the bedroom window, over to the front of the neat line of terrified children.

"Are they all here?" Dad asked Yan in a stern voice.

"Ja Baas. (Yes Boss.) This is all of them," he said, nodding respectfully as he always did.

The policeman had a pen and a pad of paper. He asked each suspect, "Did you steal Mr. Bester's pomegranates?"

During my absence due to a violent attack of the gripes, Fikile promoted himself to the post of official interpreter. He was most generously adlibbing the word "wickedly" in front of "steal."

"Hayi (No)," each suspect replied innocently.

"Do you know who did it?" the policeman then asked.

"Hayi, Baas. (No, Boss.)" Each suspect replied slightly less innocently.

Great white Mr. Plod ticked off the names of the brown children with regular rhythm. The policeman was most methodical when he pecked his writing pad with his black *Bic* pen. I had witnessed the Great White Egret "tick birds" pecking ticks off Uncle Freddy's spotless red cattle, using their black breeding beaks, with equivalent determination.

After each interrogation, the piccanins were free to leave, but they didn't go far, lingering alongside the blue weeping wisteria to see the outcome. The verdict would be a relished topic of amusement for many moons to follow.

After about ten innocent *"Hayi*'s," Sindie was now in the front of the line with Tombe standing boldly behind her. Sindie was looking straight at the policeman, wiggling her light weight from leg to leg as if her bladder was about to burst.

"Did you steal Mr. Bester's pomegranates?" The policeman asked.

Smelling a rat, Fikile interrogated erroneously. "Did you wickedly steal the fruit that did not belong to you?" He paused and elaborated, "You know the Holy Ghost can see all your actions, don't you?"

"Hayi (No)," Sindie vowed truthfully. "I did not steal the fruit."

"Why are you so wiggly, little girl?" The policeman asked, pausing as he waited for Fikile to echo his words into isiXhosa.

Taking liberty to its limits, Fikile obliged, droning like a spy with connections to the infrastructure of spirits in the sky, "Do you know who did the malicious deed, little thief?"

"Ewe (Yes)," Sindie confessed, bursting out of her skin with terror.

"Who was it?" The policeman demanded in a gruff tone.

"It was Miss Jay!" Sindie was a willing informant, but she mumbled my nickname, so he would not understand.

"Miss WHO?" The cop repeated.

"Miss Judy Bester." She confessed.

There was an audible groan. There were a lot of mumbling mixed voices; I couldn't make out all the clicking exclamations.

"All right, Mr. Bester, would you like to d-rrrr-op the charges then?" the policeman said in English this time, rolling his r's. The *rock spider* (Afrikaans speaker) sniffed at the *rooinek* (English speaker) tearing up all his neat transcriptions of evidence.

"Yes, please, quite so. *Righto* then, I'll deal with my daughter," Dad said, forcing his best manners and controlling his rising fury. Embarrassment fueled his seething humiliation.

All the piccanins and "boys" were cordially dismissed, and they dispersed rather rapidly. They were more than willing to head for the huts, to escape the wrath of my father and leave me to the consequence of my sin.

You stand alone on judgment day, I learned.

As the police truck was roaring up the hill in a mist of dust, I could hear my dad's boots banging towards the bedroom. I had quasi attack of slumber.

Seconds before he arrived, my mom entered their bedroom silently.

"Gwenna, pass me your hairbrush," Dad instructed. My mom went to her dressing table and took out a turquoise, plastic lightweight hairbrush. It was not the large, heavier silver-handled one. She handed it to him gingerly.

I was lying in the fetal position, hoping they wouldn't awake "an innocent sleeping child."

Just then Mom let out a scream. "Oooh, how ghastly, look!"

I got a big fright and peeped with one eye. There was a huge, hairy tarantula crawling on her pale turquoise curtain.

"Kill it, Boet!" she dramatized a little, even though she was the least dramatic person. "Caesar's Ghost! Squash it quickly!" Mom squealed, faking a serious attack of arachnophobia. I had seen her swat scores of of spiders quite calmly before. It was her clever ploy, delaying Dad, to allow his boiling blood pressure to subside.

Dad went over to the curtain and slammed the tarantula very hard with the spanking weapon. The hairbrush shattered into splinters, as he amputated all eight hairy legs at once.

"Oh no, my best brush!" Mother wailed, trying to be melodramatic, but not quite pulling it off. "Try not to be too rough."

Instead of cooling his temper, his fuse detonated, exploding his fury to white hot.

"Judy, come here!" he demanded.

Dad knew I was awake, even though I had added pseudo snoring for a special effect. He sat at the end of my bed, put me over his knee, and gave me the *hiding* (spanking) of my life.

"Why did you steal?" he said, as he spanked my bottom with his bare hand.

"Why did you lie to me? You are never to tell lies again. You must never ever, ever, *ever* do that again!" he said angrily, walloping me soundly.

He then tramped heavily to his office to simultaneously puff off more steam and smoke.

I was too afraid to speak to him for a long time after that. Actually, I was more ashamed than afraid because he was a good dad, always protecting and providing for us.

Dad revered honesty. He hated lies. He was angrier about the lies than about the missing pomegranates...which he never ever mentioned again.

Back at the Kasouga shack, I lay wide awake on my built-in wooden bed, reflecting on the painful pomegranate lesson. Luckily for me, this had all happened before Dad shot the policeman's murderous dog. The outcome may have not been so favorable if I had stolen the pomegranates *after* Dad had shot the policeman's pet. Timing had certainly been in my favor or I could have had a criminal record at age seven.

All of a sudden, the sky lit up. A deafening clap of thunder shook the whole Kasouga shack. I got a very big fright.

"Mo-om-my, I'm scared!" I bleated like a lost lamb. There was no ceiling in the rugged fisherman's shack, just big wooden beams for rafters. I knew my voice would be heard, even though the boys' bedroom was in-between our bedroom and theirs.

"Never mind, my girl, it is only a little thunderstorm," my dad replied in a comforting tone.

I would have felt safer in our sturdy brick home at Schelmdrift with fourteen-inch solid brick walls, plastered with cement. The wind started to gust, and I imagined the roof being blustered off the rafters. I thought of the nursery rhyme about the house made of sticks. In case the blind Kasouga River flooded its banks, our shack had to be elevated. Our fisherman's cabin was constructed on stilts. Those stink-wood poles could be identified as sticks, I supposed. I knew that lightening strikes the highest point.

Another big electric flash of lightening thunder bolted through the black night sky. The flash was bright enough that I could identify the lineup of pink flowers on our curtains. I knew that shack was not as well built as Schelmdrift.

My books told of houses being huffed down or puffed up. Or was it the house built on sand instead of rocks?

"I am frightened. Please may I come and sleep in your bed?" I begged.

I was scared rigid. If this was the wrath of God, I didn't want to be struck by it. My imaginative, informative cousin, Martin Bester, told me once that thunder is the sound of an angry God knocking down His cupboards in the sky.

My dad rescued me in his blue striped flannel pajamas. He picked me up and carried me to safety, placing me cozily beside Mom, where I nodded off to sleep.

15

BUBBLES AND GUM

Early Monday morning, Dad measured to see if a new deep freeze would fit in the corner of the Kasouga dining room. He needed freezer space to keep his I. & J. *crayfish* (lobster) and pink *prawns* (shrimp). They were fancy seafood usually used for human consumption, but Dad used both for bait.

Mom made a very valid argument, "Those frozen prawns are so frightfully expensive. Shouldn't we just rather eat the prawns?"

"No. Didn't I show you this past weekend? I'll catch you one big Jan Bruin for each prawn, making it more economical. Fish cannot resist the taste of prawns," he countered.

The smell of bacon drew me into the kitchen.

"What are you doing, Maggie?" I asked as I peered into our largest pan. The fish's eye glared back at me. Maggie was frying the fish skeleton in bacon grease, with its tail and head still attached. It was an ethereal sight and smell, indeed.

"I'm taking this home for my children," Maggie said, indicating that there was a good reason for her to leave half the flesh on the bones, when she had filleted the fresh fish.

When Mom walked in, Maggie quietly put a lid on the pan. I noticed, but I never said a word. Maggie was, after all, one of my moms. She helped raise me.

As soon as the skeleton with eyes was cooked, and Mom had left the room, Maggie flipped the fish onto a wad of newspaper. It had a picture of Graeme Pollock playing cricket at the crease. The grease stained his blonde locks, making his handsome head darker.

Maggie had no more important use for the papers. She could not read. She could not care less about cricket; it was alien to her culture. She neatly wrapped the dripping skeleton up and put it with her belongings, beside the bottles of seawater for Jane.

"Tatey loves fish and chips." She commented.

It was more like skeleton and skins.

On our way home, Mom remembered to buy bacon from Connock's butchery, in Grahamstown. She also bought my favorite Escort Pork Sausages for "bangers and mash." She packed them neatly into her blue cool box.

Dad craved newspapers as much as nicotine. He drove directly to the Ramona Café. I begged to stay in the sunny street. Mom promised to bring us sweets if I vowed not to try to smuggle Sindie in again. Hastily, Mom returned clutching a brown paper bag and soon disappeared to join Dad for civilized English tea.

Maggie handed us each a huge apricot candy ball and a piece of Wicks bubblegum. I was happy to be in the company of the cheerful Xhosas and not in the stuffy, smoky Café.

"UnoLasti uyasithanda! (NoLasti loves us!)" Maggie exclaimed when she saw the delicious bribes in the bag. She lifted out a loaf of white bread that had steam on the plastic, evidence that it was freshly baked.

Sindie chewed the bubblegum and saved the apricot in her hand, which she tried to wrap in the paper from the bubblegum. She was determined to save the wrapper as evidence to brag about how lucky she had been for once. The paper was too small, but she held the apricot half-wrapped on display so that passers-by could admire it.

I could not decide which treat I wanted to eat first, so I stuck both the gum and apricot candy into my mouth at once.

Tombe licked the apricot ball with zeal while she hid the gum safely in her clothes, in case *tsotsis* (thugs) saw it. Licking would make the candy last longer. She licked off the little red food coloring dots that made it look like a real, ripe apricot. Tombe licked long and hard. It reminded me of my cat affectionately licking her newborn kittens. If she were a cat, Tombe would have been purring. Her expression was one of ecstasy. I enjoyed watching her.

The spring weather had brought out many shoppers. Soon Maggie recognized a fellow servant from previous Kasouga vacations, whom she was overjoyed to see. She ate in the shade of the Land Rover with her hungry friend, the Dell's maid.

After a few chews my gum and apricot ball curdled. The result was a crumbly awful texture on my tongue. Bubblegum and sweets should truly practice apartheid.

Maggie stood up to stretch and spit in the gutter. "Are you not hungry, *Nohanki?* Don't you also want a chunk of bread?" she offered. My mouth was full; I shook my head so that she knew I did not want any bread. The girls held out both hands in a cupped shape.

"Look, Maggie, I can spit very well, too, like you and Jane." I clicked. Maggie never corrected my manners when I spoke with a very full mouth. I loved that about her. She was the opposite of Granny Stocks.

I tried to spit in Jane's style, through my teeth to the side, but I failed miserably. My mouth was too full to create enough pressure. Next, I tried the fashion in which Maggie's sons spat, with the lips pursed, as if they were going to whistle.

Tatcy had snorted up a bit of phlegm before he spat at the *tsotsi*'s feet. He gathered and blew a big dollop of gob. It might have helped to make the *tsotsi* slip, sort of like a banana skin. I was not sure exactly why Tatey spat so violently at the city slicker's feet.

I stood up on the back of the truck, so that I could concentrate harder and take a bigger breath to make an explosive spit. All of a sudden, the curdled candy orb flew out my mouth like a cannon ball and lodged in a webbed-looking thing. That brown bushy object had no business suddenly slipping into my spitting range.

On our ten thousand acre farm, one can freely spit in any direction and not offend anyone. I had temporarily forgotten that towns are shared with other people who get in your way.

I noticed too late that the brown ball of fuzz was the back of a moving object. It stood tall like the shape of an ant heap. The heaped head turned around to reveal a very red face on the other side. My masticated mortar had landed in someone's beehive hairdo. It was the 1960's, after all.

There was an exclusive hairdresser just near the Ramona named Tippin's. It was a very expensive salon, liable for large beehives. That hairdresser was known for making haystacks on heads with huge combs that looked like pitchforks, so they must have stolen the idea from farmers. And people paid Tippin through their noses to do it!

"*Wat was dit?* (What was that?)" The mouth spoke Afrikaans, putting her manicured hand up to her head. The glob sparkled like a twenty carat pink diamond in the sun.

She felt the goop stuck in her hair, while orange saliva adhered to her red polished fingernails. She stared at her hand in horror and then broke into loud ranting. It was a performance we had never before seen.

"*Jou swernood! I sal jou donder!* (You brat! I'll beat you!)" She kicked the Land Rover with her patent leather shoes and shouted at me in Afrikaans.

I sat down with my two friends as fast as I could.

"*Wie se donderse kind is dit, jou kaffer?* (Whose ruddy child is this, you kaffir?)" She demanded of uniformed Maggie, who had now strategically placed herself between the Land Rover and the racist. Passersby started to stare and some even stopped to witness the scene.

Maggie answered in Xhosa, "*Andiyazi.* (I don't know.)" Everyone knows what that Xhosa phrase means, as it is most commonly used—especially when one does not want to disclose useful information. Maggie and I both knew enough Afrikaans to know exactly what the melodramatic lady was screeching. Maggie lied with not only conviction, but also with the dumbest expression. That blank, defiant stare was the perfect partner to such mock ignorance.

"*Kyk na my nuwe haarstyl!* (Look at my hairdo!)" The lady yelped and tried to remove the newly attached orange and pink hair accessory.

"*Andiyazi.* (I don't know.)" Maggie repeated in humble hatred. This time she truly did not know why the witch would attach the apricot sloshy ball more firmly.

I was in the stew again. This time, boiling point was instantaneous, blowing the lid right off of the pressure cooker.

Sindie sat on top of me and tried to distract the woman by blowing a big bubble.

Tombe was scared out of her wits when she realized that the back of the truck was no longer a safe sanctuary either. One could get gobbled up anywhere, sea or Land Rover. She had not seen many white women in her life, except for our family and neighbors. She also had never seen a real racist before—a memory she might want to edit out of her journalistic mind.

"I-English." Maggie pretended not to understand any Afrikaans.

"Sorry, my Madam… *Engleeesh.*" Maggie muttered for mercy, now pretending to have Anglo-Saxon connections, which only served to incense the Boer woman more.

The woman was clawing at her hair, which now seemed to shrink significantly with each tug, like pink candy floss (cotton candy). She was literally tearing her hair out, frantically combing it with her claws.

"Who taught this white girl to spit like a bloody kaffir?" The cattish lady yelled and startled onlookers. All the Africans looked guilty at once.

"NguJane. (It was Jane.)" Maggie muttered quietly under her breath in Xhosa.

Tombe, who did not understand the English or the Afrikaans, heard her mother's name mentioned, and spilled a single tear which rolled out her big brown eye and quickly slid down her lubricated cheek.

"Who is your boss?" The *rock spider* demanded.

"Baas Sngxhoshe. Engliiish is Boss Striiict." Maggie had to answer, so she gave Dad's Xhosa name and its meaning with distinct defiance and deliberation. Only the Xhosas knew Dad by that name. It was the *dinkam* (absolute) truth, just disguised in a little language barrier.

"Wie se kind? (Whose child?) *Meneer* (Mr.) Streaked? *Sonder Klere?* (Without Clothes?)" She steamed. Now like a vulture, *"Waar?* (Where?)" Her were eyes scanning High Street for a streaker.

She wore too much make-up and her black eyes looked like an opportunistic leopard searching for prey. Only, she was hunting for the best big game hunter, who was safely shielded by *The Herald*, no doubt.

"*Andiyazi.* (I don't know.)" Maggie reverted back to her loyal lies in Xhosa. She took a sip of her Fanta grape. Then she spat a purple glob into the gutter in the true Xhosa manner.

"*Sies*, (Yuck) man!" The Boer sidestepped over the spittle. "Your Boss streaked when?" She demanded, kicking the Land Rover again.

"Always, Striiict!" Maggie now reluctantly resorted to some English. Maggie was trying to warn her not to mess with my Dad's belongings. "Striiict, every day!"

"Have you got a Madam? What is her name? What does she say when he streaked?" The cat with red claws, now dripping in orange saliva was inexorable.

Maggie had to scratch her head and think again, "My madam just say 'Caesar's Ghost!'"

"She sees a ghost?" The lady was most irate. *"Gonnas!!* (Golly!!) Your boss streaked? *Jislaak,* (Geeez,) man! And your madam sees a ghost? At the same time?"

"Ev-e-r-y day, *Miesies.*" Maggie replied.

We could tell Maggie was *gatvol* (had a gut full) of this shrill voice in her face. She partially removed her Xhosa traditional headdress that was almost as high as the white woman's beehive hairdo. Maggie scratched her skull hard as if she had fleas.

The vicious white woman only stepped back and grimaced, disgusted, as if my Maggie may have lice in her peppercorn hair. Maggie's ploy did not seem to have the desired affect of getting rid of the lady.

How was I supposed to know that it was human hair when it hardly resembled it? Birds, I was sure, would not even nest in that haystack so close to her scarecrow-like face. However, my Wicks bubblegum was not leaving its perch in a hurry.

"Where are these persons…who streak…and see ghosts?!" She shouted at Maggie in English with an Afrikaans accent.

The enraged *rock* frantically continued tugging to remove the sticky conglomerate, which merely made it cling to more hair and become a frightful sight indeed, for which I felt only partially responsible. The hairdresser surely must share some of the blame for making such a tall target.

"Andiyazi." Maggie looked the most innocent I had ever seen her look. She had plenty of practice by now.

I was so scared I pretended I could not speak at all.

"What is your father's name? Where is he?" She screeched at me.

I sat very quietly and stared back at her.

Sindie cheekily suggested we barge into the Ramona and call Dad to chase the offended creature away. I clicked and ordered her not to try that again. Sindie's next wise suggestion was that we beat the witch ourselves using Dad's fishing rod. Tombe swore the metal reel would serve just as well as any traditional *igqudu* (knobkerrie), the prized weapon of the Xhosa tribe. It was just a stick with a knob on the end, after all.

"We can easily bend the pole and break off the skinny end." Tombe was sure it would serve well as a knobkerrie, and she started to untie the fishing rods.

"I don't think my dad will approve." I assured Tombe quietly in isiXhosa.

"Do you only speak *kaffirtaal* (tribal language), and you are white?" She yelled again, aiming her diatribe at me. "What is your father's name?"

"JOOOHAAANES!" Sindie suddenly volunteered what she knew was my Dad's real name, hoping he would hear her cry or that *somebody* would go and fetch Dad to shoo the cow away.

"Did you just call me YOUR HIGHNESS? You cheeky bloody kaffir!" The woman splattered, as she aimed her tirade at Sindie.

Sindie was not willing to back down, and with no sight of my father to rescue us, decided to use trickery. She pointed down the street, in a decoy and said, "BOOOET!" She knew that was my Dad's alias. She luckily left off the Boss prefix.

"What? He is in the boot (trunk) of this car?" The tigress was grabbing at straws and her hair, which now were not that dissimilar in appearance. Her hair looked like stalks of hay interwoven with sticky pink spider webs.

"Ewe. (Yes.)*"* Sindie and Tombe both nodded in the affirmative, when she pointed away. Away seemed like a good idea to them.

The lady went to the brown Mercedes Benz parked next to us, and aggressively tried to open the boot. Luckily it was locked. She looked at me with a questioning frown, and I shook my head in the negative.

Ever-obedient Tombe sat frozen-stiff with fear. She meekly tried to give her licked apricot ball to the lady as a peace offering or parting gift perhaps. The lady rudely retreated from the well-intended sacrificial gesture and flared her upturned nostrils. She already had my generous donation of sticky spittle in her hair. That would suffice for now.

The lady only stopped her harangue for a brief moment to inspect her hairdo in the side mirror of the Mercedes Benz. Her reflection only incensed her further.

"Who is this *blerrie wit kaffer-kind* (bloody white n-child)? Can she not talk like a white person?" she seethed. Oddly enough, she looked like a Lourie, or *"go-away"* bird with a pronounced head-crest, only she would not *go* anywhere.

Maggie wickedly devised a new plan and spoke broken English with an African accent, *"My Miesies and Baas* (My Madam and Boss) is drinking brandy…by Grand Hotel Bar…forever and forever, Amen," she confessed falsely, singing slowly in a husky voice, under duress, sort of like an out of tune Bully Canary.

Maggie then launched into a crafty charade of gestures indicating that my parents were getting drunk at the Grand Hotel. The hotel was at the bottom far end of High Street. She included the Biblical phrase to her farcical confession to reinforce credibility of her elaborate lie. Maggie could not resist the temptation of sending this livid woman to call some more deserving drunk to repentance. *Teetotalers* (people who drink tea instead of alcohol) did not deserve such fury in her sober opinion.

Maggie's friend, who was still chewing bread with her mouth wide open, nodded most solemnly to confirm the Maggie's lies, and spoke in perfect Afrikaans, *"Dis reg, Miesies. Hulle suip daar by die Grand. Sy naam is Strict.* (That's right, Madam. They are drinking there by the Grand. His name is Strict.)" The Dell's servant pointed wholeheartedly in the direction of the Grand Hotel with diplomatic aplomb.

"I will go and find them. They can bloody-well pay for my hairdo if they can afford to give their *kaffirs* white bread and sweets." The vain woman with the wobbly hair, which now resembled the leaning tower of Pisa, stomped determinedly towards the Hotel. The implacable hairstyle occultist was in hot pursuit of a *"Meneer* (Mr.) Streaked."

Maggie sighed, *"Thixo, hiba nenceba nakuthi* (May God have mercy on us). "

Maggie pulled out some fresh chew tobacco that Mom had bought her and popped it into her cheek. I could see it through her shiny cheek. Nicotine seemed the common way of dismissing stress for both my tribes. She handed us each another toffee from the bag. We thanked her for her generosity. All of us were now perfectly content to sit and suck and watch the city people go about their business.

Just then, Gwenna and Boetie Bester, my splendid parents, who had missed all the High Street news, soberly strolled out. Dad tucked the fresh newspapers under his arm as he put his town hat on his head. I casually climbed back into the front, tucked safely between the two of them. Maggie climbed back up and muttered some obscenities about the Afrikaans witch in Xhosa.

Dad pointed the Land Rover north towards Schelmdrift, our home in the Karoo, far away, where no wailing witch was welcome.

I was very relieved when we reached the outskirts of town, past the golf club, finally free of all city slickers, *totsis,* Greeks, and rock spiders alike.

I never mentioned the queen bee with a hive hairdo and a stinging tongue.

16

CARD KARMA

Crossing slowly over the Fish River on Carlisle Bridge, we could see groups of Xhosa schoolchildren walking home to their various farms.

Sindie jumped up and waved at them shouting, *"Sivela elwandle!* (We've come from the seaside!) We feasted on fatty fish and chips!"

"It was so wonderful at the sea. We gorged on all sorts of food out of the ocean." Tombe aimed the news from her privileged perch on Dad's red cool box on the back of the truck, "We feasted on stacks of sweets! And we drank fizzy Fanta orange with a straw!"

I was pleased that my now well-traveled playmates had something to brag about, so I decided to keep Tombe's fear of High Street and high tide a top-secret. After all, trippers do love to boast. Surviving adventurous travels tends to swell one's self-regard. Travelers think they know more because they have seen more sights. Sindie and Tombe were now elevated to that lofty category.

Further up the road, Dad stopped when we recognized a few Schelmdrift school kids, who joyfully leapt up to get a lift home. I looked back and saw Tombe take out her bubblegum and bite off slivers for each one to taste.

The next few peaceful months were spent getting ready for Christmas. The birth of Christ could only be celebrated after much preparation. Mom emphasized that following His example— not traveling—is what makes one a better person.

Mom drove to town once more to shop for Christmas gifts. In *Simon and Barnes*, her favorite fabric shop, Mom would mutter, "Maggie loves scarlet, the bold reds; Jane likes traditional blue German print; and Lizzie prefers purple," as she flipped through rolls of floral fabric. Maggie, Jane and Lizzie received huge hampers to celebrate Christmas. Mom purchased sweets in bulk cartons.

On Schelmdrift once again, mother would try and make school fun by teaching me while we worked together, "Come on, my pet, you may help me with this chore. We can practice your *maths* while we divide up these sweets. If each child on this farm gets twenty ounces of sweets, how many sweets do we need? Don't forget to count the families that live on Goodwood. And we cannot leave out Twin and Jennet's five children."

It took the whole day to divide the sweets for each child. It was a big mathematical problem. I seemed to complicate it even more, because I added an extra handful to Sindie and Tombe's newspaper cones.

"You are very generous to our servants. They really do love you," I told Mom.

"We do our best," Mom replied.

I helped fold cones out of newspaper. That November of 1965, the headlines were all about Rhodesia becoming independent from Mother England. I was about to become independent at boarding school, not too happy about leaving my own mother. The back pages of the paper reported sensational murders, rapes and robberies, in the faraway cities.

"Good deeds never make it onto the pages of any newspaper," Mom remarked as we wrapped cones full of sweets for each child. "But God sees everything we ever do; it doesn't need to be published for Him to know about it. You should always do good deeds for others, my child. Good deeds are always recorded by angels in heaven, and rewarded openly." I believed her, even though I couldn't see any angels taking notes. I believed her just because she was my mom.

I was contemplating how my two tribes believed the same thing. Tombe knew that we never draw the curtains of our ancestors, they are always peeping at us. Mom knew that angels watch over us, so that meant we cannot lock them out of our lives either. Anyhow, grandghosts are made of air, so their spirits can move through solid doors.

"Tombe says that their ancestors are watching them all the time. Is it our dead grandparent's taking notes?" I had to figure it out.

"Perhaps—we don't know exactly. But remember we do not worship our ancestors like the Natives. We worship Almighty God, our Father in Heaven."

After we got all the sweets neatly divided, we would mix red cool drink for each family and fill an empty brandy bottle with the syrupy concentrate. It stained everything scarlet—your teeth, your tongue, and even your urine. Mom strategically piled designated heaps on the Breakfast Room tables for each Xhosa family. Maggie's pile had rich red floral material, but no leather boots, khaki shirts or trousers on it—which Dad gave to his boys. No man lived in her household.

As we sorted out gifts, Mother would tell me the Bible stories, which she seemed to know quite well. Mom attended Commemoration Methodist Church while she studied mathematics at Rhodes University. Just from reading the Bible, Mom understood the concept that the Father and the Son and the Holy Ghost are three distinct individuals. I don't believe you need a Bachelor of Science degree in mathematics to figure out that one and one and one add up to three separate beings. Gwenna Bester was blessed, I might add, with an extra dollop of common sense.

"That makes the most sense to me," Mother would say. "How can the Son possibly pray to His Father if they are the same person? A person as intelligent as Jesus is would not pray to Himself. That would be quite illogical."

I believed that she was right. They sounded like three powerful people to me, too. I distinctly recall hearing the minister always drone, "In the name of the Father *and* of the Son *and* of the Holy Ghost." I figured that if you put the word "and" between three nouns, it automatically indicted three separate entities.

"I still need to bake biscuits and fill all the rusk tins. Judy, go and ask Maggie to stoke up the fire before she goes home for the afternoon. We need a very hot oven to bake. Ask her to bring in some extra wood from the woodpile, please. We need to dry the rusks in the oven as well. That takes all afternoon."

Rusks are a part of life in South Africa. Mom made sweetened bread dough using buttermilk. I would help her roll golf ball-sized pieces of dough in flour. We then packed the balls in six rows of three in a bread pan, while she taught me my times tables.

After sliding them out of the oven, we would gently pull the rusks apart while they were still warm. Then, lining them up like soldiers spread across a wire rack, we would put them back in a cooler oven for a few hours to dry rock hard. That made them "twice baked."

"Uphi uMaggie? (Where is Maggie?)" I asked Jane, who was quietly covering Maggie's job.

"Usestalini. (She is at the stable.)" Jane said in hushed tones. Knowing Maggie lived at the stables part-time with her part-time husband, Jack, I relayed Mom's instructions to Jane instead.

Mom fastidiously prepared for the holidays. She baked rich fruitcake with plumped almonds and glazed cherries, citrus peel and crystallized pineapple. We boiled six *tiekies* (two and a half pennies) and *sixpences* (five pennies) for ten minutes to sterilize them. We practiced mathematics while we measured ingredients. Mom let me stir the clean coins into the dough that was laced with golden currants and sherry. Then Mom steamed the rich Christmas pudding in a special muslin cloth. Mother lastly immunized the Christmas cake, injecting it with brandy to preserve it from getting moldy mumps or green gangrene.

If you were lucky, you clunked your teeth on a coin while eating your steamed pudding on Christmas Day. Mom made us all lucky when she dished up. I saw her once take her *tiekie* and quickly embed it in Wendy's pudding bowl. She poured custard and brandy sauce over to hide the hole. Mothers always discreetly want their children to have good luck. There had to be a bigger Mom in the heavens who handed out treasures like *tiekies* to her favorite children. I was going to make it my life's mission to find that mysterious, elusive "someone" who divvied up luck.

Another pre-Christmas tradition entailed Mom driving Maggie, Jane and Lizzie into Grahamstown in the two-toned blue Zephyr for their annual Christmas shopping spree. Mom customarily chose new uniforms for her maids, while they scuttled to shop on the cheap side of town.

"I must remember to buy Christmas cards today," Mom remarked. Finding the right cards was a major mathematical problem. We had driven 30 miles in 100° Fahrenheit heat, searching two shops, but we found zero cards that met Mother's approval.

"I refuse to buy cards with silly snowmen on them." Mom was most indignant as she ruffled through the cards in the third shop.

"How long does it take to find cards that you like?" I inquired.

"It seems like we have to hunt harder every Christmas season," she stated flatly. This mission was turning out to be more difficult than tracking wild game on the upper banks of Bumpy.

"Can't you just buy ones with Father Christmas on the front?" I pleaded.

"I will do nothing of the sort! Father Christmas is not what we are celebrating." She was clearly annoyed.

"How about these?" I pulled some out at the fourth shop. It was a pretty picture of a house covered in snow; the house sort of looked like our stables with a cozy veranda. Often when people came to our farm for the first time, they saw the stables and thought that was our home. It did have a roof held up by cement pillars in Fikile's section, resembling many other Karoo houses. Then we would laugh and say, "No, those are the stables. Our house is behind those tall trees."

"I'll keep hunting until I find ones with suitable pictures of Baby Jesus, Mary, and Joseph, or at least the Wise Men from the East," she stated flatly, not beating about the bush on her hunt. "Snow scenes are quite unsuitable for this part of the world. It's as hot as Hades here right now." She left yet another shop, perfectly disgruntled.

"What do you suppose the significance of a snowman is in December in the southern half of the planet earth?" she asked aloud. "This is positively discreditable!"

Lastly, *NoLasti* entered Grocott's, the most expensive stationery shop in town. "We'd better find some here. I'll probably have to pay double," Mom sneered.

"These cards have stars on the outside; can't we draw Mary and Jesus on the inside?" I volunteered, doubling my efforts to end this tedious task.

"Those are snowflakes, not stars. Oh drat!" Mom grunted. "Are all these cards manufactured by silly clots? They must be imported from London for this price."

Exasperated, Mom requested politely of the Afrikaans lady behind the polished wooden counter, "Pardon me. Do you happen to have any cards with a nativity scene on them? I would prefer them without any sign of a snowman!"

"A new box has just arrived. Let me go and have a look for you, Mrs. Bester," the lady replied primly. I could not help noticing her hair. The haystack on her head looked vaguely familiar, but her smiley face threw me off.

"Thank Heaven Above!" My mother rejoiced as she spotted cards with the Baby Jesus lying in a manger, right on top of the newly-opened box.

"I think they are two rand per box, let me go and check," the friendly shop assistant informed Mom, having had no time to even price them yet.

By this time, I was ready to add up my own common cents and subtract any price for those cards.

When we declared independence from Mother England, we switched from pounds and pennies to our own South African currency, the rand and cents. The bills came in different colors. The one-rand note was brown, the five-rand was purple, and the ten-rand was green. The painted woman feigned poise as she salivated at the sight of green minted paper money. She had yellow-brown eyes like a cat with black all around them.

The feline peered curiously at me. Her whiskers made her cheeks twitch into an eerie smile as she gazed at the monetary notes in Mom's purse. She really wanted to pounce on that money, but she first played with her prey, "These cards are very grand," she encouraged the customer, "with glitter on the Star of David."

The rock spider stared at me again very hard. A slight frown of recognition crossed her forehead. The minute she frowned, I recognized the disguised witch.

Luckily for me, Mom had recently cut my hair short, removing all the curls, so that I would be all set for swimming at the seaside. I was shorn to look like a boy; nevertheless timing was in my favor. She then leaned over the counter to check if I was wearing a skirt.

I smiled my best smile, and said innocently, "How do you do?" in my most posh English manners. That is what you are supposed to say when you have never met a person before.

Mom added our fifty friends to our fifty extended family members, and then divided the total by the number of cards in each box. She helped herself to five boxes, holding twenty cards each, and parted with her green ten-rand note, rather reluctantly.

The phony shop assistant glowered at me again. "Are you Mrs. Streaked or Mrs. Bester? I do get mixed up. You are both lovely, tall ladies."

"Bester," I offered quickly.

"I am Mrs. Boet Bester. I have never heard of any Streaked family in the Albany District, and I was born and bred in lower Albany. I have lived all my married life in upper Albany, twenty years now. Sounds like a rather dotty name to me." Mom put her green money note on the counter.

"Actually, they are three rand a box." The swindler masked a very fake smile. Her eye teeth stuck out too far, like a leopard. If she was a cat, she would be licking her lips, not painting them pearly white with crushed fish scales. That pale lipstick made her teeth look darker yellow.

"Caesar's Ghost's alive! That is expensive. " Mom slapped another purple five rand note on the counter.

She snatched it with her curly cat claws, "All the prices have gone sky high. I recently paid five rand at Tippin's to have my hair done. And I had to give her a tip on top of that." The faker countered while the unscrupulous lady used the shiny silver section of the counter as a mirror to admire herself, and adjust her hairy hive.

"They're one rand and fifty cents everywhere else," Mom muttered under her breath as we exited the overpriced shop.

"Kaffer-boetie. (Kaffir-brother…unkind nickname for a white person who befriends blacks)." I heard the witch whisper as she turned around, scowling at me once more.

Mom grabbed me by the hand, "But I refuse to waste money on senseless snowmen. We are, after all, celebrating the birth of Christ. We had better go and fetch our maids. They will be waiting outside the Grand Hotel with all their parcels."

Mom methodically crossed "cards" off her list.

17

SHIP ROCK

The schools closed for the six-week Christmas holidays. Our family trekked to the seaside—lock, stock and barrel. It took a few trips to cart two maids, one man servant, and a family of six with a new deep freeze.

Dad gazed over the swirling ocean, "That warm Mozambique Current is reaching us from around the Southeastern tip of Africa. These are not very good conditions for fishing. But I still think we'll give it a try anyway." He was an eternal optimist.

"You look so funny, Daddy!" I pointed out. "Your arms and face are brown, but the rest of you is lily-white."

"It's called a 'farmer's tan' for a reason, my girl." He said it proudly as he vigorously rubbed himself dry with his towel stretched across his broad shoulders. He tugged roughly at both ends alternatively, confident in his own two-toned zebra-striped skin.

"We'd better start strolling back to the shack. Maggie will have breakfast ready by now." Mom was dabbing her reddish hair briskly. She looked stunning in her green full-piece *cozzy* (swimsuit). She had no tan at all, just brighter freckles on her slender, athletic frame.

"Br-uu—ce, Noor-man!" Dad hollered. "Come along now!"

Most holiday makers at Kasouga went for a compulsory early morning swim with their family. It was tradition. Bleary-eyed teenagers were dragged out of bed for a dip in the sea. Other swims throughout the day were purely voluntary recreation. But those early morning dips were a required family affair for us farm folks. Cattle and sheep were dipped in water laced with insecticides, to kill ticks. Likewise, we were herded and dipped in the cold ocean every morning "to get rid of the cobwebs," so to speak. We always saw the Dells, Emslies , Longs, Howards, Mills, Berrimans and other Kasouga-ites at those daily dips.

At Kasouga, there was an excess of spiders, mostly the harmless daddy long legs and flat brown house spiders. Hence, "washing away cobwebs" was not an entirely unsuitable aphorism.

Only Maggie's early morning percolated coffee—with a rusk to dip into it, of course —preceded those customary swims.

The maids sat in a group in the shade of a large tree in the afternoons. If I wanted to know any juicy gossip, I simply needed to sit silently on Maggie's lap. Servants knew a lot about their employees—too much, in fact—and freely swapped verbal news, not suspecting to ever be understood by any white kid. I caught every click. They spilled the beans:

"Boss—is rude to his wife and swears very badly."

"That boss drinks vodka with his orange juice for breakfast."

"This teenager tells the biggest lies."

"That drunk takes gin to the toilet with him."

"This madam is so stingy, even at Christmastime."

"Those two are having a secret love affair."

"Stinginess is the worst sin."

Servants usually knew how people really lived, who they really were, behind the proper public facades.

While at Kasouga, the Xhosas had to trek about 100 yards to the east of the main "European Only" beach if they wanted to swim. A few brave Xhosas swam, or rather washed, in the shallow waves while the whites took an afternoon siesta.

Dad expounded on the glitches of apartheid, when he read an amusing article, "Oddly enough, it is the blue-eyed, fair American tourists who caused further confusion at the international airport in Johannesburg." All trouble seemed to brew and breed in Johannesburg!

"The most patriotic U.S. citizens, innocently and ignorantly stood in the 'Non-European' *queues* (lines), which were intended for black people at the bus stops, public toilets and train stations. To their utter dismay, the 'Non-European' facilities were far inferior to what Americans were accustomed to back home. An American would not want to ride in a non-European ambulance, for instance. I saw how shabby they were when Moses was stabbed. What's more, restaurants have signs that read 'Europeans only,' and so they forfeit the cash of the hungry American tourists. The whole bloody idea is a mess." Dad summarized the article.

Consequently, after all the confusion, the government efficiently changed all the signs to read, "Whites only" or "Non-whites only." The newly-painted signs were better for apartheid, except masses of illiterate blacks remained baffled.

Kasouga Beach stretched like a broad deserted street paved with golden sand. The only chocolate-colored body allowed on our swimming spot would be a uniformed nanny. Usually, she'd be holding up her skirts and apron as she played with a white kid, while the mom tried to darken her tan on a towel. In these cases, the Xhosa nanny would only get wet up to her knees. If the child skedaddled into the sea, the dutiful nanny would yelp very loudly and expect a white man to rescue the rascal.

Jennet, the Carlisle Bridge Country Club maid, was a regular to fill in Jane's spot as housemaid for our annual seaside holiday. Jane never came down to Kasouga, as she had a younger family. She held down the fort at Schelmdrift, helping Maggie's oldest daughter take care of the three boys.

Jennet was an avid member of the Zionist Church. Their members loved to wear a metal Bethlehem star on a green ribbon pinned to their clothing, proudly displaying their alliance. Their African leader in *Pietersburg* was rumored to own twelve gold Rolex watches, while most of his congregation lived in abject poverty. For a monetary fee, their priests allegedly exorcised evil spirits and healed the sick.

I admired Jennet for her faith. She was constantly cheerful and preaching the Gospel, mainly within earshot of unrepentant Maggie.

Grandpa Stocks brought us basketfuls of fresh pineapples from Glenfillan Park. When Maggie peeled them for us, she left a good deal of the pine on the skin, so that her pineapple beer could be fully flavored. Unlike Jennet, Maggie was a firm believer in liquid spirits to lift the human spirit. Maggie brewed barrels of pineapple beer; I noticed when I visited them in the servant's quarters. Their asbestos bedroom was shaded by thick bush, and it was the coolest spot in all of Kasouga. I loved sitting on her antique brass bed, which once belonged to my grandmother. Maggie had hoisted her bed high up with piles of bricks under each foot. This was to guard against *Thokoloshe,* the notorious dwarf who ostensibly caused havoc in the tribe. Maggie also sold potent ginger beer in her secret *shebeen* (illegal bar).

Most South Africans considered it shameful to celebrate anything without alcohol. The spirits that came in clear bottles were the more potent spirits; cane, vodka, and gin were the ones that deceivingly looked as harmless as water.

I mulled over all this in my mind as I waited for my big brothers to emerge from the surf. Dad was sharing the latest cricket scores with Uncle Howard Emslie. Mom was talking to Aunt Doris Stirk about fauna and flora preservation.

"Come on, boys! We are heading home!" Dad yelled to them a second time, but the sound of a crashing crest drowned him out.

"NORMAN! BRUCE!" I had the loudest voice and the least patience.

Turning around, they put up one finger, indicating "give us one more minute."

My tummy was growling. The "washing off cobwebs" habit always worked up my appetite. I felt like screaming, "SHARK!" to get the boys to bolt, but then I thought better of it as my parents were present. We all knew full well that those were playful dolphins with the curly fins, speeding along the broad blue free spray.

"Let's just go without them," Wendy whined, wiping the salty drops off the tip of her nose with the towel neatly wrapped around her shoulders. "I want to go and read my book." We turned and reluctantly broke our tradition of always waiting for the whole family of six to come out of the water before strolling back to the shack.

"The water is perfect," Norman gasped as he ran to catch up with us. Bruce soon joined us. Absurdly enough, Bruce was the hardest one to get out of bed, but once he was in the sea, it was impossible to get him out of the swells. It felt heavenly to have my whole family together that day.

"The water is so clean, the fish won't even bite. The hook and sinker will be seen a mile away." Norman was wide awake now, and *full of beans* (energy). "Fish are not *that* stupid."

"Let's go and ask your Fischer cousins if they want to go up the beach with us. We'll have a picnic at Ship Rock." Mom was most cheerful in the mornings.

After a hot breakfast, Mother Hen gathered her chickens into the Land Rover. Dad tied on the fishing rods. He had his own red cool box for bait. It smelled fishy.

When we arrived at Ship Rock, there were already two blue Land Rovers parked on the high water mark. Their owners were standing on the shore, fishing.

"ANY LUCK?" Dad bellowed to Uncle Gower Dell, blocking out the sound of the running engine and the hissing waves.

"NO LUCK! The water is too clear!" He bellowed back and waved.

Dad parked in the shade at Ship Rock, a popular picnic spot. We all spilled over the sides of the truck with bright beach towels around our necks. I had a pink bucket and spade. Mom forced me to wear a big cloth hat in order to shade my face.

Dad and the boys baited up their hooks. They wrapped shearing elastic around the lobster to hold it firmly in place. At age seventeen, Bruce was quite capable of casting by himself, far out to sea.

Dad was still training Norman, who was only eleven. "Now, loosen the ratchet, and bring the rod back, like this, over your shoulder. Now swing it to the sea. The sinker will carry the line. You flick it, and then you hold the rod steady, like this, facing the sea. Never turn your back on the sea, my boy. You must always watch and be wide awake, so you can see a big wave before it hits you."

Mom had a pristine blue cool box, which she settled in the sand in the shade of a rock. She stood beside the picnic basket, holding a flask of hot tea. She poured it into insulated mugs before sitting back in the shade of her yellow beach umbrella to relax.

"Oh, look! The Dell ladies are here," Mom announced. "You can go and play with Mary-Rose. I shall chat with Aunty Joyce."

Familiar families had been going to Kasouga for generations. The Dells were the original family to start this oldest holiday resort on the Southern coast of Africa. No electricity or telephones had blemished the primeval camping experience. For miles in both directions, wild coastline stretched unspoiled, with no sign of human development. It took you back thousands of years in time.

Ship Rock looked like a small ship from far away; hence, its name. The hard rock formation had stood stoically above the eroding frothy waves, enduring eons of time. Ship Rock anchored herself on solid rock and withstood the high and low tides of life. Indeed, she was symbol of fortitude.

Mary-Rose and I played yearly in the deep rocky pools around Ship Rock. We collected shells and caught baby fish with our nets. We built sandcastles in the wet sand with our buckets and spades, adorning them with seaweed, shells, and driftwood.

Ship Rock was far removed from the wicked world. We could easily forget that the outside world even existed, a world with bothersome people. Schools of fish distracted us from the classes of education. The enchantment of the sea lured us to a respite from all such institutions and looming laws, both of land and school. This tranquil part of paradise was a perfect reprieve from reality. Somehow solitude and sea reminded me that someone superior created it all.

Mom always made me wear a modest, one-piece swimming *cozzy*. The sun tanned our little backs as we bent over, intently tiling the chimneys on our sandcastles with seashells. It was a perfect time in a perfect place with a perfect sun warming our backs.

Mary-Rose was my best "European" friend. Her family farm stood halfway between ours and Grahamstown. It was much too far to go and play at her house, but we did play at Carlisle Bridge occasionally, when her parents played tennis or cricket at the C.C. Club.

She had lovely honey-blonde hair and pretty, big blue eyes.

Mary-Rose was a talented tennis player, and she would always beat me. I would habitually hit the ball right out of the court, like "six runs" in cricket. The Xhosa kids who watched always clapped for me, thinking that was very spectacular.

"Keep your hat on, the sun is very hot," Mom warned as I defiantly took it off, only to put it right back on again. Parents watching can be bothersome. At least grand-ghosts never made you wear a hat nonstop.

"Let's go and swim in that big pool to cool off," I urged, already leading the way. Mary-Rose and I swam in a deep, natural Jacuzzi. Oysters and mussels clung to the sides of our wavy pool, opening and shutting, peeping at us like cuckoo clocks, helping us forget time for a moment.

But another clock was also ticking—one I tried to ignore—towards the rotten time when the train would transport me to teachers, "insisting on school."

The pool got deeper with each new wave and shallower as the tide ebbed. Seaweed of all shades grew on the rocks, swaying in the swirls. Edible sea snails called *gqongwes* hid under the rugged rocks. They only crawled out at night. They had hard white shells for front doors which they pulled shut for protection. Each front shell-door looked like a white pin-cushion. We paddled blissfully among our seafood delicacies.

Mary-Rose said, "My family loves to eat these sea snails with Worcestershire sauce."

"I have tasted them at your shack before. I love them, too." I was happy to have her as a friend; my family did not eat snails.

The Fischer family also pried oysters off the rocks and ate them raw. Norman tried one and told me it tasted like *snot* (boogers). I ate one, but did not like the texture on my tongue, so I spat it out. A squawking seagull scooped it up straight away. Black Mussels were chiseled off the rocks, and later boiled in buckets over an open fire for hors d'oeuvres, dipped in red wine vinegar. Squid or *inkfish* was also a delicacy used for bait, but doubled as dinner in the form of fried calamari on our seaside menu.

We discovered the white, oval flat backbone of a squid. Mary-Rose picked it up. "I'll give it to my aunt Mary for her budgie's cage." Birds like to peck them for extra calcium.

"At least you are not scared of the sea, Mary Rose, like Tombe," I mused out loud. Together, we explored star fish carefully crawling with their five legs, maneuvering and lodging on the rocks. Sea anemones enclosed our fingertips with circular fringes of short spaghetti. Baby crabs nipped our toes! Mother Nature's entertainment was both pretty and priceless.

"Yikes!" I yelped when a large octopus slid one of its long slimy tentacles out from under the rocks. It wrapped itself around my skinny ankle and latched onto my leg with its suction pads.

"HELP! DAD! HELP! BRUCE!" I screamed.

In an instant, my older cousin, Stephen Fischer, came running over, splashing with each step. He dove into the salty pool and swiftly yanked the tentacles off my foot.

"We can eat him for supper. He is a nice fat chap." Stephen was rather pleased with his catch of the day, weighing about four pounds.

As for myself, I felt distinctly like bait.

Wendy lay tanning in her new two-piece *cozzy* which she had bought herself in P.E. She had her nose in a love story, but she lifted it out to see 12-year-old Stephen, dangling the wet, wiggly octopus from a long stick.

The octopus had huge, knobby eyes that seemed out of proportion with the rest of its body. Searching and sucking desperately, its eight dripping tentacles waved freely. It was bidding a lonely farewell to its family.

"Don't you dare come near me with that slimy, creepy thing!" Wendy was not at all delicate about the delicacy.

"We are going to cook him for supper," Stephen baited, his mischievous grin wider than usual. "Do you want to come and eat supper at our shack?"

"No, thank you!" Wendy backed away slightly, pulling a face.

"I will come," I offered.

Wendy's teeth looked whiter in her grimace because her face

was tanned. The Johnson's baby oil made her glisten in the sunshine. Even her eyes looked greener and more brilliant. The sun does that. It ripens you when you are fifteen, just like fruit. She suddenly looked like a fully-grown woman.

"Look! He's got a bite!" Mom exclaimed, pointing at Bruce's bending fishing rod. Mary-Rose and I raced over to see what he had caught.

"It's a big one!" Bruce bragged. We could see the tip of his rod bending like a shepherd's crook under the weight. "I hope it is not a shark." Bruce reeled in rapidly.

"He's hooked a big one!" Dad cheered, as if we hadn't noticed, and he started reeling in his own line a little as well. Then Dad stuck his rod in a rod holder, which my Grandpa Stocks had welded from an old metal pipe, so he could come over to watch Bruce reel in whatever it was that was giving such a good fight.

"Steady now, my boy, reel him in slowly. You may snap the line if you are too jerky." Dad sounded like a sports coach, giving his son perpetual advice.

A dark streak in the sea appeared in the taller waves. It looked like a dark shadow of the log. Suddenly fins appeared as the fighting fish struggled desperately to reverse back from the shallow surf to the safety of the sea. The fish was splattering water frantically, trying to escape the shoreline with its tail fin.

Bruce maintained control, triumphantly reeling it in. The shiny hook was firmly pierced through the fat top lip. The catch was dripping teardrop diamonds of water. Its gills gasped, flapping hopelessly, regretting falling for the bait.

"You got him!" Mom exclaimed. "That fat fish will feed the family for a week."

"That's a good-sized Mussel Cracker." Dad was beaming proudly, "About…"

"UNCLE BOET, YOUR ROD!" Stephen Fischer was shouting and pointing frantically.

We all turned to see my Dad's rod get yanked out from the holder, which was now toppling over in the wet sand. Dad ran to retrieve his roving rod in the nick of time, as a roaring wave rushed to sock his ankles. He walked backwards from the water's edge while he reeled in another Mussel Cracker. We all cheered, grateful that Dad didn't lose his rod and reel or catch.

"What bait are you using?" a curious old-timer inquired. He had been watching the sports from nearby.

"*Crayfish* (Lobster)," Bruce responded politely.

"We'll have a feast of fish," Mom smiled jubilantly.

"Bring the scale, Bruce, let's weigh them." Dad was still a little embarrassed about almost losing his rod. "The scale is in the outside pocket of my tackle bag."

Bruce wiggled the hook out of the mouth of the fish, tearing the pierced lips. He hung it on the scale and used all his muscles to hold the Mussel Cracker up. "TWELVE POUNDS!" He announced it proudly, making sure we all heard. Cheers erupted.

"That's a beauty!" Dad grinned. "Righto, now let's weigh mine." Dad's was ten and a half pounds. Viewers applauded noisily.

"I think you cheated, my boy. Yours cannot possibly weigh that much more than mine! Did you stuff sinkers down its throat?" Dad pulled Bruce's leg.

"Only irresistible *crayfish* (lobster)!" Bruce was reveling in his triumph, "Once a fish tastes a tail, they will always bite, even if they can see a hook in it. It is the best bait."

I wondered how Bruce knew so much about the fish's previous diet, but I did not dare quiz the now-famous fisherman. I reflected on how he knew enough to catch a fish in unfavorable conditions. Fishing required a certain degree of skill, and then the rest relied on luck.

Bruce reaffirmed his fish facts. "The average fish caught here is from four to six pounds." He knew all about fish habits, even at the age of seventeen. I was always very proud of my big brother, Bruce Bester. He knew a lot about fishing, hunting, and cricket. Those were the things that counted most in the Eastern Cape. They established you as a real man.

Reality was starting to dawn on me, however, that Sindie and Tombe would not be able to enjoy all the things that I did. They were not going to be afforded the same lifestyle and opportunities that I had, because of both the color of their skin and the culture of their tribe. Not to mention monetary discrepancies. When I thought about that, I felt as if someone had stuck lead fishing sinkers down my throat and into my heart.

"Try this crayfish, Uncle Gower, you will get a bite." Bruce passed him a half-tail of I. & J. brand lobster.

"Thanks," he nodded. "They are not biting with *rooiaas* (redbait), that is for sure."

"Let's have lunch before you cast in your lines again," Mom suggested.

"No, thank you. The fish are biting," Dad declined. "You can go ahead and eat so long."

"Just one more cast," Bruce pleaded, baiting up his hook again. "Fish never fail to fall for lobster tail. Just like people never change, fish always fall for the same bait. A leopard never changes its spots!" Bruce now waxed philosophical, still preaching from his sand dune pulpit.

He did sound convincing, though, and he did have his proof of a big fish. Bruce's testimony persuaded a few men to change their bait, who were hoping to have the same luck.

"It must be low tide," Mom said, unpacking the Marmite and lettuce sandwiches. "Judy, please, will you offer the hard-boiled eggs around? Wendy, you may pour the cooldrink. The plastic mugs are in the basket over there." She pointed. "Maggie packed some cold chicken in, too, and these are cheese and peach chutney sandwiches."

"Thank you, Aunty Gwenna." Charles Fischer, my cousin who was my contemporary, eagerly reached for a sandwich.

"I brought crunchies to fill up the cracks." Mom announced the dessert menu.

"Goody-Goody-Gumdrops! I would love one!" Nicolas, my youngest cousin, held out his expectant hand. I loved all three Fischer boys dearly.

We saw Norman reeling in, but his rod was not bending. His bait was missing, so he had been standing there for ages, fishing with no bait. He put his rod down and waded through the soft dry sand towards us in a rather weary manner.

"No wonder I missed that big one. My bait fell off!" he said regretfully.

"Never mind, my boy. Better luck next time. Come and have some lunch," Mom said, holding out the sandwich as bait. Norm bit into it ravenously.

"Judy, will you please go and give Bruce a sandwich? He can fish and eat at the same time. He is still a growing boy," Mom insisted. "Daddy can wait." Mom knew Dad preferred to be seated when he ate.

As we reached Bruce, I saw Uncle Gower strike his rod back over his shoulder and start reeling in, his rod taut and bent.

"Look, my Dad's got a bite, too!" Mary-Rose pointed excitedly at Uncle Gower. He was a big burly man, a military commandant, as well as a Merino farmer. We watched him reeling in and walking towards the sea, with his straining, crooked rod.

There was an older fisherman with a hunched back nearby. He too declared his conversion, "Thank you very much, Brucey-boy! I'm going to give your crayfish idea a try now," we heard him say.

Great ideas must have a source, just like any river. Rains fall from the heavens, from dripping clouds. Thunderclouds are baked like white fluffy buns rising in the sky at hot temperatures from yeasty seas. Then muddy rivers with bursting banks recycle the roaring conglomerate of tiny drops straight back to the ocean. The circle of sea is simple, but how do *new* ideas form? Ideas must flow into a catchment area of the brain from somewhere. Why don't people study that fascinating subject at school?

The old, experienced fisherman's skin on his back was spotted with dark brown blemishes from exposure to the sun. Leathery skin wrinkled in layers where his love handles once were. His elbows were rough, and his arm hairs were snow-white, bleached from years of fishing. The rigid rod that he held upright was straighter than his own curved spine. He had had no luck.

Somehow, over the years, his back had calcified crooked, but not his brain. His mindset was still fluid like the deep blue swirls.

"After all is said and done, perhaps we are never too old to switch our bait." The crusty old coot appeared to be spilling his secrets to the surf. "An open mind is a deeper mind. We are humans, not leopards, we can change our spots." He simply tossed out Bruce's philosophy, as he changed his own bait. I heard him right there at Ship Rock, at the very Place of the Leopard.

In no time, his flexible rod was as bent as his back with a hefty catch!

18

IRON HEART

Back on Schelmdrift, I was feeling lonely. It was a feeling I didn't like much. All the servants had the Saturday off. My Xhosa friends had gone to a ritual party. My siblings had gone to town with my father. Mom had completed all my back to school shopping before the holidays and was relaxing with a book.

Sitting on the dirt slope with my back up against the cement silo, I was thinking very deeply. Fikile wasn't chopping wood, so there was total silence: no axe dividing logs into neat chunks; no clicking tongues to tell tales; no creaking windmills; no breeze tickling the trees. The trees stood at attention like silent soldiers. Not even the sun could melt the silence. Instead, it baked boredom in my breast.

A male Hoopoe was quietly probing the chips near the compost heap with its long skinny black bill. Its crested head feathers reminded me of the *rock spider* who swindled Mom for her Christmas cards. She was a most uncouth city slicker who stuck her beehive in the same space as my spittle in a very untimely manner.

I pondered time and space, wondering why they stood so silent, refusing to spill secrets. "Ideas" surely have a space, from whence they oft' times flowed…but where? If grand-ghosts are gawking at us all the time, are they guilty of giving us ideas? Can we return bad ideas like unwanted Christmas gifts if we do not like them?

A red ant crawled onto my bare foot. It rudely nipped into my skin, pinching like sharp tweezers. I impulsively squished it with my finger. That sucker was now just a faint smear in the dust.

"You deserved that," I told the luckless ant.

The sound of my words broke the silence for a second, but it only bounced back bigger and bolder.

Why did that ant live at all? Are we insignificant, too, like ants on the earth?

The Karoo sun brewed my thoughts to such frothy, dizzy heights that I now pondered the very reason for humans existing. A few more unsuspecting, innocent ants came creeping along. I squished them before they bit me. The reason for their existence seemed futile. One's reason to exist should reflect in your motto. Maggie's was most clear, "Eat, drink and be merry, for tomorrow we die."

Then I recalled that when Norman and I collected birds' eggs, ants had been somewhat useful. We punctured small holes in both ends of the eggs with a sewing needle. Then we carefully blew out the yolk and egg white. We hid the empty egg outside in a safe place, where no one would stand on the hollow shell. The ants crawled in the tiny hole and ate out the rest, preventing the egg collection from stinking too badly. Therefore, ants were quite useful, I decided, as long as they did not bite me. I still had not forgotten that Chris Bowker had rare Hadeda eggs, and that he did not share with me. The boy would not even swap one for a Guinea fowl egg. Stingy sod!

Presently, Rama came strolling down from the huts. He had picked up a stick and was waving it in the silent air. He came over my way.

"*Whenza ntoni?* (What are you doing?)" He asked.

"Nothing. I am bored," I replied.

"Me, too, I got left behind," he sighed, "Everyone went to Sunnyside to a *mgidi* (initiation feast), I was going to follow, but…"

"Let's ride the horses!" I suggested enthusiastically.

"Great idea!" he responded with a sudden gleam of hope.

Xhosa girls didn't ride horses, so Sindie and Tombe never wanted to ride with me. Occasionally, I enjoyed hunting, riding horses and fishing for frogs with Norman and his Xhosa mates, but my brother was not around.

"I'll go and harness the horse. Miss Judy, you go and ask for permission for me to ride, and get me a treat please," Rama directed, as he sauntered off to the car garage where the bridles hung against the silent cement wall. "Everyone is too afraid to ride Iron Heart. He is wild. So I'll only get one bridle. We can both ride Rex." Rama obviously doubted himself.

"Uligwala gqhitha! (You are a real coward!)" I called after him, clicking in Xhosa, a little annoyed. Why couldn't he be manlier, like Tatey? Rama had no Daddy to emulate.

"It's all right. We can take turns, or ride together. Norman and I have done it often," Rama tried to appease me.

"No, I want to ride Iron Heart!" I shouted as I got up and brushed the dust and sticks off the bottom of my khaki shorts. "Get two bridles."

"No! You are dilly. He'll run away with you. There's only one dad on the whole farm brave enough to ride that wild horse…and that's Jack." He spoke disrespectfully, using Jack's name.

In Xhosa, it is not polite for a child to use an adult's actual name. He should have said "Bhoyi's Dad," or "Ping Ping's Dad." But I didn't correct him. Rama was named after a brand of soft yellow margarine. He was a full-blooded Xhosa, but he had no idea who his father was.

"And you should know that Jack has been thrown off a few times, and almost cracked his skull. You will not be allowed to ride that horse," Rama grunted.

"Just get two bridles," I ordered, letting him know by the tone of my voice that he was the son of a servant, and therefore my servant, too. I understood how the food chain of authority worked. I was the daughter of the boss, and he was the son of a servant.

"Yes, *Nomhankazi.*" Rama slinked back reluctantly to retrieve another bridle. "No wonder my mother named you 'headstrong.' Once you get an idea in your head, it cannot escape."

"I'll meet you back here, with two horses," I clarified, itching for a ride.

"You will get killed! I will never ride Iron Heart!" he yelled over his skinny shoulder, making sure I didn't expect him to risk his life.

As I entered the house, silence engulfed me. Only if you live in a house in the middle of nowhere can you fully understand that kind of stillness. I found Mom deeply engrossed in her book. With ample soft pillows and a good novel to absorb her attention, she was an easy target. She did not want to be bothered. A perfect time to ask for favors!

I had discovered it was better to announce than to ask, so I merely notified her. "I'm going horse riding with Rama."

"Righto." She was not really listening with both ears, mumbling her consent.

In the pantry, I found a few peaches begging loudly to be eaten, so I stuffed my pockets. Rama loved peaches. He always ate the whole peach, skin and all.

Sometimes, I felt a slight tinge of joy that I was born white. Xhosa girls traditionally never wore shorts, and they always had to wear skirts. Also, horse riding was considered taboo for females in Sindie and Tombe's culture.

I refrained from telling Mom about Iron Heart, which only made my heart beat faster with excitement. It was the perfect antidote for my boredom. Omitting details reminded me of Dad, the day he bought Iron Heart…

"I got a big bargain at Th-Stockfair!" Dad slurred one day when he got home later than usual from his monthly trip to town.

Dad was not happy that the ten rand note with the Africander stud bull on it was green, instead of red like his spotless herd. Then his friend at the pub told him not the worry, the Jews had picked the ten rand notes before they were ripe. Dad had been celebrating for getting the top price for his Merino sheep after Stockfair. His celebrations entailed swigging from green bottles plucked prematurely off a shelf at noon at the Grand Hotel.

"What bargain?" Mom was displeased that he had spent too much time and money in the men-only bar at the Grand Hotel.

"A horthe!" His tongue was not quite coordinated.

"A whore?" Mom frowned furiously.

"No, I th-said race h-o-r-s-e!" Dad tried more carefully, steadying his hand to light a fancy cigar. "And I bought you and Judy each a Ki-Kat."

"What do you need a race horse for?" Mom quizzed. "And we don't need any more cats. Have a heart…have you not noticed all our kittens?"

"It is a well-bred *horthse. What'ths more*, it has good bloodlines, jolly good *bloodlineths,"* Dad expanded, swaying on his feet. "And I bought you both a chocolate Kit-Kat, not a cat." He took a sip of the strong coffee she brewed for him.

"Well, you have no business buying race horses; we just needed a horse to herd cattle. It doesn't have to be a thoroughbred." She was clearly ticked off. She had too many brains to ever drink in excess. "Moderation in all things" was Mother's motto.

"Thiths horthse was very *th-stubborn.* They couldn't break him in. *Hiths* name *iths* Iron Heart, because they literally couldn't change *hiths* heart!" Dad heartily shared.

"Thanks for the chocolate." She kissed him on his cheek.

Dad knew Mother's sweet spot. She loved her Kit-Kats.

"So, how much did you pay for this Iron Hearted horse?" Her practical mind was eager to assess the financial erosion after Father's flood of liberality.

"Not much. A real bargain, he *waths.* He got flogged off cheaply. A *rathce horthse* for a farm *horthse,* I'll *th-say!* I landed him for nothing."

"For nothing?" Mom knew his foolhardy shopping spree was not free.

"Well, a few 'bob,' only," Dad said, still omitting to fully disclose exactly what he had paid. ("Bob" was a nickname for a shilling which was worth ten pennies.)

"Exactly how many 'bob' did you pay for the silly horse, may I ask?" Mom was relentless in her interrogation.

"Oh, by the way, I bought a new Land Rover, too, the newest model," Dad confessed. "That was a few more bob than the *horthse.* Did you *notithce* I picked a tan one *thiths* year? Your favorite color!" Dad became notoriously more jovial and generous after a few beers.

"How was I supposed to notice it's a new Land Rover? It is dark outside already. You always buy the new model every year! I was expecting you home hours ago. I was very worried about you.

I am glad you did not land it the ditch, bargains and all!" Mom scolded.

My father was not a heavy drinker, after he saw his father suffer and die from liver sclerosis, when Dad was only sixteen. But he did enjoy celebrating success with a few cold beers in the pub. My mother saw to it that he did not get any ideas about doing it regularly.

After about a year, Iron Heart had thrown off most riders, including Bruce, and most never got back on. Jack was the only one who would remount. One must not omit to mention that Jack, indeed, had a way of charming women and horses alike. He talked in soft tones and hypnotized the horse. I suspected Jack used a little of his black magic.

Our two herding horses, Iron Heart and Rex, ran wild behind our homestead. I went back to meet Rama at the garage, but he had not yet returned, so I sat on the cement ramp, contemplating how lucky we had been. Dad had paid a few "bob" for a very good horse. Or was it actually a bad horse? It was certainly a disobedient horse. Many tried to train him, but deep down, his heart was made of iron. It would not budge with a halter. It was not soft like a sheep's heart.

I waited and waited and waited for Rama to return.

The movement of a Hoopoe bird, with similar Springbuck tricolors, drew my attention to the wood pile. There was blood on the ground where the lamb's blood had spilled the day before. When Dad was working sheep, and the dipping tank pen was bustling with the herd, Dad's laborers would open each sheep's mouth for Dad to count its front teeth. Dad would randomly pick a *two-tooth* to be slaughtered. He knew their lamb meat was most tender when the full grown sheep only had two incisors. Sheep grow two incisors per year until they have eight. Their back molars are used to crunch Karoo bush leaves, adding extra ingrained flavor to the meat.

Dad would also give an old ewe, which had finished lambing, with all eight incisors, to the servants as part of their rations. Their meat was called "mutton." It had to be cooked a lot longer before human teeth could even chew it up.

Our threesome regularly watched as two Xhosa dads and a few *kwediens* (youth), slaughtered sheep.

First, a knife would be sharpened on a smooth stone by the woodpile. When they slit the jugular vein, the lamb would bleat loudly and kick desperately. The blood squirted out into to dish, spilling on the wood chips. Gradually, its bleats would get quieter and quieter, until the lamb went silent. Lambs died without blood, and fish expired without water. Blood-born oxygen is needed in the veins to sustain life, or else life is lost to the thriving food chain. The Xhosa word for "spirit" and "air" and "wind" is the same word, *umoya.* So could that be a clue? What if ideas enter the brain surfing on oxygen molecules from the air? Spirits could blow ideas into your brain up your nose, perhaps? Maybe that was why the Xhosas used copious amounts of snuff up their noses to get rid of evil spirits. They apparently blew the bad buggers out by sneezing violently.

Xhosas peeled the woolly skin from the lifeless meat with short strokes of a knife, while the lamb lay belly-up, like a pink, sunburned lady tanning on a cushy woolen towel. Because the lamb's un-skinned head was still styled with shaggy wool around its cheeks, the meat did remind me of a blonde lady who only protected her face from the Kasouga sun. Her fair face was framed with bleached curls, while her body was roasted to a lobster pink.

Secondly, helpful *kwediens* (male adolescents) each held a cloven hoof. Then as soon as the stomach cavity was cut open, the gall bladder was quickly squeezed shut and sliced off, preventing spills of bitter bile. The little sac was tossed into the thorn bushes, sprinkling molten golden bile on its flight.

Next, the soft maroon liver and the purplish kidneys were put in a clean dish. A child was sent to deliver the organs to our kitchen, where Maggie fried them with onions for our supper. Sometimes, Maggie saved the kidneys to bake steak and kidney pie.

Lastly, they chopped open the head of the lamb with an axe. They sent the brain to Maggie to boil. Cool sheep's brains taste like the marrow found in a chop bone; it is the same texture on the tongue as the spinal marrow. Dad and I enjoyed sheep's brains mashed up on toast, seasoned with salt and pepper. Mom refrained from eating brains. She was a delicate lady raised on a pineapple plantation.

The lamb's heart was soft to the touch. My inquisitive fingers had felt the tough muscle; it was definitely not made of steel! We never ate the heart, but our servants *braaied* (barbequed) the tough heart over hot coals. My probing fingers had handled all the internal organs of a lamb before. The pale pancreas and lungs felt spongier. The servants never wasted any edible part of the lamb. They ate all the intestines, and the head, and the feet, despite the fact that they were given a whole tough old ewe to chew.

Rama looked weary as he walked towards me between Iron Heart and Rex. I held Iron Heart's reins while Rama saddled the chestnut mule and tightened his girdle. Rex was very docile, like a placid old man. He was a bit *long in the tooth* (old).

"Rex is a good boy," Rama said encouragingly. "He obeys!" He shortened the stirrups because his legs were not quite as long as Yan's, who had recently ridden Rex to herd sheep.

"Nohanki, jump up and ride behind me!" Rama tried to be persuasive. "That gray horse is too wild. I could hardly catch him. Jack mentioned he was gray like a donkey. He said it is because Iron Heart must have stubborn donkey ancestors."

"No, I am going to ride Iron Heart. He is mostly white, with a few gray mottled spots. He looks as if he should be pure white but someone has splashed charcoal paint on his coat. The horse breathed on me—he is not afraid of me. I am too little to hurt him. He is sniffing the peaches in my pockets." I could talk the hind legs off a donkey.

Rama reluctantly took a second saddle off a pole on the wall. As he tried to hoist the saddle onto Iron Heart, the horse opened his eyes wide. There was ire in his eyes as he refuted the air out his stretched nostrils. Iron Heart blew the idea of being saddled out of his nostrils, rejecting it entirely.

Rama, not quite a teenager, wasn't quite tall enough to heave the heavy saddle high enough. "Hold the horse!" he shouted as Iron Heart shied backwards.

"Wait, Rama, wait!" I commanded.

"What?" He was visibly irked at the spoiled brat white kid who always got her way.

"Iron Heart doesn't like saddles. Leave it off. Hang the saddle back up," I ordered, acting like a grownup.

Rama shook his head in apparent disapproval.

"Well, let me loosen him then," Rama was relieved, trying to take the reins.

"No, I am going to ride him bareback," I declared, yanking the reins back.

"That is a very bad idea." Rama released a big sigh of defeat. "You are free to dismiss that idea."

"You are a servant and have to do whatever I tell you to do."

As a bribe, I gave Rama two yellow cling peaches out of my pockets, one for his hungry stomach and one to stop his mouth from telling anyone.

It was a hot balmy afternoon. There were no adults around for Rama to report to. He wouldn't dream of going to the house where my Mom had her nose in a library book.

"I need a helping hand, Rama," I entreated.

Rama hid one peach in his pocket and held the half-eaten one in his teeth. He locked his fingers to make a temporary stirrup for me so I could mount Iron Heart.

The horse jerked a little as Rama flung the reins over its head to me. I reined him in tightly, which made the bit uncomfortable in the horse's mouth. I wanted to let him know who was boss. Iron Heart was already reversing. Rama was munching and mounting simultaneously. Iron Heart didn't seem too distressed. I was only a waif of a child. He kept looking at Rama and I realized that his iron heart desired the peaches.

"Give him some peach!" I told Rama.

"You've got high hopes," Rama stuffed the entire half into his mouth and shut his thick lips. He gobbled up the mass, hardly chewing it at all.

I leaned down and whispered a promise to Iron Heart. "I will give you a peach, Iron Heart, if you are a good boy," I purred, stroking his mane and neck. I spoke to the horse in Xhosa so Rama could understand, too. "I pledge to give you two peaches if you swear not to buck me off." I tried to sound soothing like Jack.

"What a waste!" Rama scoffed. "Animals should not eat better than people."

We walked the horses through the cattle kraals that a skilled stonemason had built *donkey's years* (many years) ago for my great-grandfather. Sindie, Tombe and I had previously enjoyed much amusement watching calves being branded "BB" there. Protective long-horned cows did not consent to their young being separated from them very gracefully. Neither did they approve of seeing their offspring partially barbequed with a red hot branding iron. Many a man vaulted the walls with a wild disapproving cow chasing after him, waving its white horns viciously.

Mossies (Cape sparrows) were feeding their chickens with *gogo's* (insects) in their nests tucked between the rocks of the empty cattle kraal. One perched on the gate with a hairy-poo-poo worm in its mouth. Masses of the sparrows serenaded us as we paraded by like royalty.

We rode down through Bumpy where Tombe and Sindie and I had performed rituals with frogs' eggs, but those rituals had not come to fruition after a whole year. The summer sun had sucked up the stream. There were no longer any pools to be seen.

We waded through the dry sandy bed of Bumpy, following the Land Rover tracks. The boys had packed river rocks on the banks to prevent soil erosion. Dad was, after all, the chairman of the Soil Conservation Committee. The Land Rover engine always exerted a lot of horse power to struggle up one particular bank in low gear.

I had no saddle, so I had to clutch onto the horse with all my might up that steep rocky bank. Secure in the knowledge that a horse's mane can't slip off, I clung on to the horse hairs for dear life. I tried to dig my bare toes into the horse's sides, using his rib-bones for stirrups. All he needed was oxygen to key his ignition. My legs felt his ribs expand for fresh fuel as he accelerated us up and revved over the embankment.

"I am glad you never threw me off on those loose rocks, Iron Heart. That's one peach earned!" I promised, in a husky whisper.

Rama was most surprised to see me smiling safely high on top of the mottled machine.

"Rex is the King!" Rama praised, thrilled to be riding under the open sky. He was lost in the luxury of riding and eating his second peach. Sheer pleasure!

On two parallel dirt tracks, where the Land Rover wheels had worn away the Karoo bushes, we rode side by side on the plateau called, "the flats."

"Let's race!" We sat lightly like jockeys, mere feathers on the backs of our mighty steeds.

"No." Rama didn't want to disturb the peaceful pace.

"I'm going to let Iron Heart run," I declared. As I loosened the reins, he stuck out his neck, sensing liberty. He could smell freedom in his stretched nostrils.

"Let's gallop!" I spurred his ribs with my bare heels. Iron Heart took off and I almost got left behind in the big sky, free from any specific gravitational force. Cleaving onto his mane, I glued myself to his horse power. At this point, I was the one most surprised to still be attached to the horse!

The wind blasted into my lungs. I only had to exhale. Inhaling was done automatically by the headwind. My lungs were blown up like birthday balloons. My face was so low I could taste his sweaty mane. I felt one with Iron Heart. His wild streak seemed to inject itself into my soul, elevating levels of pure adrenalin.

My horse was turbo charging for miles toward the Fish River. I was powerless to stop my racing heart. But the road would end at the Fish River. Nature would stop him eventually. I had less fear now; instead, I felt sheer exhilaration for remaining bonded to Iron Heart and gratitude for still having my own heart beating inside my chest.

Rama was lagging a bit behind, but not too far. My hair blew off my face. If it hadn't been so deeply rooted, it would have blown off my head. Rama's hair never stirred at all in the wind. It resembled a well-glued black carpet, encircling his skull like a matted crash helmet.

"Come on Rama, you can't let a little girl beat you!" I taunted, turning defiantly and taking a slight speed wobble but quickly steadying myself.

"You will die if you look back! Hold on! Don't look back!" he yelled. "Miss Judy, only look forward!"

Flying across the flats had created beads of sweat, and the exerted animal started to smell musty. The thirsty Karoo air couldn't suck up his sweat fast enough.

Eventually, I felt Iron Heart slow down his pace as his stamina was spent. A small dam glimmered in the sun to our left. His nostrils detected the water and he leaned left. "He is thirsty," I informed Rama. "Let's take them for a drink."

I steered Iron Heart off the straight, narrow road into the wild Karoo veldt, toward the muddy dam. However, he did not need my guidance as much as I liked to assume. Rama followed in single file on Rex.

His hooves kneaded the mud, much like Maggie's fists indented soft brown bread dough. His head approached the welcome water. Iron Heart's un-cloven hooves sloshed into the dam, making him seem a little shorter. All of a sudden, the ground—or should I say, water—seemed closer.

Rama pulled Rex to a halt next to me. I envied his saddle and the stirrups for his feet. We allowed them a loose rein to drink. I knew Iron Heart couldn't run away with me. His unbridled vigor was depleted. As Iron Heart lowered his head to slurp up the dirty water, I slid down his sweaty neck like a slippery slide ride. Only his big ears stopped my descent into muddy damnation.

"You will get dipped!" Rama chuckled. He was sort of happy that I was still alive. "That horse almost baptized you!"

Leisurely, we walked those weary horses home; it took the better part of the afternoon. The whole Karoo seemed thirsty. A Karoo bush's tiny round leaves retained sap longer than flat leaves that had larger surfaces for evaporation. Hardy plants adapted to dry conditions somehow. Karoo flowers were tiny yellow balls, the size of a pea, with no visible petals. They just looked like little puff balls of pollen. Plants change to survive in a miraculous way.

During a bad drought, Mom and I harvested little balls of Karoo flowers. Mom showed me the seeds at the base of the ball during

Nature Study. We gently crushed the flowers, exposing the slender seeds.

A very handy idea was shared in the *Farmer's Weekly.* We followed the magazine's advice, making dozens of clay cakes implanted with tiny seeds; we put them in the dry sun to bake on a baking sheet. After a few days, the mud balls were dried hard, like rusks. We walked around the veldt and dropped the balls on the barren soil. *NoLasti* said they would last there until the rains came. The seeds would grow and cover those ugly bare patches. Dad remarked that it would also prevent the soil from eroding. It was a brilliant idea and it worked!

"Look at those Springbuck, Rama. Do you see them? Shall we chase them? Just to see them jump?" I loved to watch them *pronk* about.

"Hayi (No), Miss Judy. We rode far already," Rama sounded like a tired tourist. "We usually don't go this far. We had better get home before they start hunting for you."

"We rode a bit too far," I admitted, noticing the sun starting to sink. "I'm going to give Iron Heart two peaches. Rex likes sugar. I will give him sugar cubes."

"I want sugar cubes, too; don't waste them on a horse!" Rama grumbled.

"OK, I will give you some, Rama," I promised. "You are a good boy, too."

"Thank you," he said with a grin.

"Iron hearts can soften if you promise them rewards. You see, Rama, Iron Heart is 'Soft Heart' now. He just needed to smell the fresh peaches. Iron Heart craved peaches so badly, that he decided he could behave after all!" I concluded as we descended the banks of Bumpy.

"You are just very lucky, Miss Judy. I think I am lucky too, because if you fell off, I would have the same fate as the policeman's dog. Your father would shoot me. Except for Jack, none of our old people will ride that horse."

Perhaps it was a bad idea, but luckily my grand-ghosts had guarded me from gravity that day, just as they had when I went flying down a hill on a go-cart with no brakes.

"Thanks. We don't have to *always* copy our old people, Rama." I smiled at him. "Think about it. We do not have to be copycats. We are not cats, like leopards. I heard that from an ancient fisherman at the Place of the Leopard."

He slowed down. "I am going to dismount in Bumpy because I hid a Hadida egg there for you. While you were away, at the Place of the Leopard, with my mom at the seaside, I found a nest with two big blue eggs in it. I took one for you. I tried to blow it out after making holes with a safety pin. Very little came out. There was blood mixed in the egg white. It was too late in the breeding season. I think the chicken had started to grow already. So I hid it under those bushes, hoping the ants would eat it out clean."

"Thank you, Rama! You earned your sugar cubes. I will throw in a pineapple as well. Just make sure you save the peels for your mom." I was ecstatic about the egg.

The Hadeda Ibis egg was perfectly cleaned out by the hungry ants; I felt renewed appreciation for the purpose of ant's lives! All of God's creatures have a purpose and a place in time, even if it was simply to be part of the cleansing chain. Why do we exist, if not to propel forward on a mission of sorts? Changing iron hearts to soft hearts would need huge horsepower of motivation. Lobster bait or some other irresistible incentive was needed to hook into our souls and change our hearts.

19

BOARDING SCHOOL

The dreaded day dawned in January of 1966. It was the day I started at Collegiate Junior School for Girls, alias, "The Snob School."

Our neatly-packed brown suitcases sat in the hallway by the telephone door. My mother had carefully prepared each luggage label in her neat handwriting. She clearly wrote our names and farm address, just in case the luggage got lost. The stiff paper labels had reinforced rings around the holes through which white string was firmly tied.

"Eat your vegetables, Judy." Mom was rather brusque at midday dinner.

"I am not very hungry." My farm life was being pulled to an abrupt halt.

"You have to eat everything they put in front of you at boarding school. So you'd better learn to eat everything," Wendy scared me even more.

School began in January and ended in November. For the first and last terms, we wore blue dresses with white socks, black shoes, and white panama hats. During the two winter terms, we wore navy pinafores, white shirts, stripy ties and straw bashers. Navy blazers with badges on the pockets were worn all year round. Under each badge was a scroll that read, "Facta Non Verba." That is a Latin motto meaning, "Deeds not Words."

"Eat up, my girl." Dad was attempting to sound plucky. "*Righto* then, we have to leave soon. We must pack the suitcases in the car, straight after dinner. We don't want to be rushed."

Jane came in to remove the dirty dishes. She looked at me quizzically, and whispered, *"Akulambhanga, Miss Judy?* (Are you not hungry, Miss Judy?)"

"Andifuni ukutya. (I don't want to eat.)" I whispered, feeling my throat closing.

She quickly put another plate over mine in one swift sleight of the hand movement. Her deft fingers created an optical illusion by placing Bruce's empty plate on top. Only I could see that the rice and gravy were squishing onto her tray.

"OonTombise baphandle (Tombe and company are outside)," She whispered in my ear.

I suddenly realized how much I loved Jane. She had been there all my life. She was the epitome of meekness, an emblem of humility, and an example of obedience. She never expected much from life. She was satisfied with her life, and had a cheerful disposition and was extremely grateful for the smallest favors. It made us want to help her more. How I would miss her genuine, generous compliments! Her calm spirit was a great source of strength to me. Plus, she seemed to have magic powers for finding my misplaced belongings. How would I survive without my Jane?

After wiping my mouth clean with my linen *serviette* (napkin), I started threading it back into my silver serviette ring with my name engraved on it. "You needn't put it in the holder; Lizzie will wash and iron it." Mom struggled to mask her emotions.

I went to the kitchen. There they all gathered: Maggie, Jane, Lizzie, Toto, Tombe, and Sindie. The girls had come to bid me farewell. Their bodies and the woodstove made the room warmer than the rest of our home.

Of course, Jane, who was less shy in the kitchen, was the first to speak. *"Akusemhle, Miss Judy. Iyakufanela gqitha le uniform!* (You are so beautiful, Miss Judy. This uniform suits you very well!)" She said, clapping her hands, but her delight was a little restrained. Then she covered her mouth with her hands and admitted bashfully, *"Uzakusishiya nesithukuthezi!* (You are leaving us behind with boredom for company!)"

Lizzie was probably thinking how much less laundry she would have. "Don't crease your school uniform before you get there." She pulled it straight. "I just ironed it."

Maggie was braver than usual. After making sure my mother was not about, she hugged me hard enough to intentionally crumple my dress, and boldly kissed me on the top of my head. Then in attempt to ease the pain with humor, she teased, *"Haba siza kuphiwa ngubani na ngoku iswekile?* (Now who is going to supply us with sugar?)" She shook my shoulders and held my cheeks in her hands. She kissed me on the forehead.

"Andiyazi. (I don't know.)" I wondered about that also.

Tombe queried, "And who will cook stew with us in our miniature hut?" The girls huddled near the back door, where Sindie nodded in agreement.

"We made the nicest stew yesterday…I am still full from our final feast." Sindie sighed. "Your uniform is much better than ours. I want to go with you, Miss Jay. Your socks are so white. And your black shoes have laces. Are you sure they are not putting you in boys' shoes?" Sindie inspected me with envy.

"No, Sindie." Toto corrected. "Those are proper school shoes."

"You are the lucky ones. I wish I could stay home and go to school at Carlisle Bridge." I managed with a wobbly voice.

"Please bring us nice things to eat from P.E." Tombe put her arm on mine gently. "You will eat very well."

"Don't ever forget us," Sindie added, also squeezing my shoulders affectionately.

"Don't crinkle her uniform, Sindie," Lizzie chided. "They mustn't think she comes from a home where the maids don't know how to iron clothes properly."

Mom bustled into the kitchen. "This is where you are! The car is loaded. Say goodbye nicely and jump into the car." She guided me out with her arm on my back.

I took one last blurry walk down the long passage and through the hall. Four kudu heads on hunting trophies stared at me with glass eyes. The mute stuffed animals couldn't say goodbye. They had no voice.

I sniffed with angst, "Goodbye, home!"

"Don't cry now," Mom said stiffly. "Bruce, Norman, Wendy, all of you, come and say goodbye to the maids this instant." She slipped into her bedroom to get her box camera. "At once, please children!"

"Shake a leg! We have to leave in five minutes! We can't be late for her first day!" Dad was stifling emotion with efficiency.

The car's boot gaped open, loaded with luggage. I heard familiar footsteps and turned around to see Sindie and Tombe, running around the front of our house towards me. Tombe's eyes were red, but her mouth was smiling broadly.

Sindie lifted my skirt slightly and bent down and peered up my skirt. "You have uniform panties too?" She was surprised by my thick navy polyester underwear. She studied my new uniform from head to toe, scrutinizing the differences.

Bruce saw her peeping, and frowned at us. Tombe noticed Bruce's disapproval, and promptly slapped Sindie's hand off my skirt.

"All the girls have to wear the same panties and hats too," I stated.

"Your shoes look strong. They won't wear out if you have to walk far," Tombe said in an effort to cover up for Sindie's manners, or lack thereof.

Then Tombe placed her right hand over my heart. "You must be happy in your heart. But don't you dare forget us! We will not forget about you." She swore an oath with authority.

"I will never forget you." I cried.

The rest of my family poured out the two front doors, followed by our clicking uniformed maids, who huddled shyly in the driveway to wave goodbye.

"Stand still please, Judy. Let me *take a snap of you* in your uniform." Mom took a photo of me with her black box camera. "You look very neat and tidy, my girl." She stiffened her upper lip.

Mom was notoriously selective with praise. She believed it was improper to shower girls with compliments, fearing that we might succumb to the traps of vanity. Vanity and pride were two of her pet hates. "Pride is a trap for people whose noses were too high to notice the spring gun!" Mom had once said.

"Come on, climb in." Dad was trying not to drag out the farewell too long.

"Yoo! Hayi, Miss Judy! Ufana no Miss Windy ngoku. Ungumtwana wesikholo nyani. Akusemhle! Uzakubogqhitha bonke. (Wow! No, Miss Judy! You match Miss Wendy now. You truly are a school child now. You will surpass all of them in beauty!)" Jane's heartfelt compliments rang in my ears.

As we drove around the old pepper tree, I glanced back at the sturdy homestead that was built in 1900. Tombe and Sindie waved rather feebly, standing arm in arm. Maggie was wiping her nose on her white apron. That was not usually acceptable, but excusable on this day. Dad drove out of the wrought iron gate, the words "Schelm" and "Drift" written in white iron on each half of the black gate.

My siblings sat in silence. They had learned to hold it in. I started to sob.

"We must be strong. You'll make new friends at school. There's nothing we can do about it, so don't cry." Mom was patting me on the shoulder, trying to reassure me. I swallowed hard, but the tears just kept squirting from my eyes.

Bruce sat behind Dad. He had just celebrated his 18th birthday. This was his final matric year at Grey High School for Boys. He was sporting his "Colors" blazer. It was called a "white" blazer, but it was actually cream with gray ribbon all around the edge. It was a prestigious honor to have "Cricket" scrolled under his school badge. Norman wore the regular grey blazer.

Bruce had been awarded his "Colors" blazer for outstanding performance on the cricket field, setting him apart like a stark white *cob* (male swan) among many grey goslings. Bruce was an outstanding batsman, coached by Mr. James Dean.

Sensing the mood of his gloomy brood, Dad said cheerily, "This Zephyr was a good buy. The boot is just big enough. I managed to fit all four suitcases in. It was a tight squeeze, but we managed. Good thing we didn't buy the car with bucket seats in the front. Judy fits in between us perfectly." He patted me on the knee. "You are going to settle down and be happy." I loved Daddy for his unrivalled optimism.

At least Tombe and Sindie had each other. I felt so lonely sandwiched between my mom and dad. We drove to Port Elizabeth very slowly.

"I don't want to go too fast; we've got a heavy load," Dad explained. Cars sped past us by the dozen as our cumbersome family car ambled along. Dad prided himself in punctuality. He always allowed an extra half hour for the drive to Port Elizabeth, just in case we had a puncture.

"We've got plenty of time," Mom noted. "We'll drop Judy off first. She has to be at the hostel by five. All the others have to be there by six. We can help her unpack and see her new dormitory."

The torturous trip finally came to an end when Dad pulled his wide two-toned tortoise up to Annerley House on Annerley Terrace in Port Elizabeth.

"I wish I could run away!" I sobbed from the stationary car.

"You haven't arrived yet," Wendy said. "It's not that bad."

"My girly, you simply can't do that. All the others have managed to adjust." Mom's steely resolve tolerated no nonsense. "I'll write to you every Wednesday and post the letter with the bus. You must write to us every Sunday also, see? I will look forward to getting your letters, my pet. I packed enough stamps with your stationery in your leather writing case."

"Just do whatever they tell you to do—it's easier to obey the rules, my girl," was all Daddy could muster. He had learned discipline from his days at boarding school and the military. He was sucking harder than ever on his pipe, wishing away this painful moment. He heaved my new big suitcase out and handed it to Bruce. "Norman, come and carry her smaller school case, please."

I could see Norman's lip quiver and he began to tear up, fighting hard to control himself. Bruce looked agitated, like he needed a cigarette, but he was not allowed to smoke. The boys carried my luggage like gentlemen. They had been taught good manners.

"Bruce, Wendy and Norman will see you at Church on Sundays, my pet. Then they will come and visit you on Sundays for visiting hours between 3 and 5 p.m., won't you?" They all nodded, committed to put family before friends. Mom tried desperately to squeeze some cheer from her other three children.

"Don't forget we are Methodists. So when the girls line up for church, get in the Methodist line. Otherwise, you'll end up at the Anglican Church and not find us," Wendy warned.

"Make sure you go to the right church." Dad confirmed.

"It's tough," Bruce said, turning away to compose himself privately so no one could see the cricket cob's soft side. He turned back to comfort me. "But it goes fast. Look at me. It feels like yesterday was my first day. Now I'm almost finished. It will go quickly for you too, Judels."

"I'm just starting! (Sniff.) I've got eight years left! I am only nine! (Sniff.)"

"You had better leave your pipe in the car. You can't smoke in the hostel," Mom pointed out. Dad went back and tossed his wooden pipe into the *cubby hole* (glove compartment).

We all stood at the door. Mom rang the bell twice.

"It's 4:15 p.m. exactly," Mom calculated while we waited. "We are a little early."

"Luckily we never got a puncture." Bruce's voice dripped with sarcasm as he pressed the doorbell again.

A thin weed of a man came to the door.

"Good afternoon. We are the Besters. This is our daughter, Judy," Dad introduced us very politely. He even lifted his hunter green hat. "How do you do?"

"How do you do?" Mom smiled, using her most charming voice. She was extending her hand and hoping to find favor with the skinny runt at the door, supposing it might transfer favorably over to me.

"You're very early." The minute he opened his mealy mouth, I cringed in disgust. "We're only expecting the girls at five o'clock." Suddenly recalling his manners, usually displayed on such occasions of introduction, he stammered, "I am Mr. Crimer."

I could tell he was a schmuck right away. He was a sniveling, shrunken figure, with narrow shoulders and pallid skin. Black hair covered his lily-white, effeminate hands. He wore thick, black-rimmed spectacles which blew his eyes out of proportion like a *nagapie* (bush baby). He stood with his feet in the "ten past ten" pose. He was a townie, a foreign breed. I chose then and there to despise him.

"We came early on purpose so we could help Judy unpack." My mother's charm cleverly became assertiveness delivered with a sticky sweet smile.

"We can wait in the car," Dad suggested politely, reversing from that odious breed of a male that Dad labeled as "pansies," but not to their fragile faces.

"No!" Mom objected. "Boet, you have to see Judy's dormitory."

Turning her frocked frame to Mr. Crimer, she gushed, "Please may we all come and see her room before it gets too crowded? We like to know where our children sleep. So when we think of them, we can imagine them safely in their beds at night."

"Certainly, with pleasure Mrs. Bester," he replied with no pleasure at all. He had no ammo with which to combat this redheaded beauty. "I just hope the matrons are ready up there." He turned to look up the stairs. "Mrs. Reddie! May the Besters come up? Their *newpot* (new girl) is here." He spared me a fake smile. I stared back in pure disgust.

"Yes, please do. We have placed her in the Green Room," an ancient voice floated down the stairs.

At least Mrs. Reddie had some manners, I thought, forgetting to cry. Dad had politely taken off his hat and now held it in his hand. My whole family was ushered upstairs to a room with five *single* (twin) beds, small metal bedside lockers, and bigger hanging lockers. Two large windows let in light through little French panes. The pale green walls were clinical and clean. The wide wooden-beamed floor reminded me of our farmhouse. We could hear a driver *blow his hooter* (honk his horn) out in the street. I could smell exhaust fumes.

"You are the first to arrive, so you may choose any bed," Mrs. Reddie said with an exhausted smile.

She must have been desperately poor to take that job at her age, I thought. Her fried in ammonia brown hair did little to hide her ghostly grey roots.

"Why don't you take this one? It is tucked in the corner behind the door. The beds by the window will get drafty and be noisier with the street below." Mom sensibly advised.

"Fine," I agreed, feeling the panic of separation draw up tears again like a windmill sucks water out of the dusty ground, rhythmically, with every throaty thump of my heart. *How will I know things like that without Mom explaining them to me?* I frantically panicked. Mom had been my teacher all my life. She dazzled me with her efficiency as she unpacked all my clothes and toiletries, stowing them neatly in the lockers. She dealt out orders, and we obeyed her. Wendy helped the most. The boys and Dad shifted about, clumsily out of place. Dad, the farmer, was like a fish out of water in the city. He gasped for nicotine and fresh air.

"You will take this smaller case to class tomorrow and bring it back full of books. We'll go and store this large suitcase in the storeroom." Mrs. Reddie was saying, her strange voice bouncing off my ears. She was hovering about. "I see it is labeled well. Thank you, Mrs. Bester."

"It is a pleasure. Please will you look after my baby girl?" Mom pleaded politely.

"Where is the classroom?" I asked. I had no sense of direction, and becoming lost in the huge city was a very real fear of mine.

"The other girls will show you in the morning," Mrs. Reddie offered kindly.

"Remember: As long as you have a tongue in your mouth, you cannot get lost. Just ask the other girls, and soon you'll be an old hat at it," Mom advised.

Other white girls and their families started to arrive.

"It's getting a bit crowded in here; I think we'd better get a move on." Dad was craving his pipe and his solitude.

"Norman is next," Mom said in a brittle voice. "Let's say goodbye here and you can stay on your bed until they tell you where to go." Mom was instructing rather than suggesting, but it was just thinly disguised nervous talking.

"Bye, Judes. I'll see you on Sunday. Only four more days!" Bruce was the first to hug me. Then he walked away quickly.

Norman hugged me tighter than ever before, and said "You'll be alright." Then he left too, smiling bravely, composing himself while greeting a few of the girls he recognized from church. "Please look after my little sister for me!"

He hurried after Bruce, who suddenly changed direction to help a single mom carry her daughter's heavy suitcase up the stairs.

Wendy hugged me tightly. "Be good, Judes. Don't cause any trouble. They are strict here." She kissed me. "I'll see you at church!" She hesitated at the top of the stairs, waiting for Dad and Mom.

"Be polite, my girl. We'll keep the home pot boiling on Schelmdrift. See you soon," Dad said with the biggest hug and kiss. "We'll fetch you for the weekend in the middle of the term." He stood beside my mom, gently putting his hand on her back for moral support as she said her goodbyes.

"Don't cry, my child. Be brave. And remember your manners." But I lost my battle to be brave. The tears squirted from my eyes like water from the open pipe at the reservoir when the wind blew a gusty gale. "We'll be here to fetch you in five weeks." She promised as she pulled away, but I stubbornly clung to her familiar-smelling, soft neck. It was the smell of *Lux* soap. She always smelled clean.

Gently, she pried herself loose and walked briskly down the stairs arm in arm with Dad. She hated abandoning me as much as I hated being left, but that was the law.

"I want my mommy!" I cried as I flung myself onto the bed and sobbed. Unfamiliar faces swarmed all over the place. Some stared at me, others just glanced. I cried and cried and cried. One girl hugged me. Her name was Helen Wilmot.

Mom had made the bed up with my new linen she brought from home. Each article had name *tapes* (tags) neatly hand-sewn by mom, marking my possessions. She knew I was going to be in the Green Room, so she had sewed a broad satin ribbon around a green blanket for me to hold onto when I went to sleep.

"I want to go home!" I howled into my pillow. Girls and parents were looking at me and whispering, but I didn't care. "I want my family!" I cried with a most shattered heart. It felt as if I had barbed fishing hooks and sinkers in my heart. I was a fish out of water, gasping for freedom.

All the parents left. Some of the new girls were weeping, too. Some *oldpots* were happy to see their friends, and they were smiling. There were eight girls squished in each of the Pink, Blue, and Yellow dormitories. We were unequivocally lucky to have the chance of getting a top class education. Collegiate was the finest school in Port Elizabeth.

I lay and hugged my "pajama dog," that Mommy gave me for Christmas. It was a fake furry Beagle, which Mom stuffed my new pajamas in. It had a zip up its back. I named him Tambo, which means bone in Xhosa.

"Line up at the top of the stairs when you hear the first supper bell," The matron, Mrs. Reddie, shouted loudly above the din.

"There's one girl who won't stop crying," a little tattle-tale told the Matron.

I hated that place. I hated Mr. Crimer. I hated the government rules.

Helen Wilmot had black curly hair and freckles. "Don't worry. You will see Norman at church. We all love your big brother, so we will take care of you."

"Who is this? Is this Norman's little sister?" another girl asked. Her name was also Helen. But she was a Pienaar from Aberdeen. Helen P. was the ringleader of the *standard fours* (fifth graders). I was a *standard three* (fourth grader). "She has the same nose as Norman, and she has his lovely smile, although I have only seen it once."

"You'll get used to this place. We are all in the same boat." Helen Pienaar had numbed the pain of leaving loved ones.

A second harsh brass bell rang, indicating that we all had to line up outside the dining room downstairs. My knobby knees conked in on the stairs on my way down. I could not control the sobs.

"Call the matron!" someone yelled.

They tried to help me move to the dining room for supper. Somehow I attached myself to the heavy wooden banister and held on. I refused to go anywhere. That was the last place I'd seen my family, so I clung to it for dear life.

The elderly matron could not detach me. "Call Mr. Crimer," she told an older girl.

He appeared at the foot of the stairs and snarled, "Get up from there!"

I refused.

He tried to yank me by the leg.

I kicked about as hard as the calf kicked me when it extracted my baby tooth. Unfortunately, I missed Mr. Crimer's ugly face or I would have probably been expelled on the spot.

"Wow!" The girls were all staring and cheering silently, expressing their shock.

"We've never had one this bad," he concluded. "Leave her here. All you gawking girls get in the dining room."

I no longer had to worry about ghosts gawking, there were plenty of girls.

"What shall I do with her?" Mrs. Reddie asked helplessly.

"Leave her there on the stairs. She'll just have to starve to learn her lesson." The cold man was very harsh now that my parents were not present.

After dinner, Helen Wilmot whispered to me, "Here is some milk. I smuggled it out for you."

"Thanks," I said numbly. I forced myself to take a sip. The milk would not go down my throat, so I spat it back in the glass."

I cried everyday for the first two weeks.

Mrs. Reddie shook her head. "We've never had one this homesick before."

I had no power to change the cursed situation. I also did not have Jane's blood or breeding. I wished I could calmly conform as she did. Tombe and Wendy and Jane all had calm natures and conformity came easily to them.

Mom must have sensed from my letters that I was struggling to obey the orderly rules. She wrote me a letter to try and encourage me to tame my wild ways.

She wrote, "Remember, my pet, life is 80% of what you yourself make of it. Life is a colorful sequence of consequences, my child—

mostly of your very own vibrant choices. You can choose to be happy or sorry for yourself." I re-read her letters and that did help comfort me. But boarding school was not my choice…

My sadness slowly curdled to sour anger, like milk becomes *amasi* (curds and whey) in a *calabash* (dried gourd). "Deeds" or "words" did not appear optional. The school was very strict. Bells rang demanding certain "deeds," and rang again for compulsory silence when no "words" were even allowed. The agony of silence was almost as excruciating for me as being separated from my loved ones.

20

ENOS FRUIT SALTS

At boarding school, the farmers' daughters from the Karoo turned out to be most agreeable. It was very interesting that we had no power to change the rules, but there were about thirty of us against three adults. Mathematically, we had the numbers on our side. We took full advantage of an opportunity for insurrection at Annerley House.

We soon shared a common goal: make Mr. and Mrs. Crimer's life miserable. Our united group of girls plotted to make their stay so unbearable that they would resign. We were determined to evict them from our lives and as superintendents of Collegiate Junior School Boarding House.

"Mrs. Crimer is a cold-hearted twirp," one girl squealed. "She is so mean, she wants to keep us locked up and not let us even talk to our own families."

"This place is worse than a prison. We have not even done anything wrong, and yet Mr. Crimer won't let us go and watch our brothers play cricket," another complained.

That was the crime of the century for girls bred in the Eastern Cape Province. Mr. Crimer was a drip who would not fully understand the level of hero worship of cricketers. Banning cricket was crossing the line! Forbidding us to watch cricket was an abomination that warranted an all-out revolution.

"They won't even let us speak on the phone."

"We are lucky he lets us go to church."

"We should all go on a hunger strike."

"That is a bad idea."

"They give us very little food to begin with!" I piped up.

"She wouldn't care if we died of starvation."

"We have to deliberately do something to make them vacate this place."

"Slowly but surely, like Chinese torture!"

That was when I missed Sindie the most. She always had good "witchcraft" suggestions. Perhaps we could partially poison the Crimers with those red berries. We did not want to kill them exactly; our aim was merely to expel them.

"Mrs. Crimer walks around with her runny red nose in the air. We should put snuff in her face powder. It would make the sniveler sneeze," one child creatively conjured.

It was true that haughty Mrs. Crimer carried herself with a cool aloofness. We could easily see up her elongated, hairy nostrils. The catty woman, with black whiskers in her nose, was about as unattractive as her husband.

"The Xhosa people use snuff to sneeze out evil spirits," I volunteered. "Perhaps she would be nicer when the evil spirits left her."

"Witchcraft does not work." One girl laughed at my idea.

"Only black people believe those absurd practices." Another confirmed.

"Her protruding eyes could pop out if she sneezed too much. And we'd all go to jail!" A timid girl moaned, dismissing my idea.

"We should accidentally bang her on the back of her head, and her eyes would pop out their sockets. She looks like those Chihuahua dogs with eyes that stick out. If you hit those dogs on the back of the head too hard, their eyes fall out." None of us had heard that before!

There was silence as we all tried to digest that information, sorting it out in our minds. Fiction and fact were often indistinguishable in ideas that I heard from peers at boarding school. I had to sort through them the same way Dad sorted a fleece of wool.

"We had a Pekingese named *Thokoloshe* that barked so hard at a burglar that both eyes popped out," a different girl volunteered. "The *tsotsi* got such a fright that he dropped my mother's jewelry and ran away. We have not been robbed since."

Mrs. Crimer did, indeed, have eyes rather like a *brachycephalic* breed, which may be susceptible to *proptosis.* Her eyes were not quite deep enough in their sockets. Besides, her eyelids were almost translucent, like tissue paper, barely solid enough to hold those eyeballs in place.

"Will you girls stop talking?" Those were Mrs. Crimer's favorite words.

She tried to silence us all the time. She never wanted to hear what we had to say. If we spoke too much, which was a problem for many of us; she would punish us with hours of detention. Her attempts to silence the young and spirited were futile, however. Detention worked for a few. It broke their spirits. But the rest of us wrote notes to release whatever it was that we so desperately needed to share.

During one dreadful Saturday detention, I felt a note pressed into my hand. I kept it there until the matron was pacing on the other side of the room. Quickly, I opened it and read, "Did you hear what happened to Linda Jones?"

I wrote back, "No, what happened?"

"Her parents are going to write to the school and say she is allergic to bread pudding so that she doesn't have to eat it any more!" the reply note read.

That triggered a deep pang of homesickness. The food at the hostel was not the same as Maggie's cooking. I longed for Maggie's wholesome bread. Our fortunate cook had escaped formal school; she just dipped her finger in everything and could instantly tell exactly what needed to be added, simply by licking her finger. The fresh farm produce was obviously a contributing factor. Mom knew how to grow tasty veggies, and Dad produced fabulous fruit. And of course the Karoo rack of lamb…

Mrs. Reddie waddled around the place and clanked the dreaded brass bell. We woke up to a bell, got dressed to a bell, and lined up to a bell. Another awful bell marched us into the dining room to sit at our assigned seats.

My place was next to Linda Jones, a quiet girl from Knysna. The dining room was a place of fear for most students, since we had to eat everything they put in front of us. The most ghastly boiled cabbage was the worst food I had ever eaten, but I learned to swallow it while holding my nose. It was a survival trick that the *oldpots* (anyone who had survived boarding school for a whole year) showed us. By doing that, we didn't taste it as much.

I had started to like some of the farm girls, particularly the two Helens. I also admired Lindsay Bennett's sense of humor. She became my first friend in the Green dormitory. She was from Fort Beaufort. As much as I hated the confinement, I started to enjoy the other pupils. Glenda Long and Janet Bradfield were prefects in Std. 5 and were extremely kind to me. They caught the train in Grahamstown, and loved my brother.

My favorite adult was Miriam. She was a tall, stout Xhosa maid who was always in the kitchen, a place we weren't allowed to enter. We rarely saw her, except when she pushed the trolley of plates into the dining room.

She came to me one day when I was crying on the stairs and said, "Stop crying. You will get used to this place." I replied in Xhosa that I would never enjoy being away from my family farm, but getting used to it seemed more realistic. I thanked her for her logical advice. Her tired face lit up when she heard me speak Xhosa.

"Your Xhosa is very deep. I have worked here many years. I have heard numerous children who can speak Xhosa a little. I am thrilled to see a white child who speaks Xhosa better than some of my black friends in New Brighton Township. We tend to mix a Zulu word in here and there. Your Xhosa is purer than mine." From then on, Miriam treated me with special kindness. She would always give me the biggest piece of meat, or the crispiest roast potato. She kindly gave me the smallest helping of disgusting bread pudding.

Instead of wasting the stale bread, the Crimers used it to make repugnant dessert called "bread pudding." They packed the slices on top of each other, soaking the moldy mound in milk. They sloshed an egg mixture over that to disguise the decay. A few raisins were tucked in between the fetid mush. It was a most revolting concoction. No one liked the slushy dessert. But we had to eat it, no matter how raw and slimy it was.

The raisins swelled and looked like overfed ticks, bleeding putrid, purplish puss, staining the sodden slices. Some things should not be resurrected; a raisin is one of them. A raisin should not try to become a grape again, it just looks too sickly. It should rather remain a raisin and be enjoyed as a wrinkly, chewy treat.

"Eat your bread pudding!" Mrs. Crimer's shrill voice would echo throughout the bare dining room.

Linda Jones, of Knysna, was white in her face. She hated bread pudding and had a phobia of it appearing on the double-decker trolley. She just sat there looking at it dolefully, trying to avoid attention. Where was my Jane when I needed her nimble fingers?

"Eat your pudding!" The icy cold voice pierced our taut nerves. Mrs. Crimer was gawking at Linda's untouched plate.

"Yes, Mrs. Crimer," Linda said politely, picking up her spoon in a mock attempt, and straightening up her back.

She swallowed one spoonful whole, trying not to taste the purplish goop. She gulped a second with equal speed. As she raised the loaded spoon the third time, her skin turned sickly green. She gagged once. Out plopped the pudding, landing neatly back in her pudding plate.

"You will eat every mouthful of that!" Mrs. Crimer screeched. "Everyone will sit here until every scrap is swallowed."

"I have a tummy ache," Linda's plea was somewhat pathetic.

"You can't possibly make her eat her vomit, Mrs. Crimer!" I spoke up, but I quickly regretted my words as soon as I saw Mrs. Crimer's face redden in rage.

"That is gobbledygook!" She screamed. "You have to learn to eat everything! And if you have any more to say, cheeky Miss Bester, I'll make *you* lick it all up!" She was truly a dragon.

Linda's hand trembled as she lifted a spoon full of regurgitated dessert to her mouth. None of us could bear to look. She ate all of what she threw up.

I couldn't help thinking of the peaceful cows on the farm. They regurgitate their *lucerne* (alfalfa) and chew it a second time. Remembering how Sindie and Tombe and I watched the cows chew their cud, once again made me long for the freedom of the farm. I wanted to be in my mud hut; instead I was in a hen hutch. Cows re-eat their food, but humans are not supposed to.

That night, girls plotted and planned what to do for revenge. "Let's put pepper in Mrs. Crimer's coffee mug." Imaginative ideas circulated wildly…

"Shall we 'apple-pie' her bed?" That was a trick the *oldpots* taught us. They made a bed with only one folded sheet, but it appears that you used two. When you get in, your feet get stuck halfway down the bed.

"How about hiding some broken glass in her sugar bowl?"

"Let's wrap *Brooklax* (potent laxative that looks and tastes a lot like dark chocolate) in chocolate wrappers and give it to her as a gift."

The older girls always had the best ideas. They had suffered far longer than we *newpots* had. It truly made me wonder how the *oldpots* cooked up their ideas. Some people just seem to be given better ideas than others. That always puzzled me…why do some people get brilliant ideas and others not? Ideas are like gifts, you never know what is going to come out of the skulls of children. In fact, one of the twelve-year-old *Standard 5's* (6th graders) came up with the most popular idea when she suggested:

"Let's put Enos in her potty."

"YEEESS!!!" It was unanimous! That idea was by far the best!

Such ideas had to be inspired by God Above. Or perhaps they came straight from the devil himself? I brushed that thought aside, as the devil could not possibly concoct such a clever idea. Intelligent ideas surely had to flow from the grandiose heavens.

"Mrs. Crimer is so lazy. She never walks to the toilet at night. She *wees* (pees) in a chamber pot. Then she comes and empties it in our toilet. It splashes everywhere, and she never wipes the seat."

Everyone became engaged and involved in the perfect plot.

"Who has Enos Fruit Salts?" a bossy girl demanded. She put up her hand, calling for an immediate response. A few of us raised our hands.

"Bring it now. We need all the donations we can get!" An *oldpot* ordered.

We scattered to our lockers and returned with our varying amounts of white crystals in glass bottles. We shook our donations into an empty shoebox. Enos Fruit Salts was a necessity at the hostel. It is an essential antacid to relieve tummy aches resulting from the vile food. After all was said and done, we pooled the powder willingly. The ceremony of donating was quite a sight. We shook our Enos Fruit salts into the box, with great anticipation.

"You see, if we pour our Enos into her 'potty,' when she *wees*…"

"It will bubble up onto her bare bottom!"

"She will get a huge fright!"

"She deserves an uprising!"

More stragglers scurried to swell the sacrificial collection to about four cups of Enos Fruit Salts, an extremely effervescent powder. One teaspoonful in a full glass of water fizzed violently. You drank the mixture while hissing bubbles popped. It was famous for neutralizing acid in one's stomach. We were hoping it could take bitter gall out her heart as well.

It was just about bedtime and we heard Mrs. Crimer's heeled footsteps approaching, so we shoved the Enos under a bed. We innocently strolled to the bathroom and brushed our teeth. We struggled to contain our excitement, but acting nonchalant was extremely difficult. Unity gave us enthusiastic strength, our insurrection was imminent.

"We need to distract her so we can creep into her room before she goes to bed." Helen P. was taking the lead, as we prepped for bed.

"How?" we inquired.

"Think of something," Helen spat out her toothpaste.

Interestingly, at this "snob school," we white girls were all on a similar footing in a socioeconomic sense. Our parents could all afford to send us to receive an upper-class education. I did not feel the pangs of guilt as I did with Sindie and Tombe when we compared pajamas.

With the bedtime bell about to ring, we had no time to waste. We put our heads together. The best decoy we could come up with was "falling down the stairs."

The older girls agreed and announced, "We are going to pretend someone is hurt. We will throw a school suitcase down the stairs and make a big noise."

"Righto then, Linda you can pretend to fall," an *oldpot* delegated the chore to the victim, for whom our mission was in honor of, anyway.

"Judy, you hurl your suitcase down." Helen P. mobilized the mob.

"Alright!" I was willing to do my part, even if it meant I had to sacrifice my new Globite suitcase.

"Linda, you must lie at the bottom and act broken."

"Okay," Linda said sheepishly, still suffering from her bread pudding ordeal.

"Hurry up!" We had no time to waste.

I got my school suitcase full of books and hurled it down the wooden staircase to create the sound of someone falling.

Linda lay limp at the bottom of the stairs.

"Mrs. Crimer, come quickly! Linda is hurt!" the girls yelled very dramatically.

We all stood around Linda in mock sympathy.

"I think she was trying to commit suicide!" one girl wailed in the most melodramatic fashion.

Linda lay with her eyes shut. She twitched her hands and feet in a fake seizure.

"Linda, open your eyes," Mrs. Crimer demanded in a bitter tone.

"She could be dead." Another girl was indignant to a fault.

The older girls were conspicuously absent from the dramatic scene. So the drama queens continued to stall and entertain, relishing the opportunity to be featured as a most helpful distraction. Farm-style first aid was administered. Linda's face was slapped. Cold water was applied.

Finally, the older girls showed up, each with a smug look of satisfaction on her face. The *oldpots* had successfully poured the crystal powder potion into the portable chamber pot. Then they had carefully placed it back in the same spot under acidic Mrs. Crimer's bed. Brave *oldpots* had dared to walk into the most "out of bounds" part of the hostel. They now discreetly mingled in the throng, with smiles that only sweet revenge can fully explain.

With the malevolent mission complete, Linda miraculously recovered. She was ceremoniously helped up the stairs, still flanked by the overly dramatic sympathizers.

The anticipation was too great to bear. None of us could go to sleep.

"I said SILENCE!" Mrs. Crimer was stomping from dorm to dorm.

"Who is talking in here?" the pugnacious female demanded as she flicked on the light. We all lay silent and unresponsive, pretending to be asleep.

"Well then, if you don't have the courage to own up, you can all have two hours of detention on Saturday," she hissed, with a tongue dripping in acrid gall.

I could not sleep so I had time to think, for a change, as I lay awake. I marveled at the talents of the *oldpots.* Talents told volumes about individual differences; some had a flair for friendliness, others a greater capacity for charity. Even if our clothes were uniform, identity was maintained by a variety of personalities. Each character was unique, and that was a miracle alone. All the girls had such a variety of talents and ideas. Characteristics stood out from each girl, making them distinctly dissimilar.

The two Helens stood out for courage. One had innate leadership skills, the other an aptitude for bossiness. Both were receptors of light and energy, which beamed from their faces.

Then there was the "favor factor." Miriam gave me the cooked corner slice of bread pudding, and Linda landed the slimy section. We were not equal recipients in endowments, even if we were born to similar farming stock. Not even Colleen and Gwendy de Villiers, the twins from Beaufort West, were alike! *Newpots* learned from *oldpots,* but all the girls were watertight recipients of accepted wisdom. We were all pots to hold ideas or pour them out. It was our choice.

Eventually, sleep overcame my restlessness.

The next morning, some of the light sleepers told tales of screams. Some had heard Mrs. Crimer shout "HELP!" Others had heard frenzied "SNAKE!" shouts. But they all had heard a big commotion, even glass breaking.

Regretfully, I was a very deep sleeper, and I slept through it all.

One girl reported that Mrs. Crimer had not been to empty her potty that morning. We deduced that she must have kicked it over during the catastrophe. Whispers of approval traveled along the formation line. The success of our mission was measured with the rapid result. The advertisement for Enos on the radio did promise rapid relief from discomfort.

Another bell rang and we filed into the dismal dining room, sensing trouble. We noticed that Mrs. Reddie, instead of Mrs. Crimer, was on duty. We walked as usual to our allocated chairs. We stood patiently and waited to say grace in unison. Before every meal we repeated "For what we are about to receive, may the Lord make us truly thankful."

Mr. Crimer barged in, but he omitted the standard ritual.

Grace was not on Mr. Crimer's mind, evidently.

"Sit down," he spat without giving thanks for the Jungle Oats porridge that was curling up on our plates.

"Who played that cruel trick on Mrs. Crimer?" His umbrage turned his colorless face purple, rather like a surgically soaked raisin. Justice was apparently foremost on his mind. He was well-educated with a good English accent, but loathsome all the same.

No response.

"Will the fiend or fiendssss responsible stand up?!" he blurted out.

No one moved a muscle. Everyone looked silently at their plates in protest.

"Who did it?!" The odious creature screamed, pockets of white matter now oozing from the corners of his mouth.

There was a strike of silence.

We stuck together, even though we had neither discussed consequences nor fully planned this part of the plot. We were all determined to not admit it or rat on anyone who had done the actual deed. Our support was unanimous. Old people need to re-think some of their hygiene habits. And some of their ragtag rules! Mean old people were not going to get away Scott free, without changing their ways.

"Facta Non Verba" was at play. We did our "deeds," and now we had no "words." We were indeed true to our Latin motto!

"Well then, you will *all* be *gated* (grounded) and none of you will go home for the long weekend. Until the guilty culprit owns up, all of you are *gated*!" the bombastic mongrel ordered. To me, he looked like a worm-infested, tick-riddled alley cat.

21

REUNION

It was a taste of hell. Getting *gated* meant not being allowed to go home for the midterm break. It shook a little of the rebellious spirit out of some. Some thirty girls moped around with stooped shoulders, as if to cradle their broken hearts inside their ribcages.

Another bell rang: we slowly shuffled to the dining room. A tsunami of sadness swept our souls. We dawdled deliberately to irritate the Crimers. Granted, it was a lesser offense, but if we all participated, it conveyed our unity. That unity gave us a glimmer of power.

We ate our cornflakes and milk, chewing it slowly, like you chew Wicks bubblegum. The mood was glum.

"Hurry up. You must not be late for school," Mrs. Crimer meowed. She rang the bell for silence, so we all stopped our conversations. If she had been a cat, she would have been an un-groomed hyena.

Mr. Crimer pranced in and rang the bell for silence again even though we were already silent. It made him feel important. Puffing up his small chest like a Bantam cock, reigning supreme among a few females, he grimaced as he spoke. "I have an announcement to make." There was a dramatic pause. "The two culprits who played that terrible trick on Mrs. Crimer came to my office and owned up last night."

None of us trusted him enough to even glance at the two brave ones. We purposely sat and looked at him blankly. Perhaps he had another scheme cooked up his sleeve to keep us in his loathsome presence. "They will remain gated, but the rest of you may go home for the long weekend." He said with a horrible fake smile.

But our happiness was tainted. We felt a lingering sadness for the two individuals absorbing the punishment. Our determination to deprive him of any hint of triumph was rock solid. He was to enjoy no satisfaction from our relief. He was not in any way to be regarded as our lifesaver; the glory belonged strictly to the heroic girls.

We showed no evidence by praising them in his presence. Perhaps the *oldpots* had not truly confessed and he was testing to see which girls we patted on the back, thereby tricking us into revealing their identities. Maybe this was merely a ploy to help Mr. Crimer find out who did the dastardly deed.

That momentous Friday eventually dawned, the school day dragged. The teachers had lots to say, touting truths about English grammar and Afrikaans spelling.

Our Afrikaans teacher pontificated endlessly about an accident being an *"ongeluk."* Directly translated, it literally means an "un-luck." I wondered why unlucky people crash their cars.

Afrikaans people were cleverer than I initially thought. They knew that to have an accident was lacking luck. On the farm, we did not have to worry about traffic accidents, mainly because there was no traffic. City life was more complicated than farm life, and seemed to contain more catastrophes with all those traveling objects moving *en bloc.*

Tombe attributed good luck to well-pleased ancestors. Sindie blamed grumpy ghosts for dealing out ghastly curses. Being so exposed to two vastly diverse cultures made me inquisitive and hungrier to find pure truth. Maybe Xhosas should not hold those glaring ghosts completely accountable!

The clock on the classroom wall ticked extra slowly that day. I had no way of lifting the curse on the two *oldpots.* Luck cannot always be shared. Luck favors people and places, no doubt. The randomness of luck was a mystery of life, one that begged to be solved! Why did school teachers not talk more about such fascinating topics?

Instead, the Afrikaans teacher warned us never to travel with smooth tires. Her best friend's car had recently slid off the road and she had been squashed to death in an *ongeluk* (accident). Our teacher blamed the lack of tire tread for the tragedy.

SPOTS

As a self-appointed detective, I was determined to discover the truth about luck. Truth cannot remain in eternal containment. As a *newpot,* I had an ulterior motive, of course; one surely needed to be a recipient of luck to survive city life.

"Judy, are you dreaming again? I said pass your books forward." The teacher abruptly jerked me out of my private world. "What do you dream about all day, may I ask? What do you think about so deeply? Pass me your book."

"I beg your pardon. What book?" I was dumbfounded.

"Your exercise book," whispered Helen Pollock, the girl who sat behind me. She patted me on my shoulder with her book. She was the little sister of the two world famous Pollock brothers, Graeme and Peter.

Helen was one of the lucky day-girls. There were about five hundred so called *"daypots"* at Collegiate Junior School for Girls. Their parents drove them to school every day with white bread sandwiches wrapped in waxy paper for their lunches. But when we came to school with kudu biltong from the Karoo, they gladly traded their salami sandwiches with us. They went home to their families at the end of each day. We didn't. That Friday, luckily, was to be different!

"Oh, yes. Thank you. Sorry." I scrambled for my book in my wooden desk.

Mathematics, Science, History, and Geography were taught in the civilized classroom, but my mind was wandering out of the classroom, freewheeling home to the smell of fresh brown bread baking. And to Sindie and Tombe and lamb stew cooked over a crackling fire in an empty KOO jam tin!

"We're going home!" I exclaimed as the final bell rang. I was bursting with excitement as I eagerly anticipated reuniting with my family and playmates.

"Walk next to your partner," the prefects reprimanded as we wiggled out of line.

The boarders marched from the school to the hostel two by two in what we called a "crocodile." Port Elizabeth was a windy city. Often the whole "croc" had to halt while a girl ran after her white hat to retrieve it by its navy blue ribbon. My practical mother had sewn elastic onto mine, to fit snugly under my chin, so my hat never blew off. She was the cleverest mom of all and I was about to see her again, after five very long weeks.

"Don't run!" I heard the prefect say sternly. Soon, the "croc" came around the corner and we saw cars parked outside the hostel with a cluster of parents standing at the gate. We all instinctively ran towards them, our pigtails flying behind our heads just as a speeding puppy leaves its ears behind in a fast dash.

The big blue Zephyr was closest to the gate. That meant Dad had arrived earliest to earn that spot! I spotted my daddy first, recognizing the plume of smoke ascending from his puffing pipe past his hunter green hat.

At five feet eleven inches, Mother towered above the other ladies. Her athletic body consisted mostly of long legs. She raced towards me, with her burnished red hair glistening in the sun like a bright beacon. She wore a green slacks suit.

Mom had earned sterling silver trophies for winning the 100 yard sprint, 220 yard race, and long jump event. She gracefully sprinted towards me. I recall her radiant smile…her outstretched arms!

Overcome with joy, I dropped my suddenly irrelevant suitcase and flew as fast as my little knock knees could go. Her speed compensated for my shorter legs.

"Mommy!" I shouted as I flung myself into her arms.

"Hello, my pet!" Mom was quite the lady, but not too ladylike that day as she scooped me up and squeezed me so tightly that she exhaled the air out of my lungs. "At last! Your hair has grown. I'll have to cut your fringe for you when we get home."

"Daddy!" I exclaimed as I looked up to see him remove his hat like a true gentleman before he kissed me. "Hello! Hello! Hello, my girl!" He was choked up with happiness. "It is lovely to see you. You have grown a little taller, I think, my girly."

"Hurry, let's gather your belongings. We need to fetch the other three children *now-now.*" Mom suddenly remembered the rest, regrouped, and reorganized. Dad was still hugging me. He hugged me so firmly that I feared my intestines might be exhaled.

"I left my suitcase behind," I confessed.

Turning around, one of the *gated oldpots,* who was not running to meet a beloved parent, had picked it up for me. She stood nearby, watching, clutching my case patiently.

"Here Judes, enjoy your weekend." She held it out bravely. I noticed she purposely dulled her own emotions as she handed me my dented Globite suitcase with a faint smile. I greatly admired her valor.

"Thank you," Mom, Dad and I all chorused.

"I'll bring you some *tuck* (treats)," I promised her, but my heart was consumed with sadness for her captivity. We all longed to be free and equal, but reality painted a contrasting canvas. Our individual choices spun our consequences into separate threads.

"I have to go upstairs and shove my clothes that are all ready piled up on my bed into here," I explained. "You can come too, Mommy. Daddy isn't allowed up."

"Righto, then! I'll stay here and keep an eye on the car. Shake a leg or we will be late for Norman. You two get a move on. Buck up now!" Dad swatted me politely on my bottom, his crinkled eyes twinkling with a tear.

Mom held my hand as if she'd never let go and whisked me up the stairs.

"Now remember to empty your books neatly onto your beds. Pack your clothes for the weekend into your school suitcase," Mrs. Reddie rambled on.

For once, we obeyed with great gusto. Seeing our actual parents was the greatest motivation, and we moved quickly.

"I have my farm clothes in my dressing table at home. I don't need that much," I informed the matron as she sniffed past my bed.

"Did you use up your whole bottle of Enos already?" Mom asked innocently shaking the glass bottle which now housed hair clips. "Is the food very bad here?"

"It is the worst," The *oldpot* answered for me, staring at my stacked possessions.

"You can't go home until your books are in neat piles," the matron muttered.

"Bye-Bye!" We scrambled to leave first. The two *oldpots* were standing there watching, leaning on each other. I felt their green envy grow, like creeping ivy, weeping silently, clinging to an invisible stoned emotional wall.

A stab of ache pierced my heart. I felt powerless, as a child often does. I resolved at that moment that when I grew up, I would try to be different from the old people of our hostel. Injustice needs to be eliminated, but what can a feeble child do?

I made an oath with myself to be better than the cold Crimers. I would strive to have more love in my heart than those heartless creatures. When I had grown a little less helpless, I would fight for justice. How could that cow expect a kid to chew her cud?

The mean old sod deserved her fizzy uprising! I was not at all repentant; rather, I felt rebellious towards the status quo.

"Hurry up now, Norman will be waiting." Mom yanked my arm in haste.

Norman was standing outside Grey Junior Hostel with his weekend suitcase. Dad drove to Wendy's hostel, where she, too, eagerly piled into the back seat. Bruce was soon seated in the family car as well, cricket bat and all. More hugs and kisses were shared.

"Move up, Norman. Mom, have you got anything to eat? I am sick of boarding house food." Bruce was never fond of school—only sports interested him, which gave him a ferocious appetite. His huge eyes pleaded for food. I had forgotten how blue Bruce's eyes were. He was a stud. Norman was also very popular with the girls.

"I brought some shortbread for *padkos* (road food)," Mom said, pulling out the familiar cake tin. Red-jacketed huntsmen on horseback, riding in the far fields of gloriously green England, adorned the square tin. "I did not know what to do with all the extra butter, so I baked shortbread."

The boys stuffed their mouths. Mom never said anything about their manners.

"I have to fill up our car with petrol. If anyone needs to *spend a penny*, there's the lavatory." Dad's voice was upbeat; he was happy to have all his Bester brood back again. "It is lovely to have all the family together again."

"My feet have grown. These shoes are too tight," Norman yanked them off.

"I can't wait to get out of this uniform," Bruce removed his tie.

"Norman! Your feet stink!" Wendy announced, winding down her window with a grimace of disgust.

"I am so happy to be out of those gates." I jumped up in my seat.

"Let's not talk about gates," Mom hugged me again.

When I gave Dad an extra squeeze, he said, "Be careful, my girl. I have to concentrate on the road." Dad was always a bit nervous about driving in the metropolis of Port Elizabeth.

"I brought you a flask of tea, too." Mom's smile was as full as her quiver again.

After a couple of hours, Daddy guided the car carefully onto our dirt road turnoff. There was a big white sign that read, "Bester Brothers Africander Cattle Stud." A rust-red Africander bull's head was painted on the white board. Real bull's horns were attached to jut out of the sign post, adding a third dimension.

Suddenly, two little black girls jumped up out of the shade of a Mimosa thorn tree. They were waving and stamping their feet in a joyous dance.

Dad slowly drove down the hill towards the gate. I waved at them with my best beaming smile, bursting to get out the car.

"Miss Judy! Miss Jay!" I heard them cheer and clap.

"It looks like we have a welcoming party," Dad nodded, waving back. He was a relaxed driver now, back on his own turf without town traffic.

"Your friends have come to greet you." Mom smiled at me and them.

As we descended the slope, they ran barefoot behind the car, chewing its dust, chattering in clicks to each other.

Dad stopped at the Schelmdrift gate. They ran ahead and

opened it, each swinging a half aside. Sindie swung on "Schelm" to the left, while Tombe drove "Drift" to the right.

"Good. I don't have to open the gate." Bruce's relaxation was not interrupted.

Dad rolled down his window and gave Tombe two shiny coins. "Thank you, Tombe. One is for you and one for Sindie. You share, you see."

"Ewe, Baas. Enkosi! (Yes, Boss. Thanks!)" Beaming Tombe curtsied as she accepted the money with both her hands cupped together as the Xhosa custom dictates.

"Enkosi kakhulu! (Thank you very much!)" Sindie sang soprano, grinning with gratitude.

Tombe handed Sindie her coin as they bounced barefoot behind the boot, down the gravel driveway, till we stopped under the pepper tree. They forgot to shut the gate in their excitement.

"Bruce, please will you go and close the gate, so the cattle don't eat Mom's geraniums?" Dad put his firstborn son in charge of the gate, and allowed me to enjoy the royal welcome of my childhood chums.

I noticed Dad did not even scold the well-remunerated piccanins for forgetting to complete their chore. On a stud farm, gate shutting was mandatory. Newborn calves were recorded religiously and both their cow-mother and bull-father were registered. Lineage was meticulously monitored for pedigree charts. No mongrels were allowed within the gates of Schelmdrift.

Happy reunions, however, mandated merriment. Dad knew when to show mercy and when to demand justice. He was a wise father, who understood when to be flexible.

"Umhlophe gqhitha. Akholanga na eBhayi? (You are very white. Is there no sun in P.E.?)" Tombe detected a change in the paleness of my skin.

My family had all disappeared into the farmhouse, so Tombe took courage and squeezed my arm, still inspecting my flesh. *"Ubhityile, Miss Judy. Akutyanga kamnandi na eBhayi?* (You are thin, Miss Judy. Did you not eat well in P.E.?)" Tombe sounded a little upset with the establishment for omitting to feed me sufficiently.

"They force you to eat boiled cabbage," I tried to account for my skinnier frame.

"I would love to be forced to eat cabbage. White people eat fresh food," Sindie challenged cheerfully.

"Did you bring us any food?" Tombe was measuring to see if she had more fat than me. Tombe was chunkier than we were and was quite satisfied to remain so.

"No," I reported. "You wouldn't want to eat it anyway. One girl puked and the wicked matron made her eat her vomit up again."

"It sounds like a cursed place, with witches running it," Sindie concluded. "I am glad I don't have to go there. I would rather go to Carlisle Bridge."

"Come and change out of your uniform," Mom called from the front *stoep* (veranda). "The girls can wait for you on the kitchen *stoep.*"

Soon after, I emerged to join them on the sunny steps. Maggie appeared on the footpath by the dairy. She had just picked up a pile of chopped wood on her way down. Maggie quickened her pace when she saw me. I ran to hug her with exuberance, causing a few logs to fall to the ground. Sindie and Tombe quickly gathered them up and held onto them with a sense of aplomb.

"Molo, NomHankazi! Unjani, mntana 'am? (Hello, Nomhankazi! How are you, my child?)" Maggie was always delighted to see us.

"I am fine, thanks. How are you? Where is Jane?" I was answering and asking in one breath.

"She is on her way. I needed to come earlier to stoke the fire. I want to make you a delicious lamb curry. It takes a little longer to simmer." Maggie smiled down at me.

Home is like heaven, I thought, miserable memories of bread pudding were now fading, but the grounded girls' faces continued flashing in my mind.

"No one on earth can cook like you, my Maggie," I gushed. Now that I was traveled and educated, my compliment was weightier. "I love your curry and rice."

"Thank you. Tell me what has become of you, *NomHankazi?* Do they beat you at school? Do you get beaten as much as Sindie here? I think the two of you have the same wild spirit. Have they tamed you yet?" Maggie demanded her own verbal report card.

"No, Maggie. I have not been tamed by those ugly people."

"I did not suspect so." She hugged me. I had missed her wood smoky smell.

She held my hand with her free hand as we walked to the kitchen barefoot. There is something about bare feet; they connect you to the energy of the earth. I loved feeling the ground beneath my feet. Maggie wiped her feet vigorously before entering.

"Let me go and light the fire," Maggie said. *"Molweni nonke!* (Hello, everyone!)" She bellowed to greet the others down the passage.

I was relieved to be home. I could breathe freely again.

"Let us go and play in our hut," Sindie suggested.

We scampered past the front of the house. Bruce and Norman were already playing cricket on the top lawn. Dad came out of his office and hollered, "I'll come and bowl to you in a minute. I'm just going to park the Zephyr in the garage. You need to practice facing a few *googlies* (spin balls). Do you face enough spin bowlers at school?"

I tiptoed gingerly on the spiky gravel of the driveway with my tender townie soles. "Ouch! My feet hurt. Did they put new sharper gravel on the driveway?"

"Your feet are really white," Tombe noticed.

"And they have become soft!" Sindie added when I limped across the gravel.

"We have to wear ugly black shoes and white socks every day," I lamented.

I realized then that I had become somewhat of a city slicker. I was most ashamed.

We arrived at the mud hut that Fikile and his crew had built for me. We could see him through the hedge, waving his *swazi* (stick) and walking behind the milk cows. He was guiding the Jersey cattle home to their green pastures. We greeted him happily.

"Please give us some milk," Sindie begged, full of brazenness as usual. "We want to make sour milk." She ran towards his bucket with our empty, corked calabash.

"We have to sweep the hut clean first," Tombe said, taking down the little grass broom and starting to sweep the dry excess dung out. "Just look at all the dust."

"I'll sweep. Sindie, you go and *theza* (gather) some sticks. Miss Judy, you can fetch some tea and sugar for us." Tombe remained the bossy mom of our trio.

"And biscuits! My mom said your mom has been baking all week, getting ready for your return." Sindie was always trying her luck.

"Miss Judy, you left us with boredom." Tombe was sounding more like Jane. She had grown taller as well.

"At least you get to live at home." I truly envied their freedom on the farm, no matter how oppressed they may have been in our nation known for apartheid.

"Our teacher is very strict," Tombe stated. "You have to do what she says or she gets very angry. I try to obey, but Sindie is most cheeky."

Sindie left to gather wood, refusing to admit her weaknesses. I secretly admired her spunkiness as strength. It takes courage to question the status quo, I thought. Doing so, I learned, can also land you in the stew.

Maybe Bruce was right, after all. Leopards never change their spots. Mrs. Crimer was even crueler after we tried to take the acidity out her heart with Enos. She forced Linda to eat cow's tongue and Linda almost puked again. Linda aptly adjusted, and pretended to sneeze and spat the cold beef tongue into her tissue. She neatly tucked her tissue up her sleeve like a lady. Linda later threw it in the hedge outside. A stray dog found the packaged tongue and ate the tongue, seconds before Mrs. Crimer picked up the tissues, castigating us for littering. Timing and luck were most definitely linked.

Mrs. Crimer was always scavenging for clues to chastise scholars. She had, indeed, not changed one bit of her spots.

But then again, I decided, Mrs. Crimer was not pretty or sleek enough to be a leopard. Her slinky walk and mangy hair was more like a hyena, for sure.

Those two *oldpots* were stuck in hades at the mansion of Annerley House. We were sitting in heaven in a miniature hut in the Karoo.

"Honestly, Miss Judy, Sindie gets many hidings for cheekiness. I just keep quiet; it is easier. I never get spanked." Tombe continued to tattle. "Go and get the food now. I am nearly finished sweeping." She was straightening the stones of our hearth. Remembering, she shouted, "And don't forget the matches!"

"Come with me then. It will be a heavy burden to carry alone." I wanted her company more than her help.

She jumped up, her buttocks bouncing in delight. They both seemed a little darker. That was probably because I was used to seeing pale Patsy Berry, lily-white Gail Pullen, and fair Lindsay Bennett in the Green Dormitory.

"You smell like a *piccanin* already," Wendy remarked coolly as I entered the pantry. Her nose was terribly sensitive. She and Mom were looking at recipes, bonding over the book of family favorites. They loved to bake and sew together.

"Howzaat?!" We heard the cricketers bellow.

"Please, may I have some tea and sugar for our hut?" I asked.

"Help yourself," Mom said, a little more generously than usual. Now I was on the receiving end of the special treatment granted to recently returned progeny.

"Please may I have some biscuits?" I decided to milk every moment.

"You may have three or you will spoil your appetite." Mom kindly agreed.

The whole kitchen smelled like fried onions and home. Jane had arrived.

After closing the hatch to the pantry, Jane embraced me. "I am very happy to see you. Tombe was waiting all day," Jane smiled. "You were missed very sorely."

"Sindie is probably waiting to light our logs." Tombe possessively steered me out.

We sat and sipped tea with much too much sugar. The girls grabbed a *crunchie* and dipped it into their tea. Only rusks are supposed to be dunked. Biscuits are supposed to be eaten dry. Granny Stocks would most definitely not approve. Nevertheless, I loved watching them savor their treats to the fullest.

"UnoLasti uyakwazi ukubhaka! (NoLasti can bake!)" Tombe complimented.

I broke the third cookie and gave them each half, purely for my own entertainment.

"No, that is yours." Tombe tried to push it back politely.

Sindie grabbed her half in case the chance never arose again, munching madly.

"No, thanks, I ate biscuits in the car already," I said, holding it out to Tombe.

"I'll have it," Sindie mumbled with a full mouth.

Tombe quickly snatched her half, not prepared to be a martyr just yet.

"So what did they teach you at your fancy school?" Sindie asked.

"The only thing I gleaned was that the new crop should outshine the old seed," I reported. "Old timers are not always quite as cultured as they ought to be…certainly not those cursed Crimers. And one teacher said you should never drive in a car that has smooth tires."

"Old people are very wise." Tombe was true to tradition.

"Not always!" Sindie noted, after marinating the idea for a moment. "The sun is starting to sink."

"The sun should never sink on this day," Tombe wished aloud.

"I agree!" If I could have held the sun up in the sky forever, I would have done it for those two little farm friends.

22

CUSTOM CUTS

Instead of waking up to the earsplitting brass bell of boarding school, Jane's soothing tone summoned me from my sleep. *"Naants' ikofi.* (Here's coffee.)"

Jane stood at my sister's bedside with an outstretched tray. Wendy sat up and rattled a bone china cup, added sugar, and helped herself to the biggest rusk.

"Enkosi (Thanks) Jane." I was groggily grateful, exceedingly glad to be home.

Jane left quickly with inaudible footsteps. Already the smell of a hot bacon breakfast wafted down the long passage. Instead of car engines, I heard cows mooing to call calves. Our vegetable garden graced our window's view, with no fenced in houses in sight.

Fragrant flower arrangements were artfully placed on white Irish lace doilies. Mother put her athletic trophies to practical use as elaborate vases. A pretty posy of scented flowers graced my dressing table. The pink blooms of stocks drinking out a silver goblet were reflecting in our mirror lined with oiled oak.

"Good morning, my girls," Mom emerged, buckling up the covered belt of her avocado green cotton frock. "What shall we do today? Would you like a game of tennis?"

"I would rather bake some biscuits to take back for our school cake sale." Wendy dipped her buttermilk rusk into her percolated coffee.

"I do hope we have enough eggs. The hens haven't been laying eggs very well of late. Or else, someone is pinching my eggs. *Leguwaans* (large lizards) do love to steal my eggs. I asked Dad to set the spring gun to eliminate the pest." Mom hastily headed out towards the pantry to count her eggs on the yellowwood egg rack.

"Morning," Bruce mumbled, as he ran his fingers through his dusty brown curls at the breakfast table.

"There is great excitement among the servants today," Dad announced as we all neatly placed our white starched *serviettes* (napkins) on our laps. "Cocoa is becoming a man."

We four children had identical silver *serviette* rings with our names engraved on them. Jane placed them in our usual spots when she set the table. She always beckoned me to help her identify the cursive engravings. Our humble housemaid had triumphantly memorized the shapes of our names, without being able to read them.

Dad's *serviette* holder was more ornate, with a "B" engraved in the silver. I always thought it stood for *"Boetie."* But Mom informed me it had belonged to his grandfather and "B" stood for "Bester."

"Francis and Dolly Bowker gave us four silver *serviette* holders for a wedding present." For Mom, everything has to add up just right. "We were very blessed to have produced two pigeon pairs, the right number of children to use them up. We had your names engraved on them, so you do not swap germs."

Mom politely put her *serviette* on her lap. She had earned her *serviette* ring, winning a race in Port Alfred. It had an image of the Royal couple's head on it, with "H.M. King George VI and H.M. Queen Elizabeth 1937" engraved in silver around the coroneted heads.

"Ja, if we'd had any more babies, we would have had to buy another farm as well as a new silver *serviette* ring!" Dad jested.

Bruce interrupted my thoughts with, "Did you hear about Cocoa?"

"Yes. It is his 'homecoming' from being a *mkwetha* (initiate) today. What do you call that ceremony?" Mom was not very gifted at Xhosa.

"The celebration is called *umgidi,"* I answered.

"Oh drat! That means our servants will be *giddy* from drinking Kaffir-beer. They will be positively useless for a few days, I might add," Mother fretted.

"Mind you, I reckon they deserve a bit of a party to celebrate the fact that Cocoa survived the ordeal in the bush," Dad retaliated. "I heard on the news that about 10% or so of these young men die from infection. Evidently the circumcision is not performed very hygienically."

"Why can't they just be circumcised as babies in hospital like we were?" Norman asked, enjoying his fried eggs.

"Simply because prehistoric Native rituals are much older than all our modern hospitals," Mom answered. "Their witchdoctor uses his own potions to heal the boys. One cannot shake those ingrained traditions off overnight."

"Poor Cocoa!" Bruce was not convinced. "He has had to suffer in the bush to morph from boyhood into manhood. He would be considered a cowardly traitor if he went to a proper white doctor."

The elderly Xhosa hierarchy enforced the cutting custom, confining the *mkwetha* to an isolated grass *ithonto* (hut), not to come out for a full week after they have been circumcised. After eight days, they may exit under supervision, but the *mkwetha* must still subsist in solitary seclusion.

"I saw about five of them with shaved heads and *ingceke* (white clay) smeared all over their bodies up in the top veldt the other day. They were sunning themselves next to the road when I went to have tea with Dolly Gradwell. If I did not know any better, I would have thought they were ghastly ghosts!" Mom exclaimed.

"Mind you, the boys did ask me if they could include some other initiates from the district. I said as long as they don't set our farm alight when they burn down that thatched hut along with all their boyhood belongings." Dad assured us he knew about the lonely lodgers. "The *mkwethas* have to walk away from the flames and not look back. Schelmdrift could go up in smoke! We were taught to watch a fire die out until it is not in any danger of spreading."

"Quite so!" Mom agreed. "Maggie tells me the adolescent *abakwetha* (initiates) eat a restricted diet such as *samp* (hominy) for the first week. During that time, they are not allowed to touch food or drink with their hands. *Nqalatha* (young boys) carry firewood and food to the students of manhood. She said Rama was assigned to Cocoa. Their smoky center fire must be kept alive all day and all night in the temporary hut. You are quite right, dear. I fear this whole affair is all quite a fire hazard."

"Cocoa said they are not allowed to drink anything for those first seven days." Bruce sounded happy to escape the scalpel as a European. "They may not even set eyes on any female. It is all very strict."

Dad continued, "You are jolly well right! Apparently, a mentor *(khankatha),* who is usually a recently post graduated man himself, visits newly circumcised Cocoa and changes his bandages made of goat skin."

"Eina! (Ouch!)" Norman sympathized, gobbling cheese and marmalade toast.

"Evidently, on the eighth day after being circumcised, the old men all visit the *umkwetha*'s (initiate's) temporary grass hut for a sacrificial killing of a goat. They asked me to buy them a white goat at Stockfair the other day," Dad recalled. "Finally, diluted corn porridge *(irhewu)* is served to the initiates at the end of the perilous week. They have to spit out the first mouthful and only swallow the second taste of liquid. I reckon that requires great discipline when you have not drunk anything for seven days. They say strips of flank meat *(intsonyama)* from the goat's right foreleg are cooked over coals smothered with leaves from a stinkwood tree *(nukani)*, adding a bitter flavor. Surely, they deserve a party after all that?"

"I would think so!" Mom shook her head disapprovingly.

"I believe that old men, or elders of the tribe, share bush secrets with the students. They speak in disguised codes, in a tongue *(isisomo)* never to be revealed to anyone besides graduates of manhood. I heard that if you reveal these secrets, you could be excommunicated from manhood *(ubudoda).* I asked Yan about it and he wouldn't divulge any secrets." Dad lit his pipe, as we had all finished breakfast. We lingered at the table to soak up each other's company.

"It all sounds rather suspicious and ghoulish to me." Mom added.

Bruce had been given more juicy details by Cocoa, "After Cocoa gets the custom cut, he has to swallow his foreskin, under the direction of the witchdoctor. Sometimes foreskin is stuck over the right thumb of the initiate. These details vary from witchdoctor to witchdoctor, but Cocoa said he was going to eat his!" Bruce bragged.

"Oh spare me! Do we have to discuss all these disgusting details?" Wendy winced.

"Do you suppose this is a proper conversation? At the breakfast table?" Mother objected.

"Yuck! And I thought boarding school was horrid, when they make you eat everything!" I gulped my last sip of milk.

No matter how many loitering ghosts were lurking and looking, eating one's foreskin is a ritual that desperately needed urgent revision, I thought.

"It sounds like a very warped version of the Mosaic Law to me." Mom was always trying to explain away rituals that she did not exactly approve of. "It does not surprise me at all that they still sacrifice goats and cattle. I think it is an excuse to have a *braai* (barbeque). There is plenty of drinking, dancing, and stick fighting that takes place."

"Anyway, as primitive and macabre as this all sounds, Cocoa will now be considered a true man. What's more, he can settle down and find himself a wife. I am glad he wants to stay on the farm and not go to the gold mines up on the Rand," Dad approved. "We need him here. He is a good worker."

"He has lots of *tombies* (girls) here keeping him from leaving," Bruce remarked.

"The Natives don't go to the gold mines for girls, Bruce. They go for the money," Mom corrected. "Daddy recently gave them all a pay raise, so I doubt they will move."

"Cocoa will never change, boy or man. He loves girls too much. A leopard never changes its spots!" Bruce insisted, as our breakfast feast concluded.

"Bruce, will you come with me?" Dad asked, getting up from the table.

I followed Dad and Bruce into the pantry out of sheer curiosity.

Dad duly unlocked the pantry bin and took out a full bottle of Bolls brandy. "My boy, go up to the huts and give this to the boys. Tell them it is a gift for Cocoa." Dad presented the prize to Bruce.

"Yes, Dad," Bruce nodded. "I'll give it to the boys."

"They are not boys. Cocoa is not a *boy*. He is a *man* now," I cheeked. "I feel sure we should not call them boys after they suffer so much to become men."

"Old habits die hard." Bruce tried to quiet me as I followed him out through the kitchen door. "Boys will be boys."

Excitement crackled in the Schelmdrift air. Masses of relatives of the esteemed *mkwetha,* our very own Cocoa, arrived on foot, horseback, or by bicycle.

Four Sunnyside maids walked past our house on their way up to the huts. They were balancing extra long bundles of wood. Two of them had babies tied to their backs with towels. They glided with the poise common only to these experienced balancers. They looked very graceful. Two teenage girls sauntered around the corner awkwardly balancing heavy buckets of water on their newly-shaven heads.

Bruce was brandishing the brandy in his right hand like a trophy.

"I'm coming with you to the huts." I followed Bruce and the bottle of brandy. "I want to go and see Sindie and them," I explained, just in case he thought I was spying.

At the top of the hill, the buzz of preparation was evident. Girls were clapping and singing to an African drum beat, practicing dancing in the dust. A brown hen desperately squawked, leaping loudly to escape the *kwedini* (young boy) wielding a short-handled axe. Hearty smells of *rooster-brood* (fire-roasted bread) baking over the coals tantalized our noses. Maggie's daughters dutifully attended to the sweet-smelling cakes on their outdoor grills. Dozens of cakes would necessitate a few extra eggs from *NoLasti*'s chicken *hok* (hatch). Luckily, there was always *Thokoloshe* to blame.

Married women, dressed in lofty layers of cotton skirts, intently stirred steaming three-legged pots. Colorful beads and braided skirts were promenaded in honor of the occasion at which Cocoa would emerge as a bona fide man.

A young mother with an infant tied on her back, had her face covered in white clay. She concentrated on stamping dried *mielies* (corn) in a hollow log. Traditionally, white clay was to warn her husband to be intimate with someone else until her baby was weaned. It was another rather raw ritual that begged apropos reprisal, I believed.

She tossed in more dried white corn, which had been soaking overnight, into the hollow center of an upright, tree-trunk-sized log. She sang sadly as she rhythmically kept beat with her blunt instrument, bashing the skins off the cracking corn. She was taking her jealousy out on the stamped corn, thus accomplishing her very own homegrown therapy.

A fresh crop of adolescent girls neatly *platted* (braided) each other's hair into cornrows, objecting loudly about the painful price of beauty. Some were washing their breasts and armpits in full view of all. Bruce's presence did not deter them in the least. Tribally festooned teenagers walked around topless, with beads and breasts bouncing boldly.

Bruce wandered off to Cocoa's family hut near the dam to deliver the gift.

"I am going to Sindie's hut," I informed Bruce, turning and parting ways.

I trusted he would deliver the brandy. He would be accountable to those beady brown eyes watching the whites' every move. Mom always told us that we need to set a good example to our servants. She was right, they stared at us.

Toto, Sindie's older sister, focused on piercing the ears of a terrified little tot. Toto enjoyed sticking a red hot needle through their ear lobes. After removing the flame-sterilized needle, she then inserted a hard, waxy white thorn picked off a prickly pear leaf, to hold the wound open. When Toto paused to talk to me, her victim bolted, holding her ear and running until she was safely out of sight. Other vain victims already wore cactus thorns sticking out the front and back of their swollen lobes.

"Where is Sindie?" I asked after the usual greetings.

Lizzie, who never worked for us on Saturdays, was bent over a large bath of clothes. She stood up and stretched her back.

"Ukwamlungu (She is at the white people's home)," Toto revealed, still sticking the needle out in a rather menacing manner.

"Sindie went to collect cow dung," Lizzie stated, returning her attention to her laundry. "You will find her if you look near the stables." Sunlight soap suds were swirling on the surface of the dusty dam water, like a creamy topping on hot chocolate.

"I will find Sindie," I promised. "Thank you. Enjoy the *mgidi.*"

I strolled off down the hill on the footpath towards the stables. Most people went there to collect dung if they were in a hurry. Otherwise they followed one of their own cows around until it expelled some fresh green dung out from its tail end.

I peered into the bull stable where Jack, Sindie's dad, groomed and fed the beasts. Ordinarily, he brushed the bull's red coats vigorously to shine them up. But on this special occasion, I found him busily grooming himself. He was trimming his own whiskers with the same hair clippers he used to trim the hair around the bull's horns!

He broke into a tusk-bearing grin when he saw me. A pink, plastic-framed mirror balanced on the top of a pole dividing the bull pens. He turned to admire himself, accidentally knocking the cheap mirror off. It cracked. He cursed and propped it back up.

A large container *(umqoboti)* of Kaffir-beer was hidden behind the manger. The fermented corn gruel smelled sour. The whitish grey brew was opaque, frothing yeasty bubbles. Black powder *(intsizi)* floated on the top to dispel bad luck.

"Looking for Sindie, lovely child of *sngXhoshe?"* Jack had a way with words.

He resumed grooming his hair. First, he stuck his hand in the bucket of red lanolin, which he had stolen from the milking stable where it was used it to lubricate the cow's teats. Jack forcefully combed out his greased hair with a comb that looked like a shrunken hay fork. He proceeded to smear the lanolin all over his face and bare chest making his skin burnish like a stud bull. I could not help staring at such a drastic transformation. Jack slanted the cracked mirror to inspect his new appearance from all angles. His image was no better from any trajectory, but he smiled with satisfaction.

He was more proficient at grooming the bulls, I thought, but entombed the thought inside my head. I admired Jack for his unwarranted swagger and confidence.

"Sindie went that way, towards your miniature hut, sweet child of *Sngxhoshe*," he pointed politely.

The Collegiate girls said that if you broke a mirror, you were doomed to have seven years of bad luck. I withheld that information from Jack, our very talented bull groomer. He looked like he was blissfully lucky in life, having the good fortune of having a light-skinned wife, Lizzie, and an "other" wife, plump Maggie.

A white kid at school also told me that if an ugly person was to look in the mirror, the glass would crack. Perhaps she was right, was it Jack's image or gravity? Boarding school had taught me that white and black people have very different superstitions. It seemed that gullible societies enjoy following spurious dogmas.

For instance, superstitious whites are not supposed to walk under a ladder, spill salt, let a black cat cross their path, or crack mirrors. I gradually realized that I was supposed to behave as if I believed all those bogus beliefs. White kids collected wishbones and horseshoes as charms to boost good luck and make wishes come true. In African culture, black witchdoctors threw bones to tell fortunes, while European witches read tea leaves. All hooey hogwash!

It dawned on me then, that if you look at the white people's superstitions from a black person's angle—or if you study the black folk's superstitions from a white person's perspective—they are both equally unsound.

From the stable, I wandered towards our homestead past the thorn trees. Recent rains had turned Schelmdrift greener than usual. A few new, tender green thorns sprouted from the branches; I picked one off and chewed on it. You cannot eat Mimosa thorns once they are woody and white. At the center of the tree, glassy sap had oozed out of the trunk and now sparkled in the sun. I carefully crept passed the thorns and gathered the gluey gum on my finger. I popped the slightly sweet treat into my mouth. I had learned to eat thorns that taste like celery, and sticky gum from my indigenous playmates. Such treats weren't served at boarding school.

I opened the "stable gate" leading to our front yard. Just then, I recognized Sindie's bottom end sticking out of my miniature mud hut. She was on all fours, smearing fresh manure on the floor. She bustled out backwards, like an aardvark, wagging her tail from side to side.

Tombe appeared from behind the hut, her hands full of dung. "We came to fix up our hut. It needed the floor redone," Tombe announced proudly, satisfied with their results. "My mother said you were taking too long to eat breakfast, so we came without you."

"I have just finished, but you can't walk on it until it is properly dry," Sindie cautioned. She stood and stretched up her arms, with what appeared to be hands gloved in green—the green being recycled grass.

"Nindincedile! (You have helped me!)" I exclaimed happily. "It was so neglected. Thank you." I was somehow not as keen as I used to be to dip my hands in fresh cow dung.

"Noble chiefs are arriving from all over!" Sindie was visibly excited. "We must make the whole farm presentable."

Tombe, as always, was the motherly worrywart. "I am very happy that Cocoa survived the blunt knife and the bush…"

"I saw that old man sharpening the dagger on a stone before he went to do the cutting." Sindie interrupted. "The *ingcibi* (traditional surgeon) looked too old and weak to be doing such a strenuous task," Sindie tattled. "Some young men do bleed and die from ancient surgeons with poor eyesight performing the procedure. Too many suffer death from the rite…it is not right!" Sindie summed it up cynically.

"Cocoa's ancestors will be pleased!" Tombe defended traditions.

"Our little hut looks very pretty." I was feeling slightly left out of the festivities.

The climax of all the action would be mostly after dark. I would not be allowed to attend the ox-*braai*. It was a Kaffir affair, and they would not want a white piccanin ruining it. Besides, my parents did not allow us to be at the hut village after dark.

"Shall I go and get some meat from our house and we can make our own feast out here?" I gestured towards the rock semi-circle outdoor hearth, which we had added.

"Yes, Miss Jay. Let's cook," Sindie enthused. "It is time to celebrate. Cocoa is a real *iNdoda* (Man)." Sindie emphasized "man," as if it was the highest rank obtainable in the human race.

One would swear that Cocoa was going to be anointed Lord Mayor of London, as one of my great grandfathers was, back in Mother England in 1884. Equal pomp and ceremony were obligatory, it appeared. I truly had one very grand-ghost in my pedigree. Granny Stocks boasted of him often.

Back in my mud hut, Sindie, Tombe and I sat and enjoyed the log fire.

"Perchance Cocoa will purchase me in exchange for his one old cow with the red blotches," Sindie hoped out loud, sighing, lost in her innocent dreams.

"Where do you get that stupid notion? You have to pop out some boobs first." Tombe dashed harsh reality into the hopes of Sindie.

"Maybe someday the new man, *ubhuRwala* (Cocoa's new title), will give my dad the rest of the *lobola* (dowry of cattle) for me when I have grown boobs. Dad loves cattle. Dad will be happy." Sindie re-stated her hopes more realistically. She wished for just one spotted cow as a down payment.

"Cocoa will be wiser by now after all the lectures *(ukuyala)* on how to be a real man." Tombe knew about the mandatory lessons he would have to memorize before graduating to manhood!

As a custom, Xhosa men literally owned their wives. Each wife obeyed the man's wishes, as she was beholden to him. Young daughters were sold by their fathers like lambs to the slaughterhouse. A wife had no right to be disobedient, no matter how abusive the husband was. It was surely the oldest form of slavery. But the trickiest part of all was that they wanted to be bought. There was a social status to becoming "a bought wife." I reckon that was what was most disturbing to me. The men got to choose, but not the girls.

Tombe crouched low, blowing into the wood fire. The flames

grew bigger with each huff and puff. "We will be singing and dancing all night with the visiting maidens," she announced. "We have to look fat and well-fed as we show off our talents. Older boys will be looking at us, choosing us for future wives."

"We will feast on the ox-steaks sizzled to perfection all weekend." Sindie smacked her lips in anticipation.

"I want to come!" I envied their feasts.

"You *can* come!" Sindie declared as if she made the rules.

Tombe shot Sindie a warning glance.

"It is a Xhosa *siko* (ritual). I think we should ask for the old people's permission. The witchdoctor may disapprove," Tombe said firmly.

"That reminds me." Sindie's face lit up. "I am going to give the witchdoctor the coin that *uSngXhoshe* gave me at the gate. I want to buy lucky beans, so that I can marry well one day." By "well," Sindie meant Cocoa, of course.

Sindie had full faith in the new man. "Tonight, the *abakwetha* (initiates) dance in a row in front of all the onlookers and the most dynamic dancer is selected from the five. I know it will be Cocoa. He is the best dancer in the whole district! I have seen those other boys—I mean men—dance before, and they are deathly dull compared to him. Cocoa will be crowned the king of dancers for sure." Sindie smiled. "Then after he is chosen from the five, black dots are painted all over the white clay to make him look like a leopard…the most agile animal in the wilderness. The other four will remain pure white without spots, until they go and wash all the white clay all off in Bumpy."

"Do you use real black paint for the spots?" I asked

"No. Charred corn cobs are used to make the black spots," Tombe taught. "Sindie is right, Cocoa will probably be selected."

"He will be known as the Leopard Man and all those hysterical bald girls will shower him with gifts galore." Sindie was aware of her competition.

Tombe continued, "The *amakwetha* (initiates) will then wash off the white ochre in Bumpy and come home to be anointed with ox fat.

The witchdoctor smears a greasy cross down their back and across their shoulders. Then their whole body is smeared in ox fat. Then they smear red ochre all over their body. They are suddenly an *urhwala* (new man) and are allowed to do anything they want. They will get new clothes, a new stick, and a new red blanket of manhood."

Sindie divulged her fears, "Toto and her friends all shaved their heads to indicate that they are all willing to be wives to these new men."

"I saw some bald maidens earlier. I thought there had been another lice attack." I added. "Bruce and I saw those girls trying to balance buckets with no springy hair to help. They had to use their hands to hold the buckets up."

"UbhuRwala (name of new man) still has to walk slowly and show that he is a respectful new man, not a seasoned old man yet," Tombe noted. "And, by the way, I will buy sweets with my coin. The fatter we are, the more the men will love us."

"Well, let's go and beg for fatty stew meat!" Sindie reasoned.

We left Tombe to stoke our fire and set off towards the kitchen.

"Cocoa is very handsome," Sindie revealed her crush as we walked past vibrant orange red-hot pokers in the flower garden. "I am going to put a spell on him. I hope he chooses me to be his wife!"

"I think you're about ten years old, like me. Isn't that too young?" I asked.

"If only I had big breasts already. I did the frogs' egg ritual again the other day after the rains, but it still has not worked. I wish I was fat like Regina. Let's get lots of fatty food to make us plump by tonight," Sindie suggested.

"You'll have to grow boobs by tonight, too," I conveyed my concern. "I have an idea! The older girls at school do it. You can stuff socks in a bra."

Her face lit up, but then it fell just as fast. "It won't work. Where will I get a bra?"

"I'll borrow one from Wendy," I schemed. "You can use my school socks for stuffing."

"It won't work. My skin is too dark. Wendy's bras are too white, Miss Jay. I have seen them on the wash line when my mom does your laundry. I would need a brown bra." She trailed off sadly. "Miss Wendy's white bra will not match my skin."

"What if we washed the bra in very muddy water?" The memory of her stained panties remained vividly ingrained in my mind. I had just seen Lizzie's laundry being washed in cocoa-colored water.

Just then, Bruce returned to meet up with us on his way to the kitchen as well.

"And what mischief have you two been up to?" Bruce asked in English.

"None at all," I replied. "And you smell like you have been smoking!"

"Hayi (No), Miss Jay!" Sindie only spoke Xhosa, laughing at my bright bra idea.

"Otherwise, you will just have to wait for the frogs' eggs to kick in," I declared.

"I may have to be Cocoa's second or third wife by then," Sindie whined, letting her hope slip away like water down a plughole. Only the finger of faith could plug the hole in her hope.

All of a sudden, Sindie's face lit up again, her faith in magic rekindled. She sucked in air deeply to refuel her fire of faith, and breathed out, "Cocoa will love me one day when I grow big boobs from frogs' eggs. I will bewitch him then."

We chewed our tasty lamb stew and licked our greasy fingers, enjoying the jubilance of the sacrosanct day, which would last forever in memory.

At sunset, African drums began to rumble and roll from over the hill, indicating the commencement of Cocoa's homecoming ceremony. The drumbeat was beckoning my buddies to attend the ritual, just as any chiming church bells called Saints on the Sabbath.

Tombe and Sindie jumped up and ran off.

23

KUDU HUNTS

At the end of the second term, the four of us caught the train in P.E., with a few other boarders from the Albany District. The mood was festive as we had three glorious weeks ahead of us for the June holidays. Mom and Dad were at the Grahamstown station to meet us early the next morning. It was the happiest sight.

I had survived half a year with those Crimers. Cocoa was not married, so Sindie was still hopeful. Our little threesome spent a lot of time in my little hut that holiday, making stew and dreaming of our futures.

Every winter, my parents organized a "family hunt," which was a reunion for Dad's family who had all grown up on our family farm. The maids spruced up the Schelmdrift homestead. Mom spiffed up flower arrangements, adding all sorts of driftwood and Guinea Fowl feathers.

Wendy busied herself baking sweet braided pastries called *koek-susters* (dough deep-fried and dipped in lemon-ginger syrup) for tea. I helped her braid the dough as I had learned to braid my own hair at school. If our hair was long enough to touch our uniform collar, it had to be tied up in pigtails, ponytails or braids.

My most favorite relative, Aunty Hulda, spent weeks on Schelm-drift every winter. She was the oldest and much older than Dad who was a *laatlammetjie* (afterthought or late lamb). She had been married just before the war to an exceedingly handsome man. I only saw one photograph of Uncle Tim Gane. I thought he looked exactly like the real James Dean from America, who was worshiped like an idol. Aunty Hulda and Uncle Tim had a baby girl and named her Marian. Uncle Tim left to fight in WWII with Dad, but Uncle Tim never came home. Tim Gane was buried where he died on Normandy Beach. Sadly, our war hero's body was *not* in our family graveyard on the Schelmdrift estate, where it belonged. It had to stay overseas. I tried to explain that to Sindie and Tombe one day.

Tombe spoke with all seriousness, "Never mind, your uncle's ghost will not stay as a guest in that faraway place. His ghost can fly like the swallows from north to south. He will be here with his own family."

Even though Aunty Hulda had suffered the loss of her beloved husband, she refused to feel sorry for herself. Aunty Hulda was the most positive person I had ever known. She succeeded in bringing cheer to others. She was one of those personalities who perfected the knack of warming your heart. One has to be a strong person to lift others.

Aunty Hulda later married Uncle Alf Smith, who loved to hunt. By that time, Marian was all grown up and married to a good-looking farmer from Graaf-Reinett, Anthony de la Harpe. The Smiths brought us huge crates of export-quality apples and oranges from Worcester, in the Western Cape Province. Even the servants looked forward to their arrival because they brought them bushels of irregular fruit. Aunty Hulda was adored by everyone for her generous love. She always brought me a store-bought *jersey* (sweater), which was such a novelty since all mine were hand-knitted.

As a girl, Hulda Bester was well-loved at her boarding school in Cradock. She was chosen to be Headgirl. Her lovable personality rubbed off on Marian Gane, who was also selected to be Headgirl of Rustenburg Girls High in Cape Town. Later, Marian's daughter, Karen de la Harpe, was chosen to be Headgirl of Union High, in Graaf-Reinett. That was such an extraordinary feat that the newspaper published a photo of the three generations of Headgirls. They knew the secret of how to be loved. Was the personality trait of popularity passed down from generation to generation by DNA or by example? They were genuine, honest, decent folks with a flair for fun. I was proud to be related to such lovable folks.

My lovely mentor, Aunty Hulda, was also an avid golfer. She had won the ladies golf championship of the Western Cape Province for fourteen consecutive years. Her hometown of Grahamstown honored her frequently on her annual return visits, asking her to present trophies at the Grahamstown Golf Club.

She always dressed extra smart on those formal occasions. She wore navy or black slimming pencil skirts. To contrast her dark curls, she wore pastel cashmere twin sets. She had them in pretty pink, powder blue, and farm butter yellow.

We welcomed the dear relations arriving early on a frosty morning for the "family hunt," traveling from Graaf-Reinett, Somerset East, Bedford, and P.E. Sometimes the Leppans traveled from East London. I dearly loved all our Bester cousins, aunts, and uncles. We had 22 first cousins, mostly boys, who all grew to be six feet or more. The reunion was a much-anticipated, happy event.

"This chilly breeze will improve our luck. Kudu have very good ears. On a windless day, they can hear your footsteps much better, and dash off. I reckon we have a better chance in the wind," Dad told the dozen hunters. "Is everyone ready? Norman, are you warm enough? The wind will blow right through that jersey, my boy, go and put on my old army jacket."

The rugged hunters sported earthy colors for camouflage. Strong army boots were a necessity to hike up the rocky terrain. They wore boots over thick hand knitted socks.

During hunting season, Mother Nature gave the elusive kudu their thicker winter coats of grey fur with white stripes down the sides of their bellies. Kudu bulls were recognized by their grand spiraling horns, measuring up to 44 inches long.

"The 'beaters' will frighten the kudu out the low-lying *kloofs* (ravines) today. The kudu will be trying to get out of the cold themselves," Bruce offered as he willingly shared his immense knowledge about kudu habits and hunting.

"We are shooting for the pot," Bruce nudged the younger lads,

Norman and Martin, known for their kamikaze habits. "Make sure you aim for the head, not the rump." Bruce had perfected his hunting skills by endless target shooting.

Once, eight-year-old Bruce Bester had earned himself a jolly good spanking from Dad. Bruce was target practicing, shooting empty beer cans on a pole. Maids were strolling through the stone cattle kraal, balancing metal buckets of water on their heads. He could not see the maids, who were safely shielded behind the solid stone wall, but the moving buckets made a more challenging target than the motionless beer cans. Bruce could not resist the enticement to display his newly polished skills. He shot a hole through a water bucket while it still balanced on a maid's head. Water started spurting out from the metal bucket where the .22 bullet had pierced the side. Somehow, the dexterous maid skillfully held the bucket on her head. Maggie and Mom rushed to administer sugar water to the shocked maid, as was a common remedy in those days. Dad bought her a new bucket as restitution. He thought she deserved a whole sack of sugar for damages to her nerves.

"Righto then! All aboard the Land Rover!" Dad started in his customarily low hunting voice. "Try not to talk too loud, in case the wind carries our voices in their direction."

Dad always drove, and Mom went along to drive the truck back home. I always snuck on the back as a stowaway to eavesdrop.

The rest of the women sat in the lounge and drank tea, which Jane served, allowing them to add their own milk and sugar. Aunty Sheila, Dad's youngest sister, was the queen of crochet. She gave gifts of exquisite tablecloths to all the newlyweds. The relatives knitted woolen socks or jerseys as they nattered. Aunty Rene, the middle sister, shared tasty treats and recipes.

The men-folk were dropped off in the veldt, rifles dangled over their shoulders, held on by thick leather straps. Brown leather bullet belts adorned their hips. Dad directed them as to where to go and *"sit voor"* (wait and watch) as they say. Daddy was extremely meticulous about safety. He made very sure each one knew where the others sat, so there'd be absolutely no mishaps. After Dad's hushed, yet repetitive, safety pep talk, they hiked varied distances over the rugged veldt to find their designated high spots. Some had binoculars; others had telescopic sights attached to their well-oiled rifles. On a very sober note, the hunt began.

Head gear ranged from knitted *bonnets* (beanies) to cricket caps to *Voor-en-Agters* (hats that shelter the front and back of your head). Style depended on age and what "fashion time warp" the various Bester relatives belonged to. Dad stuck to his old felt favorite, punctured with holes where he touched to lift it when he greeted ladies.

Superstitious hunters wore hats that they swore had previously brought them "good luck," so they insisted on wearing their "lucky hats" again. Luck played a gigantic role in farming, hunting and fishing. I had not yet discovered the source of luck, but I strongly suspected it was *not* to be found in a hat of any fashion or fad.

As soon as the hunters reached their allocated positions, the "beaters" would walk up the hill from the direction of the huts. These were the Xhosa dads and adolescent boys who wanted to join in the sport. They hollered and threw stones into the bush, chasing the big kudu bulls or cows out of the thicket. The Xhosa "beaters" wore yellow caps or bright blue hats in the hope of not being mistaken for wild game or foliage!

Maggie and Jane were very busy, washing all the extra cups and saucers and preparing food for our numerous guests. Even Lizzie, our laundry maid, was called in on kitchen duty. Maggie ordered me to collect chopped wood.

Jack had stayed behind to take care of the stables and chop extra wood for the log fires. He had a fascinating skill of detecting how many kudu had been shot. We could hear shots far off in the distance from the *woodplace* (where wood was chopped). Jack taught me how to know if each shot was a hit or miss.

"Listen carefully, Miss Judy. If you hear a shot and it has a double thud, you know it hit something. If it is just a single bang, it only hit air. It missed its target."

Soon we heard shots ring out. They sounded closer than usual. The wind must've carried the sound our way. There was a definite, double thud.

"Raakskoot! (Spot-on-the-mark!)" Jack shouted jubilantly. "Did you hear that?"

"Yes, Jack. I heard it." I loaded my arms full of chopped wood.

More shots sailed across the airwaves.

Bang! "Miss!" **Bang!** "Miss again!" **Bang-boom!** *"Raakskoot!"* we both chanted after each shot, smiling at my new discovery.

"Yo! Yo! Yo! (Wow-Wee!) We are going to feast on meat tonight!" Jack was still gloriously grinning. "Lots and lots of kudu meat."

It was cold, but I paused to watch the happiness on Sindie's dad's face. Jack's tusks looked gleeful.

The Africans had no refrigerators in their huts, so they shared meat. And then when others got meat, they returned the kind gesture.

"We are going to get lots more *biltong* (jerky)." I joined Jack's joy.

"Those *raakskote* were from your Dad or *Baas* Bruce. They will never let us go hungry." **Bang!** "Miss!" **Bang!** "Yet another miss! Your mother, she would let us go hungry. *NoLasti* cannot shoot!" Jack was laughing. "You had better take that wood to the kitchen, or Maggie will be here…" **Bang!** "Miss! … hunting for you. She is a busy woman who does not like to wait. Tell her they have hit two already. Hurry on now, sweet child of *Sngxhoshe."*

"Tell Sindie I can't play with her today." **Bang!** "Miss! I have to be polite with my…" **Bang!** "Miss! ... cousins. We can play tomorrow again." I left Jack to chop wood.

Bang-boom! *"Raakskoot*! (Spot-on-the-mark!)" We both cheered, looking back at each other. "I will tell Maggie they have hit three!" I said.

Jack looked happy to see that I was such a good pupil.

At lunchtime, everyone bundled up warmly before we loaded all the ladies into a few trucks. Then we drove to a predetermined picnic spot near the road in the top veldt. It was near the spot where Cocoa has scorched all his boyhood belongings in the temporary grass hut. The hunters all gathered in the empty rivulet, where we warmed them up with steaming coffee and tea.

The "black beaters" made a separate fire. Maggie had packed brown bread and very sweet coffee for them to enjoy with their charred kudu liver. Sugar was not a shortage when Mom left the bin keys to me.

I lingered to hear the Xhosa's clicking description of the morning's events:

"UBaas Alf does not have the heft in his heart to kill an animal."

"His thick glasses on his eyes do not help him see at all."

"Bullets were whizzing all over the farm."

"It looks like he is trying to kick up dust with bullets."

"It really looks like *uBaas* Alf is just trying to scare the kudu for amusement."

"That angry *ngulube* (wild bush pig) with big tusks decided to charge Rama."

"*Baas* Bruce knocked off the bush pig in the nick of time."

I scurried from black picnic to white picnic and heard the tales from both parties. I would join my family and relish the stories from Rob-Roy, who was a gifted storyteller. Besters did not always let the truth get in the way of a fine *yarn* (tale). I heard both stories and figured the truth hid camouflaged in the middle.

"Bruce had a big bull almost run him over! If he wasn't so quick, the kudu would've trampled him! And as for Uncle Alf, it sounded like the Boer War all over again. He must have emptied all the ammunition he had on that one old kudu cow. It looked quite tame, even after he had emptied both magazines. It probably recognized Uncle Alf from last year when he missed it at forty yards," Rob-Roy reported.

"I think Uncle Alf gets so excited that he loses his co-ordination," Bruce commented. "He shoots before he aims. I have watched him. He pulls the trigger and then aims."

"Luckily, Tony was close by. While Uncle Alf was fumbling around for more ammo, Tony finally shot the kudu cow," Rob-Roy finished.

Brian von Holdt continued, "Two more kudu came out and stood in the open veldt right after that—Uncle Alf had a cow stand and wink at him from fifty yards away. *Heerrrlikheid, Boet* (Golly, Brother),

I thought Uncle Alf never spotted them, so I was just taking aim when Mike quietly dropped the kudu. I thought maybe it died of shock, until I saw smoke coming out of Mike's barrel."

"At least my big brother, Mike, shot it in the neck, so we'll get good venison. Uncle Alf usually shoots his in the backside!!" Martin piped up. If you shot the kudu in the hind quarters, you are mocked mercilessly forever.

"SH-SH!" Bruce scolded. "He may be a bit blind, but Uncle Alf is not deaf!"

"Who shot the fourth one?" Mom asked, while pouring creamy coffee into mugs.

"Well, Nigel hit the big bull first, then Martin grazed its shoulder, then Dad dropped it," Bruce reported. "It was a bloody good shot. It was running away from Dad, at about four hundred yards, and he hit it in the back of the head."

"Magtag, Jong (Golly, Chaps), Uncle Boet aims to kill!"

"I thought that big old bull was safely out of sight."

"It was *doerrr* (far-rr-away) and gone already when he flattened it!"

"Uncle Boetie is lethal with that old .303 rifle."

"No wonder he was a sniper during the war!" Barbara's husband, Bruce Catto smiled. They were on holiday from Durban, staying at Sunnyside.

After egg-mayonnaise or lamb and apricot chutney sandwiches, the hunters hiked in their dusty boots over into Uncle Sonny's top veldt. Dad gave all his "boys" leather boots every Christmas. The Xhosa dads handed their old boots down to their sons.

A few disturbed Africander cows roamed out of the bushes. "We hope *Baas* Alf's *four eyes* (spectacles) can tell his mind that those are cattle and not kudu," Tatey clicked safely, masking his joke in Xhosa under Uncle Alf's nose.

"I am glad I didn't wear my grey *jersey* with white stripes. He might think I was a kudu," Fikile lacked in faith in a particular hunter. Fear and faith do not dwell in the same place. Faith and fear always practice apartheid in one's heart.

Fikile usually volunteered to stay and chop wood. Jack had sprained his ankle when Iron Heart bucked him recently, so Jack had traded places with a fearful Fikile.

"*NoDyasana* (Uncle Sonny) should really not allow *Baas* Alf to hunt among these precious cattle. We may soon be feasting on stud beef mistaken for venison." Yan joked. Rama heard the comments and lingered, letting the "beaters" hustle and bustle into the bush ahead without him.

"Please ask your Mom if I can have a ride home, Miss Judy," Rama asked me. "My shoes are hurting me. My feet grew too big." He wore Maggie's old *tackies* (tennis shoes).

Trekking across the veldt required more than those gaping *tackies* in winter. His toes were peeping out the front.

How could Rama know his pedigree if he was fatherless? Rama did not have a dad to hand down leather boots. I felt so sad. As a new teen boy, he was self-conscious enough without having to wear his mother's holey shoes.

"Just jump in the back." I gave him permission, without asking my mom.

Rama and I sat on the back of our Land Rover together. I noticed his black big toes sticking out the torn *tackies.* I wondered about his black tribe and my white tribe. Poverty was painful. Those Africander cattle had more ancestors recorded on their pedigree charts than Rama. I felt sorry for him. I felt angry for him.

Africander cattle ambled across the road, so Mom stopped the Land Rover to allow the herd to cross over. One hefty, handsome stud bull "served" the herd. He had a Zebu hump like a camel, made of fat and muscle, distinguishing him from the cows. Africander cattle descended from the Egyptian longhorns, and were driven down the African continent by the *Khoi-Khoi* tribe.

On the 6th of April, 1652, Jan van Riebeeck, a Dutchman, settled at the Cape of Good Hope, landing three bulky ships in Table Bay. One was the Dromedaris and we had a model of it standing in our hallway on Schelmdrift. The Dutchmen set up a "refreshment station" to grow fresh fruit, rich in Vitamin C, to alleviate scurvy outbreaks on ships heading around the southern tip of Africa. European ships sailed east to load up on spices from India, long before the Suez Canal was opened.

Dutch traders bartered beads and mirrors for these *Sanga* type cattle. The Hottentots finally figured that the trashy trinkets could not sustain life, so they invariably claimed or stole their cattle back. The Dutch took umbrage at the theft. Hence, racial tension had its roots in theft and deception. Behavioral performances, not pigmentation, was the problem. Ownership of land and cattle was in dispute while the wilds of Africa were settled by Afrikaners (Dutch, German, and French mixed-breed). Stealing and lying seemed to be the real root of racism, not necessarily skin color.

The mighty British Empire did not seem to notice that the Dutch had already colonized the Cape, so they promptly recolonized it in 1805. They sent royal red-coats to fight Anglo-Boer wars. Shiploads of British Settlers arrived in 1820 in an attempt to Anglicize the Cape Colony. Posh English accents have been heard in the Grahamstown area ever since. That accent was preserved with pride in private schools.

Africander herds improved greatly over the generations. German-bred Bester Brothers culled and castrated the ugly bull-calves, turning them into draft oxen. These "German-engineered" red oxen trekked the Afrikaner Voortrekkers north to escape the British. Selected handsome bull-calves were stabled, fattened, and groomed to sell to other breeders to upgrade their herds, producing a good lean beef breed. Our ancestors thus transformed their herd into beautiful, spotless specimens. Very hard hooves help these cattle walk on the rocky road. One needs sturdy shoes to walk on the top veldt of Schelmdrift. Rama's ventilated *tackies* did not quite suffice in that weather.

Luckily, there was peace and mutual respect on Schelmdrift in 1966.

Maggie fried onions and mushrooms in butter to make a beef stroganoff. She added gobs of thick Jersey cream at the last minute. She sucked her finger and added dashes of pepper to taste. It was served on a bed of fantastic *Tastic* rice. Green peas along with rich orange pumpkin added color. Brandy pudding, milk tart, and sherry-laced trifle were favorite desserts. Aunty Rene brought Dad's favorite vinegar pudding, which their mother, Justine Langeneggar Bester, used to bake.

A platter with stinky cheeses and Pro-Vita crackers for snacking was left in the lounge. After a day-long hunt, Daddy stood and shaved kudu biltong (jerky) thinly with his sharp pocket knife onto plates for a salty snack. Children loved to catch the pieces that ricocheted off the plate as he speedily sliced away from himself. Kudu biltong was a most delicious delicacy we enjoyed.

Bottles of booze stood on a brass tray with fancy Waterford crystal glasses. Brandy goblets, tall beer glasses, sherry sipping glasses, and wine flutes all graced the polished tray.

Dad went outside to the *woodplace* to thank the "beaters" with a few cheap bottles of brandy for a *bhasela* (bonus). Xhosa men swigged it neat out of the communal bottle like Anglicans on the Sabbath Day.

The "beaters" worked hard, skinning and dividing up the venison. We only kept the hind legs and fillet. Dad divided up those spoils with his siblings and their progeny. The rest of the ribs and shoulder cuts of meat went to the servants. The Xhosas ate the whole wild bush pig as well.

Xhosa people shared readily. It was a big disgrace to be stingy. Stingy people were detested, and rightly so. Sharing was an essential survival skill. I could never tolerate stinginess. I inherited that trait from my three black "moms."

The fire and brandy kept the skinners warm. My Anglican cousin, Martin Bester, stole a swig out of the "beater's" brandy bottle.

"Rama was almost toast. That wild pig would have spread his guts out like soft margarine." Norman joked to Martin as they both secretly shared a cigarette around the beater's fire.

"Lucky Bruce is a crack shot." Martin laughed. "Or Rama would have disappeared into the ground like yellow margarine on hot toast."

Norman, Martin and I would join in for a little while until the skinners left to continue their party at the huts. Then we would go and join our family party inside the homestead.

"You smell like wood smoke. Where have you been?" Mom asked.

"Dancing with the servants around the bonfire," I replied.

Inside the lounge of our big old farmhouse was a different culture's party. Uncle Sonny stomped the wood floor while pounding at our piano. Nicky, our Sunnysider cousin, pumped the concertina, while Lyn strummed a ukulele. Barbara played her banjo.

I heard Dad report quietly to Mom, "We got a bally big fright this afternoon." He took a swig of beer. "Right after lunch, a massive kudu bull came and stood in the open. Everyone was having a go at it. Then Fikile started shouting and wailing. He came running to me and said that Rama was missing. Fikile was convinced that Alf had accidentally shot Rama. We couldn't find the blighter anywhere! Luckily, Tatey had noticed that Rama had got a lift home with you."

Heather sang from the songbook wherein Mom had handwritten the words to *"Sarie Marais," "O Brandewyn laat my staan,"* and other favorites of *boeremusiek* (Afrikaans country music). Our family also sang a few English pub songs and waltzes with zest. *"In the Mood," "Daisy,"* and *"She'll be Coming around the Mountain"* cheered the contented crowd. Uncle Sonny could jazz up any song.

The men pushed the couches aside and rolled up the green rug so everyone could jig or jive. Whether you wore *nappies* (diapers) or used a walking stick, you bent your knees or tapped your toes respectively in time to these folk songs. Angela and cousins crowded by the piano and sang loudly, hitting or missing the notes; accuracy apparently did not matter any more. "Spot-on-the-mark" did not apply after a few spots of whiskey.

Couples waltzed, while cousins did the twist or bopped together. Some brought girlfriends or boyfriends *on appro* (for approval) to these family hunts. Uncle Sonny played by ear, having had no music lessons. He had raw, God-given talent. When he heard a tune on the radio, he could pick out the notes and play it like Jerry Lewis. It was easy to keep the beat because the floor shook as his heavy boot drummed those wide wooden beams. And so the hunt ended, not nearly as soberly as it began.

First thing in the morning after a hunt, our whole family of six had to help cut up kudu venison to make biltong. Dad carved off muscles of meat to be sliced into smaller strips to be cured in salt.

On an errand to the kitchen to collect more salt, I spotted Maggie and watched as she emptied all the crystal glasses. This was a prerequisite dutiful ritual, before Jane hand washed the valuable glassware. Maggie squeezed every leftover drop of sherry, beer, gin, whiskey, brandy and wine from the previous night's party into her enamel mug, filling it to the brim with a maroon mixture. She then downed the cocktail of dregs in one long gulp.

Our cook burped out aloud and smiled, *"Enkosi* (Thanks), *Nohanki."*

I was not sure exactly why she thanked me. Perhaps it was in anticipation of me not revealing her secrets of her creative "shindig *shandy."* Maggie was lovable inside for her caring character, even if her outside spots never changed.

Later, we baptized the wild meat in red grape vinegar to remove the salt. We sprinkled each strip with roasted, crushed coriander and white pepper. The *stuks* (slices) were hung to dry on horizontal wires, which were permanently strung along the back dairy ceiling. Metal gauze across the windows kept blue flies out of the cold back dairy.

All morning while we made the biltong, Mom expressed her concern about our musical misdemeanor. "Our side of the family shamefully lacks musical talent. Only the *Sunnysiders* can play instruments." Mother decided she was going to remedy the malady by learning to play the violin. "Our family needs more musical culture. We own the instruments, but none of us can play them. It is simply a disgrace."

"I love The Troggs' new song, *'Wild Thing.'"* Bruce beamed. "I want to learn to play it on the guitar."

"I read that The Troggs name is short for troglodyte, which means cave dweller." Dad informed us with a grunt of disapproval. "That is why their music is nicknamed Caveman Rock!"

"Once I teach myself to play the violin," Mom announced determinedly, "then I'll teach my children. We have to develop and grow our talents, or we will stagnate. Even regress to cavemen. We have to maintain our culture."

24

COLORFUL CORN COBS

As soon as her hands were free of wild kudu blood, Mom dug out an antique violin from the storeroom in an outbuilding, where we kept the Natives' food rations.

Presently, Gwenna Stocks Bester perched on the piano stool in our lounge with her long legs crossed. She looked as pretty as a bird, with her auburn hair tussled and her freckles faded with winter whiteness. She swayed her red head just like a Black collared Barbet as she counted the music beats. Smudges of smoky eyeliner from the night before were still evident, showing traces of her party spirit.

My ambitious mother announced, "I am going to teach myself to play the violin first, after which we shall all learn to play the piano. I'd be delighted if we could all buff up our musical skills." Mom was such a gifted teacher, I fully expected her to be most proficient. "Perhaps you will all stop listening to those rowdy Beatles."

As mother hit the first note, Jane, who was quietly sweeping the cold ash from the fireplace, dropped the dustpan in fright, spilling a plume of grey ashes. Jane had clearly not understood Mom's forewarning in English as Aunty Hulda and I had! Poor Jane could not have possibly prepared her African eardrums. Jane respectfully laughed at herself and muttered, *"Mta' kaKwetha!* (Child of the Kwetha family!)" That is how she always scolded herself if she broke something. Jane was sorely disadvantaged, not even knowing what a violin was for.

Aunty Hulda stopped knitting in the middle of a row, and politely hid her knitting basket. "I'm going to take a little tour of the stables and see the champion bull that Sonny mentioned last night."

Mom struck another very shrill note. Jane jumped, as if she had an electric shock. She wasn't expecting *NoLasti* to make two horrible gaffes in a row.

"Hayi, nd'othukile (No, I got a fright)," Jane said bashfully, amused at herself.

All of a sudden, two lazy, overfed cats darted out from behind the couch. The Siamese made for the light of the front door, skidded on the polished wooden floor, and then skillfully regained its footing. The black furry cat made a desperate dash for the passage door because it was nearer.

Unfortunately, Maggie had decided to occupy that particular doorway at the exact same time. She came to see what on earth could produce such an earsplitting sound. She held a glass Pyrex dish in one hand and a drying cloth in the other.

"Hintoni na engxhola kangaka? (What is the thing making that amount of noise?)" Maggie demanded in disgust.

The cat, whose paws lost traction on the freshly polished floor, got tangled in Maggie's very broad, bare feet. Maggie delivered a slight kick. The dish took flight, shattering on the floor.

At the same moment, Maggie managed to swipe at the frenzied cat with her weapon—a soggy, stinging kitchen towel. The cat got waylaid in Maggie's multiple skirts. Its sharp claws ripped at the extra layers, worn not merely for warmth, but also to enhance a plumper silhouette. The unlucky black cat crossed the wrong path, our cook's path. Maggie was quite cross! I wished that my superstitious Collegiate friends could have witnessed that black cat's fate!

As Maggie wildly attacked our cat, she lost her footing and started to fall backwards, only to find herself safe in the strong arms of *Baas* Alf, Aunty Hulda's husband. He had been roused from a nap by the various unexpected sounds.

"WAT gaan hier aan? (WHAT is going on here?)" Uncle Alf asked emphatically, reverting to Afrikaans and sounding eerily like a government official.

"Mom is going to civilize the Schelmdrift side of the family," I explained.

Mother was rather pleased to have an audience, and she promptly struck another high-pitched stroke. This made the cat even more violently frantic to depart, and Maggie more determined than ever to exterminate the cat. She had detested the ball of fur for years because it stole the cream once too often. At last, Maggie could exhibit her pent-up hatred with kicks and clouts. Her coordination was erred by earlier cocktails, luckily for the black cat that had crossed her path.

Uncle Alf posted Maggie back on her flat feet. The cat narrowly escaped with strands of Maggie's petticoat attached to its claws. They resembled white flags of surrender.

"Ndizakubulala! (I am going to kill you!)" Maggie hissed at the fleeing feline.

Jane rushed over to try and sweep up the Pyrex dish remains, hoping to restore order. Peace was soon restored, albeit for a mere moment.

Uncle Alf asked, "Where's my Hulda?" noticing his wife was not in her favorite rocking chair. He shuffled in wearing his Tartan fur lined slippers.

"She went to the stable to inspect the prize bull," I informed him.

Mom struck another cord.

"Magtig (Golly), that sounds like a swell idea. I think I'll take a stroll that way myself." He quickly scooted towards the front door.

Oddly enough, he had mentioned at breakfast that he could hardly walk. He complained that his muscles were stiff and sore from the long hike of the hunt. Now he suddenly thought walking was a "swell idea."

Mother hit another agonizing note with even greater gusto!

Uncle Alf winced, regretting he hadn't fired enough to at least dull his sense of hearing. He quickened his pace, showing no sign of stiffness, and accelerated towards the stables still wearing his slippers. His joints jerked forward faster with each excruciating violin note.

My assiduous mother simply stroked the violin more ardently.

After another painful pitch, Jane darted down the passage to empty the ashes and glass fragments on the banks of Bumpy. She sought refuge at the smelly rubbish dump.

"Ithenina la nto, ekhala kangaka? (What's the matter with that thing that cries like that?)" Jane was solely blaming the violin, not *NoLasti.* Jane composed herself, and then she smoked her long pipe on the kitchen stoep to calm her nerves.

Maggie was still loudly cursing the cat hidden behind the stove, mixing languages as well as she mixed drink dregs, to be sure it comprehended its days were few, no matter which tongue it understood.

Mom demonstrated to me as she squeaked the strings, "I don't think this has been tuned for *donkey's* (many) years."

She hit middle C on the piano as a reference.

Jane returned with the dustpan and swept up the last of the ashes, shuddering with each stroke of the bow but still politely blaming the instrument.

"Miss Judy, ivela phi na lento ekhala kakubi kangakha? (Miss Judy, where does this ugly sounding thing come from?)" She frowned and smiled, bashful as usual.

"Mother dug it out of a cupboard in the store. I think it belonged to her refined English ancestor whose husband was the Lord Mayor of London," I answered. "Mom believes it will make us all more cultured."

Jane sprang into the air every time Mom hit a note, like a ballerina en Pointe.

"Tell her please to put that squawky thing away quickly. It will chase the good spirits out of this home. They will flee back to London." Jane pleaded, very concerned. She gathered her dustpan full of ashes. "She strokes it very gently, but it squeaks in a very vile manner!" Jane appealed in Xhosa to me, genuinely smiling. "It will chase the ghosts away, even Caesar's ghost—the one she always invites over." She warned, while exiting with great haste.

Maggie, whose coordination was slightly off key due to the dregs she had consumed, almost collided with Jane in the doorway. Jane nimbly dodged her.

"Miss *Gwina, ndizokucela ipilisi* (Miss Gwenna, I have come to ask for pain pills)," Maggie begged. "And to ask for your forgiveness for the fallen dish."

"It's alright. What's the matter, Maggie?" Mom asked naively, not wanting to forfeit our cook while we had guests.

"I have a huge headache," Maggie moaned, peering accusingly at the violin. "It's that thing. The sound hurts my head."

"She wants you to stop!" I translated.

Mom innocently disregarded me. I was sent to fetch the aspirin bottle from the little yellowwood medicine chest as she carried on her practicing.

The boys and Dad were fortuitously out on the farm. Wendy had followed Dad, hoping for a driving lesson before we went back to boarding school.

"I keep telling Daddy not to give the servants so much brandy, but he won't listen," Mom muttered as she plopped four white pills in her cook's brown hand.

Soon I heard the kitchen door slamming as the maids left for the huts prematurely. My ears were also starting to sting, so I followed them.

The smell of kudu stew was coming out of every hut in their little village.

"Where have you been?" Sindie had missed me.

"We had to cut up and salt legs and legs of venison. I was also listening to my Mom play a thing called the violin. It sounds worse than a rusty windmill," I said. "You should come and see."

Maggie intervened. "Don't go, Sindie. The scraping noise made my head feel like it was cracked open with a blunt axe."

Just then, we noticed Uncle Alf and Aunty Hulda come strolling very slowly up the hill from the direction of the stables. Uncle Alf limped a little and held onto Aunty Hulda for support.

"Here come the poor houseguests. They will beg us for a bed to sleep on in our homely huts if *NoLasti* doesn't stop making that stringy plank squeak," Maggie mused. "Our white lady is oblivious to her social discord. It gave me a hangover while I was still tipsy."

Aunty Hulda and Uncle Alf made their way slowly over to the Eden Dam, to see how full it was, no doubt.

Tombe came running towards us, greeting us happily. "I have been trying to salt meat to make biltong too. We hung it on the fence. We can't eat all our meat. My father sent my brothers to take buckets of meat to my grandpa and cousins at Carlisle Bridge. And Miss Judy, why is your white uncle not wearing outdoor shoes? Tell him to put his leather boots on!"

When the Smiths got closer, piccanins wandered over to stare at the white faces.

"Thank you very much for the oranges and apples," Tombe gracefully clicked.

"They say thank you for the fruit," I repeated in English.

"It looks like they need the vitamin C with all the colds." Flu bugs were about, and most of the children had runny noses with dried mucus on their upper lips. Aunty Hulda was a nurse by profession. She caressed Tombe's outstretched hand. "I'm glad you enjoyed them, Tombe."

Uncle Alf smiled and shook their hands. The notorious black-rimmed spectacles perched on his red nose. His veined cheeks were presently purple from frostbite. He handed out some *XXX* mints that he happened to have in his pocket. The disheveled children curtsied. Some little ones ran away, too afraid to speak to the unfamiliar faces.

"Whose child is this?" Aunty Hulda asked me. "He is the splitting image of Yan when he was a little chap." She picked out Tombe's little brother, who was gnawing away on a kudu rib bone.

Aunty Hulda's character exuded charity, the purest type of love, and not only to the high and mighty. Her love extended not just to the elite, but also to the snotty-nosed piccanins. Her charity never failed to cheer up the downtrodden. Her Xhosa name was *noThandabantu* (One who loves people).

The following breakfast, my optimistic Aunty Hulda calmly announced, "I think I'm going to go into Grahamstown this morning and play a few rounds of golf. I must keep my eye in. We need to make the most of this sunshine."

Uncle Alf was quick to the draw. "I think I'll join her—not to play golf, but to go and see if I can buy a telescopic site for my rifle."

"Pop in at *Stirk's*, and ask them for advice," Dad turned to my Uncle Alf. "That shop has the best selection of gun sites in town. You may need to have your sites seen to. You will have much better luck, I reckon." Dad was holding a lit match to his pipe and inhaling deeply. "Please don't forget to buy me the newspapers," he requested, blowing out smoke.

"May I go to the huts?" I excused myself.

"If you must. Please put a jersey on, it is rather nippy out," Mom instructed.

As I neared Sindie's hut, Lizzie came out to throw a blue enamel dish of dirty water out over the fence. The grubby water flew through the cold air and sunk into the dirt. A few soap suds stuck on the wet spot. They sat for a minute shuddering at the thought of being rudely tossed out.

"Molo (Hello), Miss Jay. Come in and play dolls. Here is one for you to keep." Sindie handed me a fully-dressed corn cob.

"She is beautiful," I remarked, "and very fat. Thank you, Sindie!"

All the little children were huddled around a mature fire with glowing coals, frosted with white ashes in places. Their hearth was in the middle of their round, cozy home.

"Put a few more logs on. We don't want Miss Jay to get cold," Sindie ordered her little sister.

"And you! Call Tombe very quickly. Tell her Miss Jay is here." Sindie bossed another youngster, who flew out of the hut like a chicken whose legs had left its feathers behind.

"That is Sindie's favorite doll," a very young child stated, too young to practice tact.

"I am giving it to her," Sindie announced, not showing any regret.

"Thank you, Sindie." I was delighted. "Who made it?"

"My sister helped me make her," Sindie replied, willing to sacrifice, glaring at her squeaky little sister.

"You can't have it. Sindie loves it." The little child could not help speaking up. Little dark eyes looked at me as if I were a greedy thief of some sort.

"Sindie, let's make one for you just like it!" I was starting to feel a little guilty about the gift I had been given.

Tombe came striding down the hill with her little bundle of rags and her own corn cob doll. As Tombe entered Sindie's hut, an innocently baffled child winced in a warning tone, "Sindie already gave her favorite doll to Miss Judy," perhaps not wanting to witness any more sacrifices.

"Well then, let's make Sindie another one. I brought some extra rags." Tombe was motherly, soothing the souls of the gawking onlookers.

"There is a nice fat corn cob by our woodpile. You! Go and get it." Tombe bossed the child who acted so concerned.

The little girl ran out eagerly and soon came back with a dusty corn cob. Tombe scraped it clean with her fingers over the fire, causing crackling sparks.

"Give me that cob, I'll cover it." Sindie wrapped it with strips of fabric from a worn-out sheet. The brown sheet had once been white. But it had been washed in dam water so often that is was now a beige color.

Sindie started at the top, covered its narrow head, and bandaged it all the way down to its broader base. "This is how my sister taught me." Sindie put strips of fabric in her mouth and chewed them into a tight little ball the size of a loquat pip. "This is how you make the boobs," she said as she covered the *gobby* ball with the square. She used her teeth to tug the square cover tightly over the ball.

"Naantsi ikati! (Here's a cat!)" Someone yelped, as our black cat bolted in the door wildly.

The cat darted behind a carton box, pulling its tail in for better concealment.

"Whose cat is that?" One terrified tyke bawled.

"It is ours. It usually lives near the dairy. It is half wild. It only comes inside in the winter for warmth. It likes the heat of your fire,"

I explained. "I think it chose Lizzie's house because Maggie tried to kill it."

"Will it eat us?" an alarmed child asked. "Big cats eat people."

"It prefers mice," I said, "with Jersey cream."

Tombe tore strips to bandage the now completed boobs onto the corn cob.

Lizzie looked longer and leaner from the floor. She bent over to lift the wrought iron lid off the pot which was standing over the fire on its three legs. The heavy, black legs didn't mind the fire licking their soot-covered feet.

Steam escaped from the boiling, gurgling potage. It mingled with the smoke as they both reached for the ceiling of thatch since there was no chimney through which to fly up to the sky. Black soot crusted the conical roof.

When I looked sideways I noticed skulls of sacrificial goats stuck in the thatch right where the mud wall reached the thatch. It was on the man's side of the hut, where Jack slept. A second skull, after years of smoky fires, had gradually grown a black goatee from soot.

The goat skulls were not hunting trophies, like the huge kudu heads mounted by a taxidermist, hanging in our entrance hall. To the contrary, these skulls were eerie reminders that ancestral spirits had been honored. The once white skulls symbolized hope that protection would be awarded to Sindie's family.

Lizzie threw a chopped onion into the steaming cauldron, stirred it a little, and then replaced the heavy, black lid over the kudu stew.

"Now we need to make the buttocks," Sindie demonstrated. She chewed two even bigger balls of fabric firmly to the size of drought-stricken apricots. With the bubble butt of a purebred Bushman, Sindie reflected her own hopes in her African version of an ideal shape. It sharply contrasted the plastic Barbie dolls from America that my boarding school friends played with. The only common feature was big breasts, both cultures sanctioned those!

"Now, we need to dress my doll." Sindie was proud of her new creation. Tombe rummaged through her rags and made an offering of faded fabric.

"Come, Sindie and Tombe, let's go and look in the Breakfast Room. My mom has a sack full of material scraps," I suggested.

Our trio waltzed down the hill with our corn cob dolls. As we reached the kitchen door, we saw Jane sitting on the *stoep*, smoking her pipe. They had come in early to make kudu bone soup. Xhosa women traditionally smoke very long-stemmed pipes. This is so they don't drop ashes on their babies, who are always suckled on their breasts.

Jane was talking to Maggie. "No, mother of Rama, I can't do that. I am afraid."

"Come then, let's hide it in the store, where it has been sleeping for years. My ears are hurting. It sounds like that black cat when I pulled its tail," Maggie bemoaned.

"How will we get into the storeroom? *Nolasti* has the keys." Jane was sucking her pipe extra hard for an extra dose of nicotine, talking as she exhaled smoke.

She spat. It landed on the ground about six feet away.

"Look, Jane, I can spit too, like you taught me," I spat through my top teeth.

Mom opened the bathroom window just in time to see me aim and shoot saliva.

"What on earth do you think you are doing, my child?" Mom winced.

"Spitting!" I stated. "Watch! I'm quite good!" I tried again, but not too successfully. I had run out of saliva. "Look! Sindie gave me a doll. It was hers. She made herself another one."

"The doll is very pretty. Spitting, on the other hand, is most vulgar. Please come inside and allow me to teach you how to play the violin instead." She said as she shut the window.

Our trio hesitated and huddled on the steps of the *stoep* catching the last rays of weak, watery, wintry sun.

"Miss Judy! Hurry and get the store keys! Right now! Steal them if you have to!" Maggie burst onto the back stoep with a log of wood, holding it in a threatening position. I feared she might pelt me with it. "Run! Before I take that squeaky wooden thing and use it to stoke my fire," Maggie threatened.

I jumped.

"NoWintsi! (Jane's Xhosa name!) You go and grab it out of the lounge! We will stuff that squawking plank back in the storeroom where it belongs!" Maggie commanded. "You can pretend you were just tidying the lounge."

She was acting like a sergeant major. Maggie had declared war on the peace shattering instrument.

"Mom said it cries worse than a hungry cat," Tombe tried to fill Sindie in.

"Maggie warned us," Sindie responded.

"No, I am too afraid." Jane was smiling at Maggie for mercy.

"I'll get the violin *and* the keys," I volunteered. Mom taught that literature, music, and Christianity refined moral character. Quite to the contrary, Maggie considered carved wooden instruments and paper books as combustible materials, useful only for log fires.

"No wonder the black cat has moved in with Sindie's family," I chuckled as I got up, thinking how mistaken old folks could be.

"Mom, may we please have some leftover material for our *mielie* cob dolls?" I called out.

"Certainly, I'll come and find the off-cuts for you," Mom called back. "Your little friends may come and play in the Breakfast Room. It is too chilly to be out. I am surprised Aunty Hulda is still playing golf."

"I am not surprised at all," I muttered under my breath.

I went to the piano and saw the violin lying in an open, fitted case. I quickly shut the box and clipped it closed. I tried to escape to the kitchen with it.

Mom stopped me. "And where do you think you are going with my violin?" Mom asked huffily, "To play it for the servants?"

"Maggie said if this instrument doesn't go back in the storeroom, she is going to look for a job at Sunnyside. Then we won't have a cook anymore." I stood firm.

"Oh drat! It is not *that* bad. I am still learning." Mom seemed most indignant.

"It is *very* bad…the poor servants! The cats have disappeared to the huts! Maggie thinks it will make good firewood!" I told the truth.

"Firewood?" Mom queried crossly.

"Yes. Maggie wants to cremate the violin. Jane said, just now, it would burn very well. The antique wood is brittle and dry." I elaborated, but I needed bigger ammo, so I continued. "Why do you think Aunty Hulda is playing golf in the freezing sunshine? And Uncle Alf ran away too on his sore, stiff legs?" I spoke of all the recent refugees. "In his slippers!"

"Fine, I'll have to teach myself another time, and then I'll civilize you properly," Mom finally realized her practicing was not popular.

"I am going to put it away!" I said. "Where are the keys?"

"Next to my bed," Mommy said, with a sigh of defeat. "I suppose I will go and have a cup of tea instead then."

"Thank you!" I smiled with relief.

"Enkosi!" Maggie and Jane echoed in Xhosa and nodded enthusiastically.

"I shall find you the bits and pieces of material." Mother was composed and resolved not to discuss the violin any further. She stiffened her British upper lip.

My little friends were overjoyed at the colorful array of fabric. We spread the floor with colors—mostly turquoise, as that was Mom's favorite color.

"Thanks, Mommy." I was grateful for her kindness, and I hugged her.

Sindie snatched scraps of rich red. Tombe reached for the blue hues.

"Our mother cobs need babies to tie on their backs," Tombe enthused. "I know how to make them." She rolled a little piece of yellow fabric into a scroll, the size of a dried date, and that became the baby. We all copied her fast fingers folding tiny squares to make triangles, which we neatly bent over to form a contrasting baby bonnet.

"I want a pink bonnet. My baby is a girl," I pretended. "Pink is for girls."

"Why do girls wear pink? Who started that strange tradition?" Sindie wanted to know.

"I am not sure who started pink for girls, but I like it so I will keep doing it," I answered.

"I want my baby to wear blue, so does that make it a boy?" Tombe asked.

"That is what Miss Jay says," Sindie reasoned. "We can copy the white people sometimes, too."

"I don't think we can change who we are. That old fisherman at Ship Rock, said we keep our old core cobs, but we can adopt good habits from all kinds of folks. I don't think we are leopards. We should be able to change our spots, if our *ngqondo* (minds) are not so *qingiwe* (constipated). He said we must have a fluid mind, a mind like the sea, always accepting a fresh flood of ideas." I clicked perfectly.

"Can we do that without that dreadful squeaking plank?" Sindie checked.

"I hope so," I answered.

"When I grow big boobs, I am going to be as pretty as this doll." Sindie smiled as she held up her freshly-adorned corn cob, "I am going to knock the spots off Cocoa, our newly crowned Leopard Man."

We were going to have all three dolls dressed the exact same. Deep down, I dreamed that one day I would dress like my Aunty Hulda and wear pearls with cashmere.

"Will you forget Sindie and me when you are grown up?" Tombe asked earnestly.

"No, Tombe. How could I be so callous?" I assured her.

"Don't you dare forget about us when you go back to school next week!" Tombe demanded. "I will not allow you to forget us, even when you sink into the white society."

We made the next generation of fabric babies out of superior cloth. Complete with Xhosa headdresses, the dolls wore stripy towels to strap their new babies onto their backs. They were clad in equally vivid colors, but their inner cob was covered in dust-stained fabric.

"Let's go and show our moms in the kitchen," Tombe urged triumphantly.

"One day we will all be wives with big boobs like these dolls!" Sindie dreamed.

"I am going to tie my babies on my back too. Even if white ladies are not supposed to do it, I am going to adopt your custom," I declared.

"Those frogs' eggs had better work!" Sindie smiled cheekily.

"Old people know it works." Tombe stated soberly.

"We must find out the truth for ourselves, even if we have to hunt for it with a telescopic site. My mother says your old people talk rubbish and your old people think white old people talk tripe, too. I want to start a new tradition of being friends with you both forever," I declared, fully intending to apostatize from apartheid.

"We will be your friends, forever and ever." Tombe declared with a broad grin.

"Our lives may go different ways, but we will always come together again and be friends forever." I swore with all my heart.

Posting her corn doll in the air, Sindie danced into the kitchen, chanting in English, "Forever and ever and ever..."

25

CULTURE COLLISION

One hot December day in 1966, my family of six, two maid servants, and Cocoa, the new manservant, all squished into two vehicles. Huge stainless steel tins of *rusks* and homemade biscuits stood between the fresh produce on the back of our brand new white Land Rover.

I had survived a whole year at boarding school, and Cocoa had survived circumcision. We thus set off to Kasouga to celebrate the Christmas season.

"Who-can-see-the-sea?" Dad was his cheerful self.

Cocoa had a big smile on his face as we drove over the Kasouga hill in convoy. This was to be his first Christmas as a real man. That was status to be revered. He would be fishing for a wife, no doubt, while he washed our cars, gutted the fish, and cleaned the boat. No wonder he was so smiley! He looked as pleased as Punch. He stood up in the back of the Land Rover, smelling the cool sea air through his huge Native nostrils. I was proud of our Cocoa for his survival skills.

I wished I could encourage him to buy Sindie for that spotted cow. Or at least I could ask Daddy to persuade Cocoa to choose my friend.

Staring at Cocoa, I saw a fleck of red ochre fall from his face as he grinned widely. After passing the bush test, he was expected to paint his face red daily for a full year. If he had been a cat, he would have been a Cheshire cat, with that endless grin.

"Cocoa, will you help the maids with these heavy boxes, please?" Mom supervised the servants, while Dad knocked out his pipe on the front wooden step.

"Doesn't this sea air smell good?" Dad carefully unloaded his fishing rod. Dad knew how to relax and unload his mind. I admired that about him. He looked at Mom. "I can't wait to go and catch a big Jan Bruin for you," his smile deepened his dimples.

Familiar families from all over Albany District were in different stages of unpacking. Each one looked a little older every year as we summered at the seaside.

The men-folk talked about the exact same subjects year after year: cricket, fishing, and recent rains. The ladies loved to discuss the weather and who was engaged, married, or pregnant.

"I want to go over to Port Alfred tonight. I hear they have a very good band playing at the Langdon Hotel." Bruce sloshed an excessive amount of butter on his fresh green *mielies* (corn on the cob) as we sat around the supper table. "I heard they play Wilson Picket songs, Mustang Sally and In the Midnight Hour very well."

A few days later, Mom was making posters to advertise a Kasouga Dance. Our parents were volunteers on the Entertainment Committee. While Dad fished, Mommy wrote in her neatest teacher handwriting with a thick black *khoki* (marker) pen:

KASOUGA SESSION

FRIDAY 16th DECEMBER 7 p.m.

KASOUGA HALL

BAND: THE GULLEY CRABS

Admission R1 Cool drinks 25c

"Here, Norman and Judy, will you two please pin this one up on the notice board around the corner? Everyone will see it on their way to the beach. Our Committee will make more profit if we have a good turnout. Our entertainment committee needs funds to pay for a new generator for the Kasouga hall."

Handing Norman the box of sharp tacks, Mom added, "Auntie Joyce will take posters to put up at Kenton-on-Sea, Kariega, and Bushman's River Mouth. I will put some up at the Kowie (Port Alfred) this afternoon when I go grocery shopping. Please make certain you do it properly. It must be straight." Mom was well-known as a competent organizer.

Sixteen-year-old Wendy spent all Friday fussing, washing her hair in an enamel washing basin. She wrapped strands of damp hair in brown paper, and then she ironed it to straighten the fizz out. She used the heavy iron that Maggie heated on the gas stove. After that, Wendy painted her nails a pearly pink shade. I just stared at her in wonder. There was a distinct cosmetic change in her appearance.

"Turn the volume up," she commanded while blowing her fingernails dry. "Rock and Roll is fab." She was doing a shy jig. It was a heartless attempt compared to Sindie's salacious efforts. The Troggs were hissing *"With a Girl like You,"* over the radio waves.

"That does not quite qualify as music. It's just noise," Mom sniffed, exiting the shack with her library book and straw hat. She sought refuge with her parents next door.

Suddenly I heard a song called *"Satisfaction,"* and I was on my feet. My body responded by jumping onto the spare bed, swaying my hips and shoulders with all my might.

"Judy! Who taught you to dance like that?" Wendy shouted, still shaking her nails dry. "You look like an Af." She was both smiling and frowning at the same time.

"I am an African. And I am rocking with-no-sat-is-fa-a-ction!" I cheeked.

"White people don't dance like that! You are supposed to be white. Don't dance like a Hottentot!" She was shaking her head, but the frown never shook off.

"I'll teach you the twist, like this," Wendy wiggled. "Now practice."

I copied her twist, but I also added my flavor to it by sticking out my buttocks.

"We can't take you anywhere," she retorted with a smug smile of a satisfied instructor who recognized a slight improvement in her pupil. "After a whole year at Collegiate...you must not dance like a piccanin in public!"

The Entertainment Committee members arrived at the rustic hall an hour early. Servants had swept the spacious wood floor. Mom was now busily sprinkling Johnson's Baby Powder all over the dance floor.

"What are you doing? The maids just swept the floor!" I inquired indignantly.

"This will make it nice and slippery. My mother used to do it exactly like this. It is easier to slide your shoes and make gliding waltz steps." Mom carried on.

I had visions of people skidding. "You will make them slip and fall."

"It will do nothing of the sort. We will smooth it out with the broom, so it does not look quite so patchy." Mom insisted.

"But what about the smell?" I objected. "It smells like a baby's bum in here."

"A clean bottom, I may add. And you should not use the word 'bum,' it is not ladylike at all. You should say 'bottom.' " Mom hurried on, puffing out white clouds of talcum powder with very determined movements.

"This is the 60s, Mom. People don't waltz anymore at dances. They shuffle and twist nowadays," Norman piped up, carrying a package of paper cups.

"*Ja,* we bop and jive to Rock and Roll." Bruce and the boys neatly lined the perimeter of the hall with long wooden benches.

"We had many dances here when I was young. In the olden days, we waltzed gracefully around with Aunty Les Todd playing the piano. She knew all the Frank Sinatra tunes…that was proper music," Mom reminisced. "Aunt Les was not available once, so they hired your Uncle Sonny Bester to play the piano for our ball. He played Bing Crosby songs. He brought his younger brother, Boetie, along with him. I met your father at that dance on *this* very spot." She identified the exact hallowed spot, anointing it with an extra sprinkle of powder. "It was much more elegant in those days. We had a little book and the gentlemen would ask us for a dance. We would write their names next to a number. Daddy romantically booked the last dance with me," she smiled with pleasure. "It was a slow waltz. And *that* was *that!*"

"You are starting to look like a snowman." I noticed her hair had accumulated white flakes. "Fashions in dance change! We don't need the whole place slippery any more!"

"Nowadays, children convulse their bodies." Mom plunked down the empty talcum container. "There is a distinct lack of class in the way hooligans shudder and shake. Screeching is not singing at all."

"Let's put the table in this corner," Dad pointed to the left corner as he walked in. "That way, we men-folk can keep an eye on you ladies while you sell the cool drinks."

The James Ford Kasouga Hall was built perched on stilts. It was donated by Mr. Ford, who stipulated in his will that no alcohol was to be allowed on the premises.

Uncle Dudda Ford arrived, all 6 feet 6 inches of him. He was to be the "bouncer" to toss out any trouble-causers. He helped his son, B.J., carry in band paraphernalia.

"Testing, testing," the singer spoke into the mike. Mary-Rose's cousin, Greg Price-Lewis, strummed a chord on his electric guitar and I almost fell out of my skin. It was lovely and loud. The strings inside of me were struck by the music. My body responded and I just started to wiggle. He sang the first few lines… "If I were a carpenter, and you were a lady, would you marry me anyway…" Greg sounded exactly like Bobby Darin. He looked like the lead singer of The Troggs, Reg Presley.

"Judy! Behave yourself!" Wendy sternly shook my shoulder.

"Let's get your hands stamped before the crowds get here." Dad took out his leather wallet and paid for his four children. "You two younger ones don't get in the way of the older teenagers," Dad warned. "Dance over there by the window. Here is a few bob for a cool drink." He gave us each some cash.

"Thanks, Dad." We all chorused.

"It's my pleasure. Now go and let your hair down!" He grinned, hoisting his pipe into the summer sea air.

Bruce was all kitted out in his pale blue stripey Beatles shirt. A gold pin connected the white collars with tiny gold squares sticking out. He did not smell like he'd been fishing at all. Now he smelled like Old Spice, all decked out in his navy *stove pipes* (skinny pants). His black Chelsea boots with pointy toes and no laces were the latest fashion. Bruce had the perfect athlete's body to squeeze into those tight jeans. His hair was neatly combed; however, no amount of grease could stop it from curling. Sheila Vogler and her friends adored Bruce Bester, and for good reason. He was very attractive.

Dad took the cash at the door and counted out change. Uncle Gowar Dell stamped teenagers' wrists with a blue ink stamp. Broad-shouldered Uncle Dudda Ford just stood and stared. That was really quite adequate to deter any trouble.

My lovely friend, Mary-Rose, and I each bought a Fanta orange from our mothers.

The band struck up and my heart almost jumped out of my chest. We walked over to the window next to the band and sat down in a most ladylike fashion.

I stared at the drummer. His name was Alan. The Gulley Crabs were a homegrown band of Kasouga-ites. Alan was about twelve, with straight blonde hair. It was clean and fluffy and light. He pounded those drums like a rock star. His blonde fringe bobbed and bounced up in the air before flopping down in time with the beat…he mesmerized me.

The sound drew in many more teenagers.

Alan saw me staring at him. He smiled. I smiled.

Wendy wandered over to check on us. "You have to sit and wait for a boy to ask you to dance." She was clearly concerned that I would embarrass her. She strolled towards the Ladies Room to check on her pearly pink lipstick. Mom had informed me once that they grind up fish scales to make cosmetics shimmer. I did not fancy using pearly products.

We rocked to the beat of "Ticket to Ride" by those singing Beatles, covered by The Gulley Crabs in the Place of the Leopard.

The older teenagers danced closer to the door. That way, they could get outside faster to refuel with alcoholic beverages stashed in the boot of their cars. Older kids stared at us. I heard one say, "Look at those teenyboppers dance!"

Kevin Vogler and the Berriman brothers danced with us. Sandra, Dawn and David Emslie were also enjoying the dance. We urged our brothers or cousins to dance with us if no one else asked quickly enough. Jenny Currie looked pretty with her sun-bleached blonde hair. We rocked and rolled heartily.

We soon became quite hot, so we opened the sliding wooden window. Outside, the off-duty servants were also enjoying the beat, kicking up the dust. They were not allowed inside the dance, but they peered through the window.

"That's good, Miss Judy. We can hear better now." Maggie was doing the *xhensa* (dance) to the beat of *Black is Black* by Los Bravos. I recognized her new white *doek* (head scarf) in the sea of black faces. She had taught our threesome to *xhensa,* and we copied her with no counting involved. It was a healthy high to dance to the rhythm of clicking and chanting and clapping at Schelmdrift. I learned rhythm from the best.

All of a sudden, Uncle Dudda's deep voice boomed in my ear. "We have to shut the windows and keep them locked. Otherwise, we will get those blinking ducktails (white *tsotsis)* from Jo'burg climbing in here without paying." No one argued with Uncle Dudda, the gentle giant of Kasouga. The window was promptly locked.

"*Just like a Woman*" by Manfred Mann was the next song. I was shocked to look up and see Alan standing in front of me.

"Do you want to dance?" Alan asked, taking my willing hand.

I glanced at the electric drums. Alan's older brother, Lindsey Dickinson, was drumming the beat, giving his little brother a break.

It was a slow dance, so we put our arms around each other. "I requested this song for you." He had a shy smile. "I dig the way you dance."

"I love the way you play the drums." I had my first innocent crush.

We danced the night away until our parents took us home. Mother was thrilled with the enormous success of the dance. The Kasouga Hall had been full to capacity.

The next morning, Bruce called towards the servants' quarters, "Cocoa, please come and help me launch the boat into the river."

Cocoa promptly replied from out of the bushes. "I'm on my way." He soon swaggered around the corner, still smearing his face with wet pasty ochre. *"Awu, Baas* (Oh, Boss) Bruce, please ask your father to allow me come here every Christmas. I love all these fat maidens."

"Hayi (No) Cocoa, how can you say fat girls are beautiful? Check out this chick parading down the road! Look how luscious she looks in a bikini. She's Helen Dickinson. Now that is beautiful. She just won the Miss Johannesburg beauty queen title," Bruce said, trying not to let his eyes stray too much.

Cocoa glanced in her direction for a very brief moment out the very corner of his dark eyes. *"Hayikhona! Baas* (No way! Boss) Bruce, she is most hideous!"

"Mind the car!" I bellowed as they almost scraped it with the boat.

"Yes, *Baas* Bruce, look what you are doing! Stop ogling that malnourished girl! She would be a very poor food gatherer. Her hip bones stick out like a cow during the drought. That's not very comfortable!" Cocoa chuckled.

"Comfortable?" Bruce said steadying the boat and looking at Cocoa.

"Yes. We men prefer our women more padded. You white boys, you know nothing." Cocoa boasted like a real Xhosa man.

"Helen, do you want to go scooping with us tonight?" Bruce blazed his big blue eyes at Helen as she got within earshot.

"That would be lovely, thanks. What time?" Miss Johannesburg sparkled her pearly white teeth at Bruce.

"Just after dark, we'll come and fetch you," Bruce committed.

Helen glided on towards the beach in a swanlike manner, displaying her beautiful body in a white bikini. She minced her hips as she waded through the air. A blue towel lay draped over one golden brown shoulder as she modeled her shapely physique down the dirt road. Kasouga Road, alias, the best modeling ramp on earth, was lined by shacks on the left, and the Kasouga River on the right.

"Hayi kwedini (No boy) what's the matter with you?" Cocoa was shaking his head and grinning. "You don't know how to pick a good sturdy woman! You should find one who will bring you lots of chil-

dren and be strong enough to breastfeed and work hard. Now look, I'll have to teach you. Look over there," he said, while pointing at The Spring tap, where a few uniformed maids were filling buckets. An unmarried nanny with a short skirt was washing clothes by hand with her buttocks in the air. "There is Beauty. She is not a sickly, hungry bony beef!"

"*Ag! Sies!* No! She looks like a hippopotamus," Bruce grimaced. "Cocoa, be careful! Hippos kill more people than lions in Africa. Hippos are more dangerous than big cats."

"You're not even a man. I am a man already. Look!" He patted his finger on his clay-crusted face. "I am a *rwala* (new man). Real men know more than boys."

"Well, I've been a man since I was a baby," Bruce bantered.

"You haven't been taught. When you are an *mkwetha,* old wise men teach you secrets about how to deal with females," Cocoa continued convincingly.

Bruce argued, "You'll never change. Didn't they teach you that 'A leopard never changes its…' "

"SPOTS!" I interjected. "I got that right on my English exam. Thanks to you, Bruce, you say it so often." No one was interested, but that did not stop me from yakking away. "You two are going to fall in the river if you do not watch out."

"Suddenly you think you know everything just because you have been snipped… Watch the pothole! Stop gaping at hippo butts!" Bruce laughed.

'Poor Sindie,' I thought. 'She'll never be chosen by Cocoa.' She was long and lanky. She resembled Helen more than the hippo butt, Beauty.

"Can I come scooping with you, too?" I asked Bruce.

"Maybe another time...the boat will be too full tonight. I've invited a ton of people," he nudged me affectionately, ruffling my curls.

"A bunch of bloody bony butts! Of course there will be room! Skeletons don't take up any space at all." Cocoa was my advocate.

"Well, if I invited hippo butts, the boat would sink!" Bruce mocked.

Cocoa knew he was not actually invited. He enjoyed the gesture anyway. We all accepted that blacks and whites did not socialize together during the heyday of apartheid.

"I saw you dancing, Miss Judy. You dance better than any of those other white kids. Who showed you how to dance?" Cocoa clicked at me.

"Sindie!" I replied with pride.

"Awu! (Aha!) Sindie," he said, "She has taught you very well indeed! You would have been chosen as the Leopard Lady, like I was chosen as the Leopard Man for being the best dancer."

"Sindie would make a very good wife. Please will you marry her, Cocoa?" I had to take my chances as they presented themselves. Make hay while the sun shines!

"Sindie is too young," Cocoa smiled sweetly. "And she has a twin brother."

"Oh please, Cocoa. Can't you just give Jack your spotty *Nguni* cow?" I pleaded.

"Judes, why don't you go and play with Mary Rose? Cocoa wants to teach me new tricks," Bruce said scathingly. Cocoa was Bruce's mentor in one way, and his servant in another. "I don't think you're quite old enough to hear."

"Fine," I relented; disappointed that they finally noticed I was present enough to be dismissed. "Please, Cocoa! Sindie is superb!"

I loved listening in on their conversation. What rendered females attractive was clearly a topic of high interest for both boys. Black and white males had opposite tastes. It was a curious culture clash, which clearly modeled illogicality. I wondered to myself if their conflicting ideas were genetic or purely cultural. Was it in their breed or in their creed? What if a white family adopted a black boy—would he admire skinny or fat girls?

Noble qualities such as "character" were glaringly absent from their communications. Bruce and Cocoa definitely had that omission in common. A woman's shape, albeit opposite shapes, according to their programmed minds, was obviously all that mattered in both cultures. It was black and white.

Their oversight revealed that they were both mere boys, I noted to myself. Sindie had spunkiness galore, but that did not seem to count. I sat alone on the swing and thought how much I missed Sindie and Tombe.

They would soon be painting their faces with red or white ochre, and shaving off their peppercorn hair. To me, shaving off hair that turned fizzy in the sea air sounded somewhat sensible. But I would be expected to copy Wendy's ways. She used eyeliner made of *kajal* or soot. She smeared pink whale blubber on her lips and painted her toenails coral with paint made from smashed fish scales. Was I destined to succumb to using pearly products? Oh, blush! I worried that conflicting vain traditions would split our little trio apart. How I missed the two of them.

I smiled to myself as I recalled the amusing moment when Tombe leapt off the swing like a *pronking* (jumping) springbuck. Bruce and Cocoa reminded me of two springbuck rams with hooked horns locked, their cultures clashing. Neither was going to change his stubborn mind.

Bruce and Cocoa were now near the jetty, knee-deep in the river, laughing and sharing secrets. Not wanting to be chased away again, I swung as high as I could.

After thinking long enough to make me sad, I decided it was a bad idea to think too much. Sindie was not going to win Cocoa in the near future.

I jumped off the swing and wandered across the green to Mary-Rose Dell's shack. The two of us played a game of croquet on the green in front of the Dells' shack.

Every year as we got taller, it seemed that those wooden croquet mallets got shorter. In fact, when we learned to play, the mallets were taller than we were. Now, we expertly maneuvered our mallets as we smacked the wooden ball through the hoops to reach the end post.

At twilight, we played a game called tenniquoit. Grandpa Stocks had a tenniquoit court in front of his house. A rubber ring was tossed to and fro over a net.

"We are taking some girls scooping." Bruce relinquished his spot on the court.

"You are fishing *with chocolates* (for girls), are you?" Dad asked, taking a sip of his sundowner and facing Bruce. "You must please be a gentleman and don't let anyone drown in the river. Chocolates make very good bait, my son."

"Don't do anything foolish, my child. Wendy will be with you; treat the girls like ladies, please," Mom added. "You are the oldest, Bruce, make sure you don't tip the boat."

After supper, Norman and I sat and played rummy with our younger Fischer cousins. We could see the lamp on the boat, beaming its light over the sparkling river ripples. David and Donovan Murray, our teenager cousins, were with Bruce and Wendy.

Springers are slender fish, which leap out of the river towards the spotlight. The seafarers in the boat try and snatch the slippery flying fish with their fingers. Two people on either side used a scoop net to catch fish that could be seen swirling just under the surface. Sporadically, a scooper may lose their balance and fall overboard. They were pulled back onto the boat, dripping wet. Some sport lay in keeping the stash of fish inside a bucket. Flipping fish often shot back out of the bucket, devilishly attracted to the spotlight. Shrieks of delight frequented this unpredictable play. The splashing left all the participants soggy. Some even peeled off their drenched outerwear and dove into the river for a midnight dip.

"Just listen to those children having fun out there," Dad commented as we heard loud squeals echo towards our shack. "It's all good clean fun."

"I hope they are being sensible." Mom worried.

Springers were recycled as live bait to catch bigger fish. Grandpa Stocks knew a special spot upstream where they planned to fish the following night for Leery.

Later, I lay in bed and pondered with fascination the springing gazelle and flying fish. Both Springbuck and Springers flew up in the air like diving dolphins. The beauty of nature's parallels began to lull me to sleep.

It seemed such parallels in nature, only spotlighted the differences in humans. Camping at "The Place of the Leopard," people's true spots seemed less disguised. Mommy's freckles became more pronounced in the sun, so she constantly sought the shade, while Wendy worked hard on her suntan. What's more, Maggie went to great lengths to paste her dark complexion with white clay to appear paler. All tried to conceal their blemishes, while anxiously trying to attract to the opposite sex.

As I was drifting off to sleep, a wet Wendy came traipsing into our bedroom.

"Was scooping fun?" I whispered.

"The Todd girl swallowed a springer!" Wendy spoke in hushed tones.

"How did she swallow a live fish, a few inches long?" I was a doubting Thomas.

Wendy spoke softly, "She was laughing with her mouth wide open and a small fish just dived down her throat."

"And you expect me to believe that rubbish?" I quizzed.

"Ask Bruce! I would not believe it if I had not seen it with my own two eyes. It is absolutely true, I promise you!" Wendy insisted.

The next morning, Bruce convinced us that it was evidently so!

26

FISHING COMPETITION

One sunny morning, while sitting on the front step looking over The Kasouga Green, I watched Uncle Freddy Ford's cows mow the grass. One never heard a lawnmower disturb the peace at tranquil Kasouga.

Maids hoisted heavy buckets on their heads at the Spring and walked gracefully to the various shacks where they were employed. Others were sweeping *stoeps* or shaking out rugs before the heat of the day.

Uncle Peter Long walked past, carrying his throw-net on his way to catch mullet in the river shallows. He was early enough to catch them before the bathers chased the schools of fish away. The stocky Berriman lads lugged a pump to suck up prawns for bait. A younger *"boetie"* (little brother), Kevin, followed faithfully at a distance, swinging a blue bucket.

Most fascinating to me were the European Swallows flying low around The Green. The agile birds swooped down on a swarm of *muggies* (insects). Again and again, the birds circled and dive-bombed their prey with pinpoint precision. How did they not crash into each other? Swallows must be guided by exceptionally accurate radars. They sped up at the exact right speed to capture the haze of insects with their beaks. The red-faced swallows glided around slowly, on outstretched wings, balanced by forked tails. They circled to create new momentum to plummet down for another taste, missing each other by millimeters, snatching the moving, *muggie* meal.

Why do bugs live, if only to be eaten all up?

Do humans live to chomp up animals?

My mind was full of unanswered questions. Norman, who sat beside me waiting, said I irritated him no end when I asked too many questions, so I was attempting to figure it all out silently.

Our early morning swim had been delayed. Bruce was a little slow in rising.

My thoughts turned to the food chain. I pondered about who eats whom.

Was life solely about eating and sleeping and breeding good-mannered children?

"Has Bruce surfaced yet?" Mom asked as she came out of my grandparents' shack.

"I haven't seen him." I shifted aside for her to step up into our beach cabin.

"What have you got there?" Norman inquired.

"Honeycomb. Grandpa collected it from his hives on Glenfillan Park yesterday." She lowered the plate to give us a lick.

I started to think about how bees busily collect pollen and turn it into honey for us to enjoy. Grandpa Stocks said that bees did more than merely manufacture honey. They served to pollinate his pineapples with six tiny feet. He explained that they were a very useful part of the food chain, so perhaps we should forgive God for making them sting so sore. Grandpa said we should never kill a bee. I was secretly glad that they died after they stung me, nonetheless.

"Grandpa brought a load of queen pineapples back as well." Mom was elated. "These sweet little ones are my favorite. He said we must help ourselves. Please will you take an empty basket and go and collect some out of Granny's pantry, Judy?"

Mom presently returned and nudged me out of my dreams with a basket.

I strolled in between our shacks, swinging the wicker basket. Bruce was coming towards me from "up the garden path," which was the "proper" way Mom used to describe the "long drop" toilet. Cocoa loitered outside our kitchen door, holding an enamel mug of aromatic coffee that Maggie had slipped to him.

"Cocoa, will you go and clean the boat for me please? We messed it up a bit last night. Please, before my Dad sees …" Bruce pleaded.

"Sendigqhibile. (I have done it already.)" Cocoa clicked his tongue.

"Thanks, Cocoa," Bruce's taut face relaxed.

"Yes, Boss Bruce! I found *stompies* (cigarette butts) and *dumpies* (beer bottles) and other things that *SngXhoshe* would not want to see," Cocoa broke into his usual telling grin. "You owe me a *bhasela* (reward) *kwedini* (boy)."

"You helped me out. Thanks," Bruce said, holding his head. "I have bad *babalas* (hangover)."

"I could be silenced for a few cigarettes," clever Cocoa bribed Bruce.

Bruce pulled out a packet of Lucky Strike plains from the inside pocket of his black rugby shorts. He was allowed to smoke, as he had just matriculated.

"I have to impress the girls here with white cigarettes," Cocoa's smile broadened.

Remembering my mission, I slipped into Granny Gwen's pantry. Filling the basket with pines, I could still hear and see the boys through the wooden slats of Granny's outside cool pantry.

"Your advice paid off." Bruce spoke in low tones.

"Good. We can't have homemade *zols* (tobacco wrapped in brown paper) here like at the farm." Cocoa caressed his stash, "I-Lucky Strike!" He mimicked the radio advertisement. "I want to 'strike it lucky.' " Cocoa loved to show off using a few English words. *"Enkosi kakhulu!* (Thank you very much!)" He reverted back to Xhosa.

Maggie was frying tomatoes when I entered through the kitchen door. Her eyes lit up at the sight of the pineapples.

"Nomhankazi, will you give me one? I want to make *i-drink-i*." She used an English word with a Xhosa prefix and suffix. I knew her pineapple "cider" was more fixed to be beer, but I casually donated a couple of pines, courtesy of my grandpa.

"Cocoa, run and hide these in my room. Do not be seen by anyone." Maggie whisked the pineapples to Cocoa who was still lingering about the kitchen door, counting his Lucky Strikes. "High up where *Thokoloshe* cannot reach them," our cook instructed.

"Kumnandi eKasouga (It is good at Kasouga)," the new man declared lustily, fully loaded with the spoils of a good life. "I am coming here every year!"

Dad was in the lounge, loading new batteries into the radio at the coffee table.

"Righto," he called out, "come along children, we need to shake a leg and get our early morning dip right away. The cricket starts in an hour. The *Ozzies* (Australians) are playing our Springbucks for the final test of the series."

Bruce perked up. *"Ja,* I will listen to cricket all day, no more fishing for me."

After our compulsory morning dip in the sea to remove hangovers and cobwebs, it seemed as if all the radios were tuned into the same station across The Green. Charles Fortune, a legendary commentator with a posh British accent, was praising the Springbucks in his eloquent speech:

"There are not enough adjectives in the English language to describe the superb Springbuck cricketers this season. Young Graeme Pollock hits a magnificent six with such ease that he makes it look effortless. His timing is as flawless as his coordination! Such athleticism can only be a God-given talent. Watching him inspires young and old alike to strive for greater artistry in batting. And here comes the Ozzie bowler…with a long run-up…his pace is quick…and his delivery…is deadly accurate! But Pollock miraculously manages to deflect the ball for four runs! You can hear the crowd, no doubt. The air is electrified at this glorious spectacle. Graeme perfectly placed the center of the bat to the ball; he belted that ball into the grandstand. He seems to get his whole body weight under his three-pound bat. It seems like an optical illusion, until he does it again! His technique and strength have taken batting to innovative levels of excitement. Indeed, it is apparent by watching the expressions of his enthusiastic fans…who are scrambling to retrieve the ball in the grandstand. This six-foot-two blonde chap receives such a response from his adoring fans, it is akin to worship. Only a splendid batsman keeps a crowd on their feet, roaring like lions. I hope you can still hear me...above the applause... which is deafening!"

Everyone was glued to their blazing radios. When Graeme Pollock confidently cracked that hard red ball for another six runs, you could hear the united ovation echo across the Kasouga Green. Howard Emslie jumped up from his deck chair and cheered. Minds were tuned into the cricket. South Africa was on top of the food chain of the British Commonwealth cricket world. Conversation respectfully ceased and no one dared talk to Dad. Interrupting Charles Fortune was not advised.

"Mary-Rose and I want to go fishing in the river. Can Cocoa take us?" I tried asking Mom for permission.

"You may go and find him and ask him yourself. Last time I saw him, he was flirting with maidens at the Spring, while he washed the Land Rover. That new white model shows the dust much more than our old tan model used to." Mom was attached to the wireless herself, keeping score of figures...Denis Lindsey scored 606 runs in the test series; Eddie Barlow batted with a winning attitude, and bowled so well, the batsmen did not know where the ball was coming from; Mike Procter took seven wickets; Peter Pollock oozed talent to become a legend with his brother, Graeme.

Cocoa obliged and soon filled my pink bucket with prickly prawns from the river bank. He helped us onto the boat with all our tackle. He rowed us out to the middle of the river in Grandpa Stocks' wooden fishing boat. Cocoa was not allowed to use the engine with horse powers. He threw out the anchor in the deepest, dark, teal water.

The two of us knew how to cast and bait our own hooks. Cocoa sat dozing in the sun lazily. He neither owned a radio nor cared about cricket. The boat rocked him to sleep. Mary-Rose and I fished and fished. We filled buckets with silver *flatties* mostly. We caught a few little *zebras* and *steenbras*.

Cocoa woke up when we tilted the boat. He lit a Lucky Strike cigarette. He only smoked half and stubbed it out carefully to save the rest for later. He kept his cigarettes in a small English toffee tin with a lid so they would not get wet.

Mary-Rose and I were the only fishermen on the river that day. We were only two little girls who could swim, with one new man servant, who could not swim.

"Hayi (No), Miss Judy, your bucket is overflowing with fish. Can we go back home now?" Cocoa begged. The sun was sinking in the sky.

"No. We are practicing for the fishing competition which takes place tomorrow." I was resolute. "First prize is a rod, second prize is a reel, and third prize is a bag of sinkers. I want the rod!"

"You can't even eat those little fish. You are wasting time." Cocoa grunted, and pulled his Lord Ivy cap over his eyes for a second snooze.

After we had reeled in a few more fish, Cocoa began pleading some more. He even lit the other half of his cigarette to calm his nerves.

"I only need the first prize…desperately. This rod is too small for me. I have outgrown it," I preached to the water, hoping Cocoa knew that the Xhosa words were pointed at him and not at Mary-Rose. "You have to *qonda* (understand), Cocoa, I do not want third prize either. Dad can make me lead sinkers in his special mold. I have watched him melt the lead and make sinkers. Father Christmas brought me this new reel, so I definitely don't want second prize either. What would I need two reels for? This rod is old and the eyes are rusty, and it was a hand-me-down. I want that glass fiber rod very badly, so I have to practice. Practice makes perfect."

"Hayi (No), you talk, talk, talk too much. Can we go back to shore now, please?" Cocoa was getting somewhat desperate.

"Not yet." I was unwavering, striking another catch. "You may carry on with your siesta, Cocoa." I ordered.

Half an hour drifted passed. I deliberated about milking the moment so I could bribe him to marry Sindie.

"Look, little child of Sngxhoshe, the *Hadedahs* (Hadeda Ibis) are flying home to their nests. It is time to go home now." Cocoa was becoming more and more distressed.

The big birds with heavy, broad wings sounded their familiar "Ha-Ha-Ha-a-a," above our heads, heading for the tall wild chestnut trees on the far west bushy bank.

"I am going to keep you here until you have smoked all your fancy cigarettes. You won't have any left to impress Beauty with." I smiled, putting my loyalties with Sindie's high hopes. I was ranked higher than this "new man" on the food chain of South Africa; I had to take full advantage of my whiteness.

"If you promise to marry Sindie, we can pull up anchor and row back to shore," I blurted out the blackmail. We relished the fact that Cocoa could not swim, while I intentionally rocked the boat.

"Hayikhona! (No way!) Miss Judy, I will do anything for you, but I can't do that. I told you the reason why yesterday already. Miss Judy, Please! Please! " The real man winced. "Mayday! Don't sink this boat! Mayday!"

Cocoa was a good catch. I wanted Sindie to reel him in. It was unrealistic to cast our hopes so high. But we hoped, regardless. Perhaps we should tip the boat over to induce the type of humility that assures full contrite submission.

"One more cast then," I was unyielding, re-baiting my hook. "And if you promise…"

"Hehala! (Holy Moly!) There will be no fish left in the river!" He tried a different approach. "Think, child of *SngXhoshe,* if you catch all the fish today, there will be none left for tomorrow's competition. The fish will be *phelile* (all gone)."

I ignored him.

"I will get up early and pump you lots of prawns tomorrow. Please!" Bribery was common to both our cultures. Besides, it had worked for him earlier that day with Bruce.

I struck and reeled in another fighting fish before caving. "Fine then! Alright, Cocoa, you may pull up the anchor now." Then turning to Mary-Rose apologetically, I revealed, "This Cocoa has big fat hippos to hook."

Mary-Rose remembered a request. "Oh yes, I almost forgot! Cocoa, our boy had to go back to the farm for a funeral. Please, will you pump me some prawns for tomorrow? We will need a lot of bait."

"Yes, child of a white man. I will get enough for both of you girls. Miss Mary-Rose, please promise not to win the competition. Miss Judy here will make me sit on this water every day. We will have to practice until she wins next year." The grinning new man was terrified of water.

Cocoa was a Xhosa man. I was a European child. He worked for my father, so he had to obey me. That is how the political food chain worked. But had my life been in danger in any way, he would be the adult and protect me, even if it was against my will. That is the unwritten law of a loyal and loving servant. Although, if the boat sank, we would probably have to rescue him!

"You must pay him with a packet of Lucky Strike," I told my pretty friend.

Cocoa emptied our buckets overboard. "See you again tomorrow," he bid farewell to the freed *flatties.*

The following day, we gathered for the competition with most of the boys and a few of the girls from Kasouga on the far side of the river, away from the bathers. There were no houses on the wild, west bank of the Kasouga River.

Uncle Athol Emslie was talking into a handheld horn loudspeaker: "You can fish anywhere between that fence and the river mouth. You have to fish off the bank, not a boat. You have to cast for yourself without any help from an adult. Try not to stand too close to each other. We don't want any accidents with sharp hooks and heavy sinkers."

Mary-Rose and I stood next to each other. My grandpa suggested that we choose that spot, where the water was deeper. Mary-Rose kept losing her bait and pulling in an empty hook, dripping strands of seaweed.

"Grandpa Stocks says you must strike as soon as you feel the bite. Don't wait to let the fish nibble off the bait," I told her. "We have plenty of prawns. Don't worry. Cocoa is here. He will get us more if we run low." We put our fish into our individual big metal pails, half full of river water in the shade of a coast silver leaf tree.

Mom's large beach hat shaded her fair skin. Aunty Joyce's red beach umbrella shaded their picnic baskets, laden with sandwiches and thermos flasks full of hot tea. Children played in the sand, but no one was allowed to swim on the west bank of the river that day. A few swimmers splashed on the east bank. This was the only day of the year that the west bank was more popular. The water's edge was fenced with a line of wriggly, suntanned boys and girls, each proudly holding a fishing rod. That many fishing rods looked like fake fence of poles, each manned by a barefoot white child.

I concentrated on casting into a deep pool, where the river was darker green and where I had hooked my biggest *flattie*. I was trying to cast in the same place to catch the rest of that *flattie's* family. Dad had given me a slightly heavier sinker, which helped me cast farther. Grandpa had tied a new sharp hook on for me with a fisherman's eye knot.

The prize lime green fishing rod stood at attention on display, all wrapped in translucent plastic, next to the table of three judges. A red and white stripey beach umbrella shaded them. That magnificent reward rod motivated me to cast fast, striking, reeling, and tossing fish into my bucket rapidly. I was too busy to talk or eat.

"How many do you have?" One overly-anxious parent peered into my pail.

"I don't know. I lost count," I replied, not offering to count or make conversation.

"We'll throw them back and catch them again next year," Mom told the curious kids peering into my bucket of restless fish.

At 4 p.m. sharp, a loud whistle was blown and we all had to reel in. The judges came around with pen and paper. The fish were counted, the biggest ones were weighed.

"Mary-Rose has 24 fish," the judges announced. Cheers erupted from the crowd. That was the highest number so far. She always beat me at tennis. We were even at croquet. I was not sure about fishing. It looked as if we were tied; both our buckets were squirming with squishy fish.

"Now, we have Judy Bester. Her Grandpa Norman Stocks has been a fishing legend here at Kasouga. He taught many a man how to fish. Her dad and brothers have won numerous competitions. Let's see if this young lassie can follow in her family's footsteps," Uncle Athol, Dawn's dad, announced over the loud speaker.

"26, 27! 28!" Uncle Brian Clarke was out of breath from counting. Some fish were only two inches long, but they still counted, no matter how tiny they were.

"We have two more competitors' fish to tally up. Does anyone have more than 28?" Uncle Athol called out, just to be sure.

I held my breath.

"No." The last two disgruntled boys conceded.

I exhaled in relief.

"I believe we have a winner here. Congratulations, Miss Bester." Uncle Athol patted my shoulders. He put lot of effort into organizing such fun entertainment.

I stared at the rod and smiled. "Thank you very much."

"Now all gather around the table over yonder for the prize giving," Uncle Athol announced. He was the unofficial mayor of Kasouga. Athol Emslie also chaired the Entertainment Committee.

I walked up to the table with my *kiewietjie* (Crowned Plover) legs and shook the hand of a dignitary of Kasouga, Aunty Doris Stirk, and gratefully accepted the fiber glass fishing rod. My soul was filled with joy!

Cocoa clapped the loudest and even let out a roar, which was not very proper. Maybe it was relief, not pride, which made his teeth stay visible so long, locked in a grateful grin. "You had many lucky strikes, Miss Judy." Cocoa suddenly spoke English with a thick Xhosa accent to impress Beauty, who was a nanny to a white kid. Our proud Leopard Man danced a jig of joy while he roared like a lion.

Mary-Rose won the reel. Phillip Berriman received the sinkers. John White caught the biggest *tottie* (fish) and received a cash prize.

When we arrived back at the shacks, Norman snarled, "You shouldn't have won. David Dell helped you."

"He did not!" I thought he meant that David cast for me. "You can ask Cocoa, I practiced all day yesterday. My shoulder still hurts from yesterday's practicing."

"Yes, David did," Norman snorted.

"He did not!" I argued.

"He did," Norman taunted.

"Rubbish!" I stated.

"He fancies you and wanted you to win. He gave up half way, and stopped fishing. Then he came and dumped his flatties in your bucket when no one was looking," Norman insisted.

Euphoria was gobbled up by sudden shock. Shock was followed by fiery fury.

"Mommy, Norman says David Dell put his fish in my bucket. Did you see him do that?" I asked, desperately not wanting to part with my rod and its shiny stainless steel eyes. I had already pulled off the plastic and attached my reel, which I got for Christmas.

Norman always tormented me, mostly because he was bored and wanted to get a reaction out of me. David Dell did the same to Mary-Rose; they were equally bothersome brothers. Perhaps David *had* cheated, so his little sister would not show him up?

"I am certain he did nothing of the sort. Cheating is very bad. There were so many spectators milling about. I can't say I was watching every second of every minute."

Obviously only grand-ghosts could boast about twenty four seven surveillance.

Mom was busy rattling teacups. "I certainly would not expect that type of base behavior from a lad like David. Aunty Joyce fair gloated about what a good chap he is. Surely he would not possibly cheat?"

"Ask David!" Norman's challenge was rather glib.

"I will!" I snorted back, storming out the door. I marched across The Green.

"David! David!" I yelled, as I saw him trying to leave his house. "Wait right there!" I was out of breath. He turned and waited. "Did you put *your* fish in *my* bucket?" I demanded.

"No, what for?" he said innocently, appearing surprised.

"Good! Norman said that you threw your fish in my bucket," I blurted.

"He was just teasing you," he said casually. "Just ignore Norman."

After strutting back to our shack, I attacked Norman with a pillow, fully intending to cause grievous bodily harm. Being stronger and bigger, he just held my skinny wrist.

"Do you want a Chinese bangle?" he asked, twisting my skin painfully on the wrist opposite ways. We came to big blows. I cast a few, but I hardly landed any. Norman was the typical big brother that tormented me for his own entertainment, but would defend me against strangers and *moer* (beat up) anyone else who tried to harm me. I loved that feeling having big brothers and many male cousins to bail me out of trouble. Luckily, Bruce was out the same protective mold.

Bruce had to come to my rescue. "Leave her alone. Pick on someone your own size." Bruce was the best big brother, always saving me. "You won a rod! Can I see…?"

"Kawuleza, Baas Bruce, zenomphu. Naantsa inyoka! (Hurry, Boss Bruce, bring a gun. There is a snake!)" Cocoa was yelling at the front door this time, rather than the usual kitchen door.

Bruce grabbed Dad's gun and followed Cocoa to the bush behind the shack.

The vilest yellow snake lay coiled over a dead branch on the ground below some weaver birds' nests. Bruce fired and took off its tail. The snake sat up and puffed out its neck to look like two fish fins, fanning its black forked tongue. He shot again and removed half the snake's head. It was still slithering with one black eye, writhing and churning up dried leaves. Cocoa grabbed an axe from Granny's woodpile and sharply chopped off its gaping, wounded half of a head.

"You are so brave. I am not surprised you have many female fans," Bruce teased.

"Good shot, Bruce! That is a gigantic Cape cobra." Norman praised him, also proud of our big brother.

"Who is firing shots?" Uncle Gowar Dell, the unofficial policeman of Kasouga, came along to inspect why loud gunfire disturbed the peace. A crowd of "would-be" bathers and family members came to see what the hullabaloo was all about. Cocoa was holding up the slippery serpent like a trophy. Its scaly body was dangling from the axe, glowing golden in the sun.

"Now its mate will slither into your bed in the middle of the night," Norman spluttered in my ear. "Cobras can climb trees and creep up onto bunk beds."

"I'll *klap* (clout) you," I spat.

"Aunty Pat, please may I come and sleep at your shack tonight?" My skin crawled at the sight of the vomit-yellow snake.

"Yes, you may, with pleasure, Dearie. I would be delighted," she agreed affectionately. "I always wanted a daughter. I will make special seafood paella for you for supper."

Aunty Pat was always kind to me as she only had three sons, Stephen, Charles, and Nick. Aunty Ione Murray only had boys too, David and Donovan. I grew up tough with so many big boy cousins and brothers, but snakes scared the wits out of me.

At dusk, our older cousin, Donovan, arrived home from surfing at Port Alfred, where the waves were cresting higher.

"It is time for a cup of tea. Who wants tea?" Granny Stocks offered, gathering her nine grandchildren with a plate of Scottish shortbread that she had baked using real farm butter. She was very generous to us.

"Guess what happened to me? I was surfing and all of a sudden I saw a dark thing in the water. I thought it was a long log of driftwood until I noticed the fin!" Donovan knew the sea very well. We all listened as he told the scary story. "It was a great white shark. I paddled as fast as I could. When I saw the triangular fin, I almost walked on water! The eight-footer followed me right to the shallow water before turning out to sea again."

"You were jolly lucky. You have to have a healthy respect for the sea," Grandpa Stocks instructed his grandchildren. "Sharks think of swimmers, seals and surfers as supper. That is simply the way the food chain works."

"And six-foot snakes, too," Norman hissed in my ear. "Looking out…sliding up…especially for girls who cheat at fishing competitions."

"Stupid fool!" I slapped my insufferable sibling across the back of his head as hard as I could with many male witnesses and one genteel female witness looking on.

"*Judikins,* now that is not very ladylike." Granny scolded. "Etiquette and eloquence elevate you in society. You desperately need to improve both in order to be a lady. It appears your constant association with uncivilized savages has not helped your behavior. Your mother allows you to play with piccanins much too much. Manners maketh…"

"The man!" Wendy finished Granny's sentence with high regard for manners and culture and civilization.

"He deserved it," I declared without wincing. "He tells lies. I did not cheat."

Grandpa Stocks changed the conversation with this statement: "Life is full of imminent dangers. You just need to keep your eyes wide open. There are always camouflaged snakes and swift sharks about. My late mother taught me from the Bible: 'Beware of dogs, beware of evil workers, beware of concision' or devilish deception. You have to have your wits about you at all times. You can never destroy all predators, either. They serve a purpose for their existence in the food chain," Grandpa warned wisely, sipping his tea. "Nature is a splendidly powerful thing, indeed. I sincerely hope that you children learn to respect Mother Nature and preserve it for future generations. You should never take leave of your senses." He went on and on.

"Why did God make spiders and snakes anyway?" I asked. "Did your mother tell you that?"

"I think it was to keep you on your toes, my lovely girl…to keep us all on our toes." Grandpa Stocks sipped his tea like a well-mannered gentleman does.

I slept safely at Aunty Pat's shack that night.

27

SNAKES AND LADDERS

"Caesar's Ghost! Bruce passed his matric exams!" Mom cheered jubilantly, holding the newspaper wherein the matric results were published, on New Year's Eve. Bruce had survived boarding school and graduated. His example gave me hope.

Dad popped corks off bottles of champagne. The corks bounced off the wooden rafters of the Kasouga cabin. Dad raised his glass to toast Bruce's achievement, or rather in this case, luck.

"To Bruce!" fellow revelers echoed.

After a few days to recover from the celebration, we started packing up. Dad put my new rod safely with his on the high rack, to rest there until the next summer. We trekked back to the farm, all sunburned and sandy. We felt rejuvenated by the sea air.

Sindie and Tombe wore their new dresses and *jerseys* (sweaters) despite the sweltering heat of the Karoo in January 1967.

"Aren't you hot?" I asked, noticing they were wearing woolen jerseys.

"Not at all," Sindie was twirling her dress to show me. "Look, this is my Christmas gift. *Ndiphiyiwe!* (I was given!) It is brand new. It never belonged to Toto. Look, Miss Jay. "

Sindie's attire made her swagger like royalty and Mom received a curtsy as well. Her Christmas clothes seem to put a kink in her knees that hadn't been there before.

"Did you eat well at the seaside?" Tombe wanted to know.

"What did you bring us?" Sindie was already hinting. She had spotted the basket of fresh, ripe pines on the back of the Land Rover. "Did you bring us a pineapple?"

The three of us ran over to my little hut with a dish full of sweet pineapple slices to celebrate our reunion. Maggie kept the peels.

"Grandpa grows the sweetest little 'queen' pineapples in the world," I said. "The bigger ones are called 'giants.' They are sourer."

I educated my friends on pineapples grown in the Eastern Cape. But they didn't care at all. They blissfully indulged with pure delight, licking the juice off their fingers loudly.

"Mmhh, Mmhh, *Azisemnandi?* (Aren't they delicious?)" Sindie smacked her lips.

"Did you bring us any fish and chips?" Tombe inquired.

"No, but I caught lots of fish in the river. I even won a rod in a competition," I informed my friends. They did not seem to care about the rod, they only wanted fish.

"Look, Miss Jay," Sindie suddenly jumped up. "I got new panties as well." She lifted her dress to reveal pale pink cotton knickers. "Tombe did too." Sindie smiled, pulling up Tombe's skirt to display hers as well. "Hers are bright blue. Didn't you say that blue is for boys?"

Tombe paid no attention at all to Sindie; she was still lost in the ecstasy of a slice of tangy pineapple. She savored it by keeping it in her mouth to extract the full flavor before reluctantly swallowing.

"I wish I was a cow," Tombe suddenly divulged.

"Why?" I was confused. Tombe looked so happy in her own skin that day.

"Because then I could puke up this pineapple and taste it again. Haven't you watched the cows? They eat leaves until their stomach is full and then they burp like this." Tombe demonstrated, making heaving sounds. *"Urphg... Urphg.* You can see the lump of food behind their skins as the ball travels up and bounces up their necks. The blob lands in their mouth and they enjoy it all over again."

"We've all seen cows chewing their cud. When they swallow the second time, the food goes into their second stomach, remember?" I jerked her memory, while mine flew back to Linda Jones.

"I'd only chew my cud when I ate delicious things." Sindie looked longingly at Tombe's last piece of pineapple as it vanished behind plump, pineapple-juiced lips. "I only want a second chance if it's a good one!"

"I certainly wouldn't want to re-eat that bread pudding at boarding school," I lamented. "But I agree, I would repeat eating this divine pineapple."

"I wish that witchdoctor could change me into a cat. Cats lick up cream all day. Have you seen how fat the cats are that hang around near the dairy?" Sindie asked. "My mother says they steal cream."

"Magic will not work for you, unless you obey all our traditions. The door of this hut faces west," Tombe noticed reflectively. "White people don't have the same beliefs we do, Sindie. All our huts must face east. The good spirits come from the east with the rising sun. You see, Sindie, witchdoctor magic won't work for Miss Judy either; her hut faces west. But it doesn't matter, because she's white." Tombe then added comfortingly, "White people don't need magic. They already have everything."

After pondering her own speech with a pause, Tombe spoke again. "Cocoa built it wrong," Tombe accused. "He should've made this hut face east."

"No, he couldn't," Sindie defended Cocoa. "*NoLasti* told him to build it like this, so he just did what *NoLasti* told him to do. White people are lucky, as you said. Miss Jay eats nice things every day."

"Well, if this little hut faced east, the door would be right up against the hedge. We'd have to make a hole in the hedge to get out," I spoke up, reflecting my mother's practical mind.

"It doesn't matter; white people don't have to obey Xhosa customs. She doesn't sleep in this hut, anyway. It is just for playing in. The big white house where she sleeps faces east. That's good enough." Tombe ended the discussion.

"Did Cocoa find a wife at Kasouga?" Sindie inquired.

"I don't know," I replied. "If he did, she didn't come home in the Land Rover."

"What else can we eat?" Tombe queried.

"Cocoa was admiring a fat girl with her bum in the air. Bruce called her a 'hippo butt,' " I reported. "She probably couldn't fit in the Land Rover."

"Let's go down to Bumpy," Sindie suggested. "Rains always bring more frogs' eggs. I saw some on my way to Sunnyside with Toto."

As we reached the peppertree, we heard birds creating a raucous racket in the branches above us. They chirped and fluttered frantically in objection. Birds have very sharp eyes, and they always shriek to alarm each other if there is danger nearby.

"Jonga, naantsa inyoka! (Look, there's a snake!)" Sindie screamed, pointing up into the tree. A long brown *boomslang* (tree snake) balanced silently on a brown branch, hardly visible. Sindie had a gift for detecting camouflaged evil.

Running into the farmhouse, I breathlessly alerted my mom. "Hurry! There's a big *boomslang* in the pepper tree!"

"Oh no! You lot, go and keep watch so it doesn't escape. Oh drat! I'll go and get the gun. The boys and Dad went over to Sunnyside to take Uncle Sonny the latest newspapers." Mom hurried towards the office. She grabbed the double-barreled shotgun off the gun rack. She snatched a box of full of cartridges loaded with buckshot instead of birdshot.

Meanwhile, Sindie and Tombe stood guard under the poisonous serpent. The maids had dropped everything to join the hunting party. Wendy instantly discarded her baking to follow the throng.

"NAANTSA! NAANTSA! (THERE IT IS! THERE IT IS!)" Sindie and Tombe shouted, pointing at the huge *boomslang*.

It was about six feet long with a bulging belly full of bird's eggs.

"Boomslangs come out on hot days like today." Mom used the teaching moment effectively. "These snakes have more poisonous venom than a black Mamba, so stand back! Some dimwits think that because their folded fangs are so far back, they can't bite you unless you stick a finger down the snake's throat. That is a myth. Where are the men when we need them?" Mom exhaled exasperatedly. "Wendy, phone Sunnyside and tell the men folk to come home this instant! At once!"

Wendy hesitated, not wanting to miss the action.

"Dubula! Miss Gwina! Dubula! (Shoot! Miss Gwenna! Shoot!)" Maggie was instructing my mother now, in a rapid role reversal.

Maggie was, after all, a tough single mother, and matriarch of the whole farm. Even Dad listened to Maggie's advice most of the time. Her dominance crowned her the Queen Bee of Schelmdrift.

After loading the gun, Mother gingerly aimed and then pulled the trigger. Leaves rained from the tree. Terrified birds took to the sky for cover, alighting straight up like helicopters. The snake merely slid onto a higher branch.

"This blinking shotgun kicked my shoulder!" Mom hesitated to shake her shoulders as if she was warming up to run a race.

"Dubula weer! Miss Gwina! (Shoot again! Miss Gwenna!)" Our cook commanded, mixing Xhosa, Afrikaans, and English words together, adding a zesty tone of urgency to the blend.

In an emergency, born leaders take over the reins. Maggie was a commandant by nature. She barked commands in many tongues to be clearly understood by all relevant parties. By her sheer confidence of delivery, you could tell she expected swift compliance.

"Where is it? I can't see it," Mom asked, craning her neck.

"Naantsa! (There it is!)" The Xhosa chorus harmonized, pointing upwards.

"How does this gun work?" Mom muttered, mostly to herself. She cocked the gun and pushed two new cartridges down the barrels. "I sincerely hope I have loaded it correctly."

BOOM! BOOM!

Gunpowder lofted through the air. Mom reloaded.

BANG! BANG!

Empty cartridges littered the driveway

She stared down at the weapon. "There are two triggers, one for each barrel." Mom's mathematical mind clicked into action.

She packed more buckshot into the heated barrels.

"Just pull the trigger!" I urged.

She carefully positioned her arms, dividing her hands equally to fit a finger on each trigger.

"NO! Not both at once! " I suddenly became her instructor.

Mother had no brothers, so she was ignorant of most things masculine.

Noticing her dilemma in unfamiliar circumstances, I egged her on. "It's a big snake, and you can't possibly miss it. Aim first and then pull the triggers, one at a time! Shall I fetch your glasses? Can you see it? It is lying so still!"

Mommy might have missed the snake, but she would never miss a teaching moment. "Quite right! I see it now! A *boomslang's* deceivingly small head is divided in half by a very stretchy mouth. The truth is it can bite you anywhere. And don't you be fooled by those large, innocent-looking eyes; indeed, it has stereoscopic vision. No need to fear, I can see its vile little head quite clearly now."

Mom fired with great gusto. The puff of gunpowder smelled like the fireworks on Guy Fawkes Day. Many more leaves descended like green snow. She pulled the other trigger. More foliage floated down.

"Uphosile! (You missed!)" Sindie stated rather irreverently, but her disgust was safely disguised in the Xhosa tongue, which Mom could not entirely comprehend.

"Dubula WEEER! (Shoot AGAAIN!)" Bossy Maggie demanded further fire. The instructor was strongly suppressing her desire to grab the gun and shoot the snake herself.

Mom reloaded, this time less gingerly. "Now, you lot, keep your eyes on it, make sure it doesn't escape…mind you, I have its head in my sights now."

She took aim more carefully, blasting the peppertree again and again. Thunderous consecutive shots rang out. The Frontier wars fought decades ago along the Fish River were now being soundly rivaled. Big bits of branches were blasted off, and fell onto the leafy bed below.

"WAT MAKEER MIESIES? (What's the matter Mrs.?)" Jack bellowed, appearing somewhat startled from the direction of the stables. He was shielding his head with his elbow. His tusks shot out from behind his lips in a startled smile.

"Naantsa inyoka! (There's a snake!)" Sindie pointed at the safe,

sedentary snake stretched across a sturdy branch, presently catching a tan in the middle of the shade tree.

Plenty of pellets recently embedded in the rough bark now rendered the pepper tree in severe danger of lead poisoning.

"I think I'd better go and phone Dad and ask him to come home," Wendy surmised independently, having ignored previous instructions.

"No! Wait! Let me try one more time. I can see the serpent more clearly now with a few less leaves in the way." Mom re-stuffed the barrels.

By this time, curious spectators had descended from the huts, hearing the shots shattering the silence of the Karoo. They held their ears as they walked.

"Please may I try?" I pleaded. "I have fired that gun before."

Mom would have nothing to do with that idea, which was now shared by most onlookers, including Jack.

"There are hardly any leaves left for it to hide in," I continued.

Mom was shooing us behind her with her free right hand. That was the proper protocol a professional hunter would employ. No clamor was to alert the endangered snake.

Maggie yanked Mom by the sleeve into a better stalking position. Mom crept closer, with Maggie's firm hand pulling on her arm. One would think Maggie had colonel stripes on her sleeves judging by the way she bossed Mom around!

BOOM!

And with that final shot, the venomous snake fell to the graveled ground, freshly paved with peppertree fragments. There was only one glitch in Madam Gwenna's victory. The serpent was neatly divided into two pieces—both slithering violently. It looked like two snakes, each roughly three feet long.

"Yuu! YUU! Yoo! YOO! Qha ihleli! Hayini! (Wee! WEE! Wow! WOW! Only it's alive! No!)" The Xhosa chorus howled in a crescendo of wails.

Doeks (scarves) fell to the ground as married maids took off in different directions. Girls jumped into the garden, squashing delicate flowers, crunching the gorgeous cannas, which were normally treated with great respect. Maids stampeded, hurdling over each other to escape. Skirts and petticoats speedily assailed the vista of blooms, turning pink petals into confetti.

Maggie was the only gutsy one. She was the bravest woman, indeed. Even Jack stood at a secure distance near my little hut, in case he needed to run into it for cover. Actually, he feared "Miss Gwenna with a gun" more than the deadly snake.

Our master cook stood united by my mother, still instructing. *"Dubula, weer! Miss Gwina! Uyichanile kwakanye futhi*! (Shoot, again! Miss Gwenna! You actually hit it once!)"

From a safe distance, behind the crushed cannas, Jane could see no wrong in *NoLasti,* or her hunting skills, for that matter. "So what if it took a few hundred pellets of buckshot?" Jane was advocating. "The goal was achieved eventually."

Jane had the patience of Job. Her compliments were never ending, never scarce, never insincere. The worst hunter on Schelmdrift, maybe even further afield, in Jane's eyes, had done a good job, and she deserved ardent praise.

"Heke! Mlungkazi! Uyigcanile! Uyakwazi ukudubula! (Good job! White lady! You hit it! You can shoot!)" Jane was nodding her head and smiling, knowing Mom didn't understand Xhosa very well at all. Her body language clearly conveyed her approval.

Recognizing her housemaid's tone of voice and hand gestures of praise, Mom nodded modestly to thank Jane.

Jack, who just couldn't stand any more female foibles, pleaded earnestly in Afrikaans. *"Hou op skiet! Miesies! Asseblief tog!* (Stop shooting! Mrs.! Pretty Please!)" He stuck both hands up just in case. Then Jack bravely stepped forward, leaned down, and borrowed a rock from Mom's rockery. He instinctively resorted to the rock, the most widely-used weapon in all of Africa. Jack smashed the gaping head of the snake with clinical accuracy and instantly inflicted death on the deadly serpent, known to have the most concentrated hemo-toxic venom.

"There is simply no antidote serum available in our Albany District. Any injection from those fangs would prove fatal indeed. As a matter of fact, its poison causes your inner organs to bleed and you end up drowning in your own blood. Thank you, Jack!" Mom was relieved to be rid of the demonic serpent.

Cheers of approval and claps of delight filled the Karoo atmosphere.

"The tail is still alive," one skeptical maid observed.

"It doesn't matter; it can't think or see." Jack beamed broadly. "It will die on its own. That is what happens when you can't think or see properly."

"HEKE! GALEKILE! UYICHANILE! (GREAT WORK! Jack's Xhosa Name! YOU HIT IT!)" Jack soaked up the loud applause. Sindie was extra bouncy, holding onto his shirt tail, an unusual display of affection and kinship.

"Well, it was a team effort." Mom was exhausted from all her futile firing. "Maggie, will you please put the kettle on for tea?" She soon resumed her role as the madam once the arduous task was over. "I feel sure Jack deserves a big mug of tea too."

Mom and Wendy sipped their tea served on a tray as they sat on the front *stoep*. I chose to drink mine on the kitchen *stoep* with the servants. They relived and retold stories better than most fishermen.

"I am very glad *NoLasti* doesn't come on the kudu hunts with us in winter, or we'd all go hungry!" Jack joked. A chuckle of amusement and agreement ensued. The number of bullets fired grew bigger and the snake was almost a python by the end of teatime:

"Only the trunk is left on the poor peppertree."

"She almost shot up the heavens."

"We hope our ancestors were undercover behind the clouds."

After tea, the men folk returned from Sunnyside. "What happened to the peppertree?" Dad asked as he entered the house. "Whole branches are lying on the gravel!"

"I told Jack to clean it up. Where did he disappear to? You can never find him when you need him. Now where's Maggie? She's gone, too," Mom tried in vain to change the subject.

"Mom shot a big *boomslang!* And parts of the peppertree! She just had to blow away a few leaves first so she could see the snake better," I explained.

Beaming smiles broadened their faces, as the men chuckled. Mom indignantly left the room to go hunting for Maggie, who was quite safe at the stables, no doubt.

"Well, the peppertree certainly got peppered," Bruce quipped, enjoying the visual. Turning to me he asked, "What gun did she use, the elephant gun?"

"No, she used the shotgun. I think she loaded buckshot into it instead of birdshot," I tattled. "She held the gun like you hold a tennis racquet."

"Did she pull both triggers at once?" Norman asked smiling.

"Almost," I replied as Mom re-entered.

"Don't you dare laugh! We disposed of the snake appropriately. While you weren't here to help, I might add." That silenced the boys' snickering mirth.

"Mind you, the tree will grow back." Dad sucked his pipe to help hold back his smile. "What's more, peppertrees have very deep roots. That is how they survive the droughts, and other calamities." Dad was very reassuring. Nobody was going to mock his beloved Gwenna with a gun.

That night, I could not sleep. My legs ached from growing pains. The thought of another *boomslang* searching for its missing mate did not improve matters.

"Wendy, are you awake?" I whispered across the pitch dark. There were no streetlights in the Karoo. Without any moonlight, you couldn't see your own hand millimeters from your eyes.

"No. Be quiet. Go to sleep," Wendy directed.

I tried very hard to sleep, but I kept thinking of all the warnings Grandpa Stocks had given his grandchildren. He warned of the deceptions of life. He explained that we need to be aware always; and wide awake. My grandfather lectured, "In order to survive, you need to know and observe the difference between a shark and a dolphin. I want you to remember; like Donovan did….it is the shark that has the straight fin, and the hooked teeth. You have to understand that in the concrete jungle, the deadly black mamba is a deceptive shade of gray. Deception is most deadly."

Now, I heard Grandpa's warning echo to be wide awake while Wendy ordered me to sleep.

"I can't sleep. What if there's a *boomslang* (tree snake) in our house? We were at Kasouga so long that the slithering snakes took over Schelmdrift," I worried out loud.

"Every summer, we expect snakes. This is Africa. You just have to watch where you put your feet," Wendy warned, providing no comfort at all.

"Please can I sleep in your bed?" I wailed.

"I suppose so," she conceded kindly, rolling over to make space.

I took a running leap onto her bed, making very sure not to touch the floor.

"Careful!" she yelped, as I almost misjudged in the pitch dark.

I cuddled up to her back, while snakes slithered into my thoughts. Jack claimed you needed to *see* and *think* in order to survive. The night was as dark as devils. I was thinking in the pitch dark. Cocoa and I had survived eating unthinkably bad stuff, but would we survive the jungle of life?

"Can we put bricks under this bed to make it higher?" I begged.

Maggie's beds, both at Kasouga and in her hut, were hoisted up with at least three bricks under each foot. *Thokoloshe*, a very short, mythical goblin, could apparently only reach up to your knees. The hairy devil had terrorized the Xhosas for generations.

"What? Don't tell me you believe in *Thokoloshe* now, too?" Wendy queried. "You are white, so perhaps you should start acting a bit more civilized."

"I would just feel safer if we put bricks under our bed," I revealed. "Then the *boomslang* could not reach us."

"If a *boomslang* can climb up a peppertree, it can climb up your bed, no matter if we put a hundred bricks under it," Wendy reasoned, still not offering too much comfort.

"Shall we get the shotgun?" I suggested.

"No. Shut up and go to sleep or I'll kick you out of my bed," Wendy threatened, eager to avoid any further fiasco.

I never uttered another word. But my mind kept thinking about growing up because the pains in my legs reminded me that I was growing taller. Growing up and changing held many dangers. Attractions and traps, baits and bites, dangers and devils, hopes and heaven, one had to watch…but how are you supposed to see in the blackness? I didn't dare ask Wendy.

Sindie's high hopes of being able to choose her own husband were destined to be dashed as far as Cocoa was concerned. Tombe was more sensible. She would not dare break any tradition. Tombe leaned towards her ubiquitous ghosts, while Sindie relied more on the magic of witchcraft.

Grandpa Stocks' face looked most earnest as it popped into my mind. He had an honest spirit with him when he preached to his progeny, "You need to know that the worst breed of deception is when you laud evil as the norm; and Godly good as not so acceptable."

Fear of snakes motivated me to temporarily turn towards Christianity, and I prayed for safety. Presently, Wendy breathed deeply. I knew she was asleep. My thoughts wandered to the board game of snakes and ladders. I loved playing that board game with my cousins at Kasouga.

When you throw the dice, you move along. If you land on a ladder, you get hoisted up. But if your luck lands you on a serpent, you slide downwards. But you can throw the dice again, and get another turn, no matter where you land, until the game is over. I loved ladders a titanic amount more than snakes.

Bruce barely passed his matric exams, but he was a crack shot. Mom was highly educated, but that did not help much if she could not shoot straight. Education was only part of survival, not all of it. Luck helped you to leap up the ladders of life.

Champagne corks popped in my imagination; or were they shotguns booming in my mind? Jack was correct, thinking and seeing were both essential to survival. We needed to *see* clearly to avoid the sinful serpents along our pathway. And we needed to *think* straight to take full advantage of the ladders of life. But who rolled the dice of luck in the universe? That elusive answer remained to be uncorked.

Surviving was the best option, but if I succumbed to a snake bite and died, I wanted to win first prize and go to heaven. So I said another quiet little prayer, just in case.

As I was sinking into sleep my last thoughts were happy thoughts. Sindie and Tombe both acquired new panties for Christmas, just like the ones I received from my Aunty Ione. I felt a very deep gratitude for that change. It removed my guilt and made my shame subside. It was evident that our little threesome would eventually go in different directions. Our lives would be poles apart. Would our friendship endure adolescence and adulthood?

I wanted our friendship to survive so desperately. Society needed to shed a few rotten spots to make that a reality. As humans we have the privilege to adjust our habits and abolish evil traditions. As I drifted to sleep, I dreamt I was a leopard who could lick off my own spots and they tasted like black licorice. I got such a fright, I woke up.

"It is possible!" I shook my sister. "We can lick—I mean remove—our spots!" I woke Wendy up to tell her.

END OF BOOK ONE

Judy (Bester) Brummer was born and raised in the Karoo, the outback of South Africa, where Bester Brothers bred stud cattle. This memoir is about her experiences growing up in the heyday of apartheid, forming friendships with Sindie and Tombe, two Xhosa girls and daughters of her mother's maids.

She was homeschooled by her mother for 4 years. She later boarded for 6 years at Collegiate Girls School, and matriculated from Victoria Girls High School in Grahamstown.

Judy studied English at Rhodes University for a year and half, but does not remember a thing she learned. Most of her education comes from watching people of all stripes and observing how they talk, walk, eat and behave!

She has been married to André Brummer for 30 years. He is a founder of YouWho.com.

They raised two gorgeous daughters and two tall, spirited sons.

Judy loves to cook, garden, sew, swim in the sea, tan, walk five miles a day, knit, talk to her friends, throw parties and shop. She loved writing this book, as it made her laugh until her bellyached. It also made her homesick and weepy. She says, "I feel like I lived this fun life, and relived it as I wrote. I hope there are some helpful lessons to learn in these pages. My mistakes are not mistakes I would want my kids to repeat. It took a few hard knocks of life to teach me some wisdom."

Despite her dislike of flying, she has set foot on five continents. Judy is fluent in English, Afrikaans, Zulu and isiXhosa. Judy learned to speak isiXhosa, with native ability, growing up with her black friends and interacting with their families. She later studied isiXhosa at Rhodes University, where she learned to read and write it.

Judy is a popular public speaker and has spoken at more than a hundred firesides. She has now written her story down with a thousand times more details. She strongly believes that all humans can change and become spotless with the help and grace of God. This is her testimony in the form of an entertaining memoir.

For more information on the

SPOTTY BOOKS TRILOGY

go to

www.spottybooks.com